SERIES IN PHYSICS

RICHARD M. SUTTON

EDITOR

INTRODUCTION TO ATOMIC AND NUCLEAR PHYSICS

ROGERS D. RUSK
MOUNT HOLYOKE COLLEGE

APPLETON - CENTURY - CROFTS, Inc.
NEW YORK

PREFACE

The great present-day interest in atomic and nuclear physics stems both from the basic nature of the problems attacked and from the technical applications, which are of world-wide importance. An understanding of the foundations of the subject, together with some of the chief results and trends, is a necessity for students of science and engineering and is assuming increasing importance for the general student.

This book was written as an introduction to the subject either to follow more or less closely the general physics course or to serve as an integral part of the first two years' work. It is the outcome of many years of teaching the subject. For the general student the aim has been to present the fundamental principles and experimental results in as clear a manner as possible without the prerequisite of more than average mathematical training. For teachers who wish to give an introductory course to those who have had a minimum of mathematical training I would suggest that the chapters on wave mechanics and quantum statistics be omitted or touched on lightly. For students of science and engineering it is believed that a brief introduction to these subjects should form an integral part of the course, and that the simplicity of treatment will enable the student to gain some understanding of them and of the direction in which science is progressing. The book may then serve as an introduction to the more advanced courses.

Because of their growing importance mks units receive sufficient mention in the earlier part of the volume to enable the teacher to emphasize their use if he so desires. However, in other portions the sanction of custom and the requirements of references and tables still make cgs units more convenient for the general student. Usually the relations between units in the two systems are so simple that there is little trouble in transferring from one system to the other, and many students will want to familiarize themselves to some extent with both systems. The problems are for the most part of an elementary or intermediate level of difficulty, but they should furnish ample opportunity for the student to test his knowledge. Enough references are given at the end of each chapter to make it possible for the student readily to find suitable material for supplementary reading.

I should like to acknowledge my many debts generally to friends and fellow workers in the field of physics and particularly to those who have assisted by their critical reading of the manuscript. The advice of Professors Richard M. Sutton and Arthur H. Benade of the Case Institute of Technology has been invaluable. I am deeply indebted to Sarah E. Rusk for her constant encouragement and her indispensable contribution in the unenviable job of typing and otherwise helping to prepare the manuscript.

R. D. R.

CONTENTS

3

EMISSION OF ELECTRONS FROM METALS

4

ELECTRIC DISCHARGES IN GASES

5

X-RAYS AND CRYSTAL STRUCTURE

6

QUANTUM PROPERTIES OF WAVES AND PARTICLES

7

THEORY OF RELATIVITY

8

THE HYDROGEN ATOM AND SPECTRA

12

RADIATION AND BOSE STATISTICS

13

THE SOLID STATE AND FERMI STATISTICS

14

NATURAL RADIOACTIVITY

15

PARTICLES AND RAYS

16

TRANSMUTATION, INDUCED RADIOACTIVITY, AND NUCLEAR PROCESSES

17

NUCLEAR STRUCTURE AND NUCLEAR FORCES

18

PARTICLE ACCELERATORS

19

FISSION, ATOMIC ENERGY, AND NUCLEAR REACTORS

20

COSMIC RAYS AND NEW PARTICLES

APPENDIXES

INTRODUCTION TO

ATOMIC AND NUCLEAR PHYSICS

CHAPTER 1

THE ELECTRON

1-1. Introduction

The discovery of the electron was one of several near the beginning of the twentieth century that led to a revolution in scientific thought and opened up vast new fields of investigation first in atomic and more recently in nuclear physics. Chief among these discoveries were: x-rays (1895); radioactivity (1896); the electron (1897). On the theoretical side came Planck's quantum theory of radiation (1900) and Einstein's special theory of relativity (1905). These developments were preceded by Maxwell's formulation of the *electromagnetic theory of light* (1862-64) and by the discovery of the *photoelectric effect* by Hertz in 1887 which was later found to require the quantum theory for its explanation.

Not since the time of Galileo, followed by Newton in the seventeenth century, had such a period of revolutionary discovery and change in viewpoint occurred. Since their day it had come to be universally accepted that the only true method of science must rest upon experimental investigation and that the results of any theory must be submitted to experimental test. During the time from Galileo and Newton to the end of the nineteenth century steady progress was made in the subjects of mechanics, sound, heat, light, electricity, and magnetism, where the phenomena investigated were for the most part in or near the realm of common experience and direct observation. Now came developments in the realm of the atom and the electron, far removed from ordinary experience and direct observation.

It is this new age of physical science which is often referred to as the age of "modern" physics; more recently it has become known as the "atomic age." It is an age in which many older ideas have had to be revised and some have had to be supplanted by radically new ideas. It is an age in which many ideas previously accepted as "common sense" have had to be replaced by ideas which may have seemed at first to violate common sense, and the limitations of simple mechanical explanations of things have been transcended by new methods and ideas. The new methods and ideas have been strikingly justified by the brilliant achievements to which they have led, encompassing the entire gamut of physical phenomena from atoms to stars and to the large-scale release of nuclear energy.

1-2. The Atomic Nature of Electricity

The new concepts of the electrical nature of matter came with the discovery that all matter contains elementary electric charges of the same magnitude. During the nineteenth century electricity had sometimes been likened to an incompressible and continuous fluid, a fluid of such mysterious character that it could apparently permeate or flow through a "solid" such as a copper wire. However, it had been found that copper wire, along with other kinds of matter, is composed of individual particles or atoms, which are the ultimate units of the various elements, and by the latter part of the nineteenth century the atomic theory of matter had been generally accepted. Then the discovery was made that electricity is also atomic in nature, and the smallest individual unit of electricity was called the *electron*. This name had been suggested by Stoney in 1874 for the charge on a singly charged ion which acts as a carrier when electricity flows through a conducting liquid.

The discovery of the electron in 1897 by J. J. Thomson was the culmination of the work of a number of investigators including Crookes, Lenard, Townsend, and others, but to J. J. Thomson of the Cavendish Laboratory in England must go the credit for making definite measurements and demonstrating in a convincing manner that these tiny units of electric charge actually exist and are found in all types of matter. The later, more precise measurement of the charge of the electron by R. A. Millikan extended and confirmed Thomson's work.

1-3. Cathode Rays and the Discovery of the Electron

The passage of electricity between two electrodes in a glass tube from which much of the air has been evacuated was studied by many people. In 1859 Plücker in Germany found that when the tube was highly evacuated and the voltage sufficiently high the glass of the tube itself would fluoresce with a greenish yellow light. He attributed this fluorescence to rays from the cathode, and he discovered that the rays could be deflected by a magnetic field. Plücker's pupil, Hittorf, showed more conclusively that the rays came from the cathode and demonstrated that when a solid body was placed in their path a shadow was cast. Goldstein extended this work and named the rays *cathode rays.*

Later in the century Sir William Crookes in England performed many interesting experiments and advanced weighty arguments to support the idea that cathode rays were charged particles shot off from the cathode and that they were not a form of wave motion as thought by some. He recognized, however, that they were not ordinary particles and that they were unlike anything already known. Perrin in 1895 deflected the rays into a little cup inside the discharge tube and found that the cup acquired a negative charge, thus demonstrating directly that the rays carried a negative charge.

General recognition of the discovery of the electron came when J. J. Thomson carefully measured the deflection of cathode rays by electric and magnetic fields. The direction of deflection was always such as to indicate that the rays carried a negative charge. To confirm the idea that these rays were actually particles it was desirable to measure their mass. Although it was not at first possible to measure separately either the individual charge or the mass of the newly discovered particle, Thomson performed an experiment in which he measured the ratio of charge to mass, e/m. On the assumption, not immediately confirmed, that the charge e carried by a cathode-ray particle was the same as that carried by a singly charged ion in a liquid, he found that the amount of the deflection indicated the rays did possess definite mass although it was far less than that of any known particle. Thomson further found that the individual particles of the cathode rays were always present regardless of the material of the cathode or of the kind of gas in the tube. Thus came about the discovery of the electron and recognition that not only do these tiny particles of negative electricity exist in all matter but that, despite differences in the atoms of different substances, the electrons are all alike.

1-4. The Deflection of Electrons by a Magnetic Field; e/m

The ratio of charge to mass for the electron was early obtained by measuring the amount of its deflection in a magnetic field. Several refinements of method have made it possible to secure a very precise value for this important quantity, but the basic method may now readily be repeated by the student in the laboratory. Electrons emitted from a heated filament (cathode) in a large evacuated glass tube, as at C (Fig. 1-1), are accelerated toward an anode A (sometimes in the form of a grid) held at a positive potential with respect to the cathode. The glass bulb is placed in a region of uniform magnetic field at right angles to the direction of motion of the electron stream, and the electrodes are designed so as to confine the electron stream to a narrow beam which is deflected by the magnetic field. After leaving the region of accelerating potential the electrons travel with constant speed across the magnetic field and experience a constant deflecting force at right angles to the direction of motion and to the field. Under the action of this force they are deflected in a circular path the radius of which is determined by the charge, the mass, the velocity of the electron, and by the magnetic flux density.

When an electric charge q moves across a magnetic field at right angles to the field a force F is exerted upon the charge. The direction of this force depends upon the sign of the charge, but it is always at right angles to both the direction of motion of the charge and the direction of the field. The magnitude of the force is given by the relation

$$F = Bqv \qquad [1\text{-}1]$$

where B is the flux density of the field. In mks units F is in newtons when q is in coulombs, v is in m/sec and B is in webers/m^2. In cgs units F is in dynes when q is in abcoulombs, v is in cm/sec and B is in gauss.

If an object of mass m moving with constant speed experiences a force of constant magnitude always acting at right angles to the direction of motion the moving object is then constrained to move in a circular path. The required centripetal force is given by the well-known relation $F = mv^2/r$. We now find that this formula, which describes the behavior of ordinary objects, can also be applied to the motion of an electron (Fig. 1-2). If m is the mass of the electron the required centripetal force can be provided by a magnetic field across which the elec-

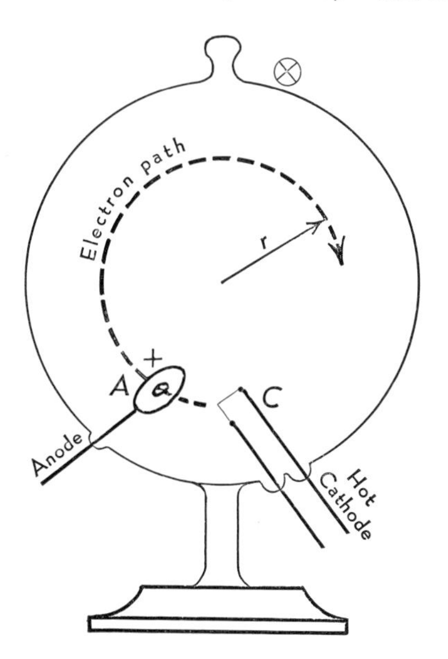

Fig. 1-1. A high-vacuum tube for measuring e/m for the electron by magnetic deflection. Electrons from hot cathode C accelerated toward positively charged electrode A pass through and are deflected in a circular path of radius r by a uniform magnetic field at right angles to plane of the figure. If the charge of the electron is known the mass can then be determined.

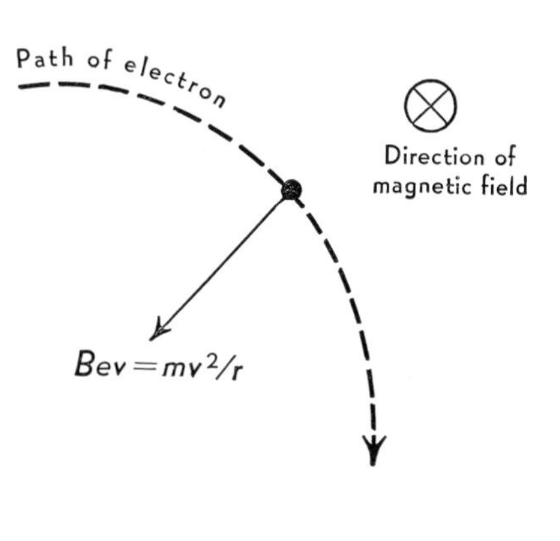

Fig. 1-2. A uniform magnetic field exerts a deflecting force Bev on an electron moving at right angles to the field, the force being at right angles to the field and to the direction of motion. The cross in the circle stands for the feather end of an arrow and represents a field directed away from the observer. A dot in a circle represents a field directed toward the observer.

tron moves, and it is Bev where e is the charge of the electron. For circular motion then,

$$\frac{mv^2}{r} = Bev \qquad [1\text{-}2]$$

From this the ratio of charge to mass is

$$\frac{e}{m} = \frac{v}{Br} \qquad [1\text{-}3]$$

when it is assumed that all quantities are measured in the same system of units.

To find this ratio it is only necessary to know the magnetic flux density B, the speed v of the particle, and the radius r of the path. The ratio e/m can then be computed. These quantities may readily be obtained. If a small amount of gas is left in the bulb (Fig. 1-1) some electrons will hit gas molecules and excite them to emit visible radiation, making the path visible in a darkened room. The radius of the path can then be directly measured. The measurement of magnetic flux density can be accomplished by standard methods or it can be computed, but the speed of the electron cannot be obtained so simply. It could be determined by a separate experiment such as the method of balanced deflections (§ 1-6), but it is often more convenient to compute the speed by Eq. 1-10.

Accepted values of e/m are

$$\begin{aligned} e/m &= 1.759 \times 10^{11} \text{ coulombs/kg} \\ &= 1.759 \times 10^{7} \text{ abcoulombs/gm} \\ &= 5.273 \times 10^{17} \text{ statcoulombs/gm} \end{aligned}$$

It is often desired to find the radius of curvature of the path of an electron in a magnetic field of uniform flux density B when the ratio e/m is known, and when the speed of the electron is known. This is readily obtained from Eq. 1-2, which may be conveniently solved for the radius of path, giving

$$r = \frac{mv}{Be} \qquad [1\text{-}4]$$

From this equation it is apparent that the radius of curvature of path is directly proportional to the speed when the mass is constant.

1-5. The Deflection of Electrons by an Electric Field

A simple type of cathode-ray tube such as that in an oscilloscope affords a ready method of studying electron deflections by an electric field. The tube, as shown in Fig. 1-3, includes at one end a source of high-speed electrons known commonly as an electron gun. This consists of a hot cathode C which emits electrons and, some distance in front of the cathode, an anode A with a tiny hole in it. Since the anode is made positive with respect to the cathode, electrons are accelerated toward the anode and will gain velocity continually until they either strike the anode or pass through the small hole. Electrons passing through such a hole behave in a manner similar to a stream of bullets emerging from the muzzle of a gun. Since they have left the region of an accelerating

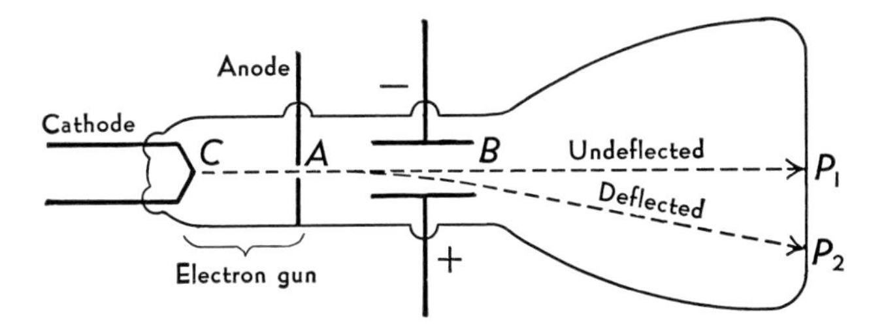

Fig. 1-3. Deflection of electrons by an electric field. Electrons from hot cathode *C* pass through a hole in anode *A* and are deflected by electric field between plates at *B*.

field they now travel forward with uniform velocity or speed unless interfered with by collision with gas molecules. They then strike the end of the tube at P_1 if not deflected. If they are deflected by an electric field between the plates at B they may strike at P_2.

Electrons travel so fast that in their brief transit time the distance they fall under the action of gravity is not appreciable and they travel through a discharge tube in almost straight lines. If the opposite end of such a tube is coated with fluorescent material, the position at which the electrons strike can be observed directly as a luminous spot on the fluorescent screen. If electrons pass between two deflecting plates D_1D_2 (Fig. 1-4) with the lower plate positively charged, they will be accelerated downward by the field between the plates in much the same way as a rifle bullet is accelerated downward by the force of gravity. The deflection s can be computed as follows:

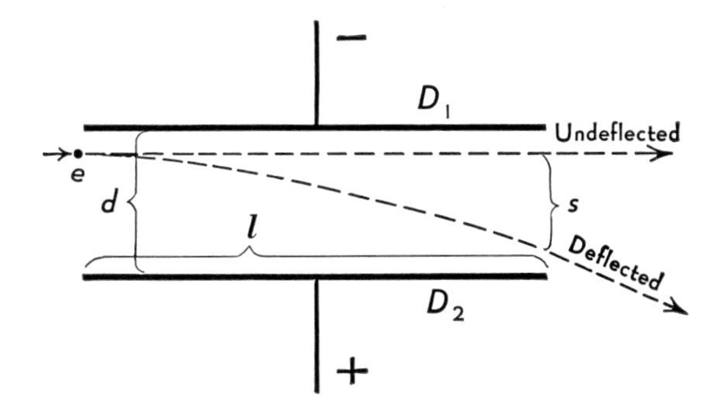

Fig. 1-4. When electron *e* enters field between deflecting plates D_1D_2 it is accelerated toward the positively charged plate. The deflection *s* can be computed (see text). Correction should be made for nonuniformity of field at edge of plates.

The *electric field intensity E is defined as the force per unit charge exerted by the field on a test charge.* The force on any particle of charge e then is Ee, and by Newton's second law, $F = ma$, the acceleration is Ee/m. In the position shown, the force on the electron is downward, and it will be accelerated downward. The distance s that it falls while in the accelerating field is given by the relation

$$s = \frac{1}{2}at^2 = \frac{1}{2}\frac{eE}{m}t^2 = \frac{1}{2}\frac{eE}{m}\left(\frac{l}{v}\right)^2 = \frac{1}{2}\frac{eV}{md}\left(\frac{l}{v}\right)^2 \qquad [1\text{-}5]$$

where l is the length of path of the particle in the field and v is its average velocity. The amount of deflection s may be readily computed if e/m and the electric field intensity E are known, provided that the time during which the electron is in the field between the deflecting plates is also known. The field E is equal to the difference in potential V between the plates divided by their distance d apart, but to find the time involves knowing the speed or velocity of the electron.

1-6. The Speed of a Moving Electron

Determination by experiment It was J. J. Thomson who showed that the speed of an electron may be obtained by a comparatively simple experiment. When one considers that the problem is to measure the speed of a particle far too small to be directly observed and that this speed may be hundreds or thousands

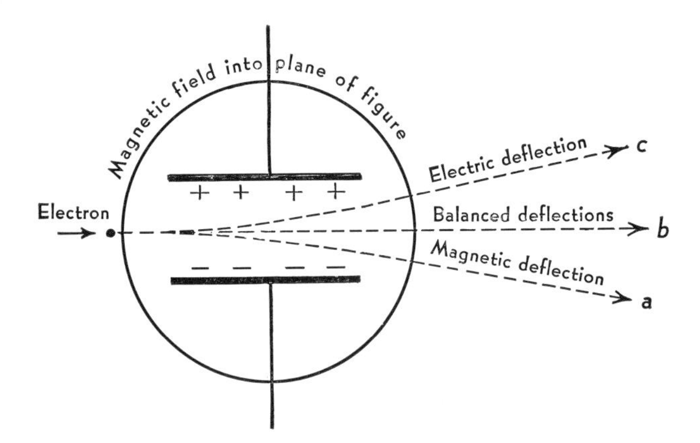

Fig. 1-5. Method of determining electron speed by balancing electric and magnetic deflections.

of miles per second, the idea of measuring it presents an intriguing problem. Thomson found that, if an electron stream is passed through a region in which magnetic and electric fields are superposed in such a manner as to produce deflections in opposite directions, the fields can be so adjusted that the effect of one just cancels the effect of the other. The electrons for which the fields are thus balanced would go through undeflected (Fig. 1-5). For such a balance the magnitude of the force Ee of the electric field E on the electron must be equal to the magnitude of the force of the magnetic field Bev, or

$$eE = Bev \qquad [1\text{-}6]$$

and the fields must be at right angles to each other. The charge of the electron cancels on the two sides of the equation, and the speed v is given by

$$v = \frac{E}{B} \qquad [1\text{-}7]$$

Thus to obtain the speed of the electron it is only necessary to measure the magnetic flux density and the electric field intensity and take their ratio. This is called the method of balanced deflections.

It is of course implied in the equation that E and B must be measured in the same system of units. In mks units B is in webers/m^2 and E is in volts/m. In cgs units if B is in gauss (em units) and E is in statvolts/cm (es units), it is then necessary to write the equation

$$v = \frac{cE}{B} \qquad [1\text{-}8]$$

where c, the velocity of light (3×10^{10} cm/sec), is the ratio of the units in the two cgs systems.

Determination by theory Often it is simpler to obtain the speed of an electron from a computation based on the difference of potential through which it has passed. If an electron starts from rest at the cathode it will be continually accelerated by an electric field until it reaches the anode. The kinetic energy which it would then have would be given by the well-known formula $mv^2/2$. The problem is similar to that of a falling body. An object raised to a height h possesses potential energy mgh. On falling to its original level the potential energy is converted into kinetic energy and $mgh =$

$mv^2/2$. In the electrical case if we were to move the electron against the field, that is, from anode to cathode, the work done would be eV. This is apparent since the difference of potential V is defined as energy acquired per unit charge and *the volt is defined as a joule per coulomb.* When the electron moves from cathode to anode under the action of the field the potential energy eV becomes kinetic energy, or

$$eV = \frac{1}{2} mv^2 \qquad [1\text{-}9]$$

and the final speed is

$$v = \sqrt{\frac{2eV}{m}} \qquad [1\text{-}10]$$

When the ratio of charge to mass is known the velocity of the electron can readily be computed for a given potential difference V; in mks units it is in meters/sec. When e/m is measured in cgs electrostatic units (esu), as is sometimes done for convenience, the speed is in cm/sec. The potential difference must then be in statvolts, and it is convenient to remember that volts/300 equals statvolts.

1-7. Electron Energies and the Electron Volt

From Eq. 1-10 it is seen that the speed of the electron is proportional to the square root of the accelerating potential and also to the square root of the ratio of charge to mass. A "1-volt electron" has a velocity of 5.93×10^5 m/sec (368 mi/sec) and, by Eq. 1-10, a "100-volt electron" would then have 10 times this velocity. The energy of the electron on being accelerated by a difference of potential of V volts is conveniently specified in terms of the unit the **electron volt.** For instance, in falling through a potential difference of 100 volts an electron is said to gain an energy of 100 electron volts (100 ev). For electrons of high energies the unit is 1 million electron volts (1 Mev). This unit will occur frequently when we study particles of very high energies and speeds.

$$\begin{aligned} 1 \text{ electron volt} &= 1.6 \times 10^{-19} \text{ joules} \\ &= 1.6 \times 10^{-12} \text{ ergs} \end{aligned}$$

The term *electron volt* should not be used as a unit of velocity or speed. It is true that all particles of the same charge and mass such as electrons acquire the same velocity after falling through the same potential difference, but particles of different masses, even though possessing the same charge, gain different velocities. Velocity depends not only on charge but on mass, and the larger the mass the smaller is the acquired velocity, whereas all particles of the same charge falling through the same difference of potential gain the same amount of energy regardless of mass.

In § 1-4 it was desired to find the ratio e/m. This can now be done by eliminating the velocity v between Eq. 1-3 and Eq. 1-10 thus giving e/m in terms of easily measurable quantities.

$$\frac{e}{m} = \frac{2V}{B^2r^2} \qquad [1\text{-}11]$$

1-8. Velocity Selector

The apparatus of Fig. 1-5 may serve as a "velocity selector" when electrons of different speeds are present. Faster electrons will be affected more by the magnetic field and bent downward as at a, whereas slower electrons are affected more by the electric field and are bent upward as at c. Only electrons of a particular speed will pass through undeflected in the direction b. The same basic method has been applied with streams of positive ions to select those of a particular speed.

1-9. Millikan's Precise Measurement of the Charge of the Electron

The universal character of the electron as a "building block" of all matter and its basic importance in all phenomena of electricity made it most desirable to have a precise measurement of its charge. Robert A. Millikan, then at the University of Chicago, subsequent to the pioneering work of J. J. Thomson, J. S. Townsend, and C. T. R. Wilson, devised an improved method of measurement of the charge e of the electron. Thomson, Townsend, and Wilson had tried to measure the charge of the electron by forming a cloud or mist of small, charged droplets of water in an ionized gas. The cloud would fall at a rate that depended on the size of the drops. The total charge per cm^3 of the cloud divided by the number of drops would give the average per drop which they hoped would be that of one electron when the drops were small. It was later found that any one droplet might have a charge of more than one electron, and the method though ingenious was sadly inaccurate.

Millikan believed he could study one droplet at a time. To avoid loss of weight by evaporation he used droplets of oil. These could be conveniently formed by an atomizer, but they were so small that they had to be observed by means of a magnifying telescope in a brightly illuminated field of view. The method he perfected is described below.

If oil droplets are sprayed into the region A (Fig. 1-6) some of them fall through hole B into space C between two charged plates where they may be observed. Millikan found it possible to hold a charged droplet balanced in an electric field for a considerable period

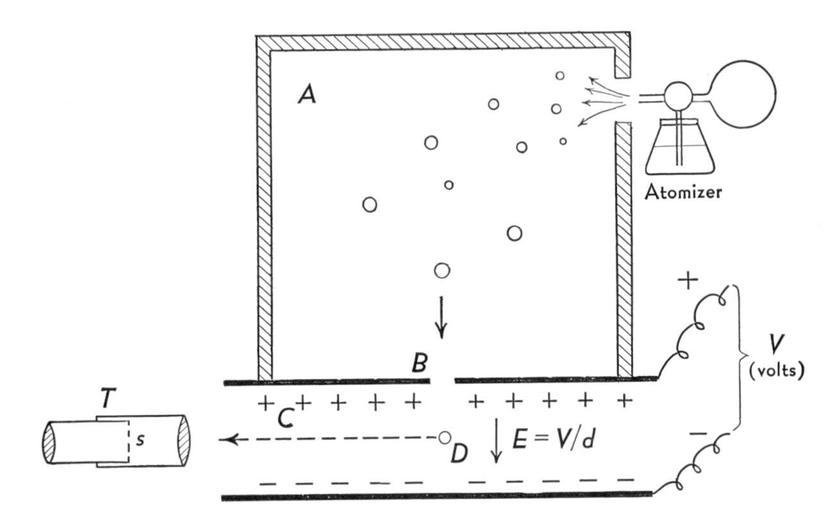

Fig. 1-6. Millikan oil-drop experiment for measuring charge of the electron. Charged droplet *D* falls through hole *B* into region *C* of electric field between charged plates, where it is illuminated by intense light source and observed through a telescope *T*. Latter has transparent scale *s* for measuring distance that droplet moves. Droplets acquire charge when blown out of atomizer into *A*, or they may be charged by ionizing action of x-rays.

of time before it would either disappear from view or lose its charge. Then the upward force Eq of the electric field intensity E acting on a droplet of charge q is adjusted until it just balances the downward force acting on the drop. The net downward force acting on the droplet is the pull of gravity mg less the buoyant force of the air. The buoyant force is the weight of the air displaced by the drop, which is the volume $4\pi r^3/3$ of the drop times the density d' of the air times g. Then the forces are balanced when

$$Eq = mg - \frac{4}{3}\pi r^3 d' g \qquad [1\text{-}12]$$

$$= \frac{4}{3} \pi r^3 g(d - d') \qquad [1\text{-}13]$$

where d is the density of the oil forming the droplet.

The charge q on the droplet can be obtained from Eq. 1-13 if the other quantities are known. Most of these are readily obtainable including the electric field intensity, which is the potential difference between the plates divided by their distance apart. However, since the droplets varied in size and no direct method of obtaining the mass or of measuring the radius could be applied, an indirect method was resorted to. This involved the law established by Sir George Stokes for the terminal velocity of a spherical body falling through a resisting medium. Any medium such as molasses or water or even air possesses viscosity or internal friction. A body falling in this medium experiences a resisting force which increases with the velocity. As the velocity of the falling body increases the resisting force also increases to the point where it is equal in magnitude and opposite in direction to the net force downward. From this time on the falling body is no longer accelerated but moves under the action of balanced forces with a uniform velocity called the **terminal velocity.**

With very tiny spherical droplets this terminal velocity is reached in air in as little as one hundredth of a second, and we may then apply the Stokes law which states that the retarding force F is given by

$$F = 6\pi\eta v r \qquad [1\text{-}14]$$

where η is the coefficient of viscosity of air, v is the terminal velocity, and r is the radius of the drop. When the terminal velocity is reached, the retarding force and the net downward force balance, and

$$6\pi\eta v r = \frac{4}{3} \pi r^3 g(d - d') \qquad [1\text{-}15]$$

In the interest of maximum precision a correction is made, because for a very small droplet the air no longer behaves as a continuous resisting medium but acts as if it had "holes" in it. For simplicity this correction will be omitted in the present work.

If the viscosity of air is known from other experiments the radius of the drop can now be obtained from measurements of its rate of free fall. Thus the quantities to be put in the equation are all known, and the charge q on the droplet can be computed. Millikan found the charge q always to be an integral multiple of the smallest observed

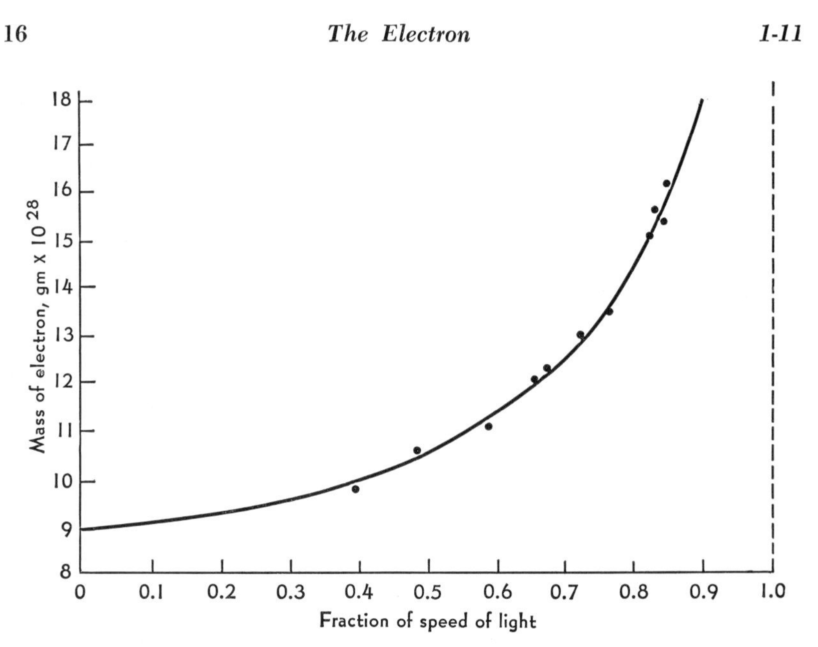

Fig. 1-7. Variation of mass of electron with speed. Experimental points lie close to theoretical curve, and curve approaches infinity as speed approaches that of light.

If the mass of a particle at rest such as an electron is m_0 (called the rest mass), the mass at any speed v is given by the Einstein and Lorentz equation

$$m_v = \frac{m_0}{\sqrt{1 - \frac{v^2}{c^2}}} \qquad [1\text{-}17]$$

where c is the velocity of light. This equation indicates that at ordinary speeds the variation of mass is too small to be detected. However, the mass of the particle would approach infinity as its speed approaches the speed of light (Fig. 1-7).

Equation 1-9 ($eV = \frac{1}{2}mv^2$) for computing the velocity of an electron accelerated by a potential difference of V volts is consequently only valid with small voltages or low velocities where the variation in mass is inappreciable. For high voltages the variation of mass must be considered. Up to 7000 volts, the error is less than 1 per cent. At higher voltages the error rises rapidly. The theory of relativity, however, indicates that Eq. 1-17 cannot be put directly into Eq. 1-9 to obtain the speed of an electron at high voltages. The reason is that not just the mass but the total energy as well must be considered. Einstein has shown (Chap. 7) that the energy equivalent of any mass m in grams is mc^2 where c is the velocity of light.

The energy equivalent of the mass of an electron at rest is m_0c^2 whereas the energy equivalent of the electron moving with speed (or velocity) v and possessing mass m_v is

$$E(\text{energy}) = m_vc^2 = \frac{m_0}{\sqrt{1 - \frac{v^2}{c^2}}}c^2 \qquad [1\text{-}18]$$

The difference of these energies must equal the energy eV supplied by the field. Therefore for an electron accelerated from zero to the maximum obtainable for a potential difference V the following equation becomes necessary to compute the velocity.

$$m_0c^2\left(\frac{1}{\sqrt{1 - \frac{v^2}{c^2}}} - 1\right) = eV \qquad [1\text{-}19]$$

It is often convenient to use this equation to obtain the speed of the electron in terms of the speed of light c, a few examples of which are given in Table 1-1. It will be noted that the speed of light is always approached but never reached.

TABLE 1-1. RELATIVE ELECTRON SPEEDS
(in fractions of the speed of light, c)

Electron Energy (ev)	Electron Speed
1,000	0.063c
10,000	0.196c
100,000	0.588c
1,000,000	0.942c
10,000,000	0.999c

1-12. Properties of Electrons

What do we know about electrons? The answer is that we know a very great deal, and some of the more important properties are listed below. Other important properties, some of them more revolutionary in nature, will be encountered later.

1. The electron is the fundamental atom of electricity.
2. Its mass is 1/1836 that of a hydrogen atom, or 9.11×10^{-28} gm, or 9.11×10^{-31} kg.

3. It has a negative charge of 4.8×10^{-10} esu or 1.6×10^{-19} coulomb.
4. It is extremely small in size in comparison with a hydrogen atom, which is the smallest atom.
5. The effective mass of an electron increases with increasing speed.
6. If moving with sufficient energy it will ionize gas molecules.
7. In an electric field it behaves like any negatively charged particle.
8. A moving electron can be deflected by a magnetic field.
9. The spot where electrons strike a photographic plate will be "exposed" and appear black after development.
10. Where electrons of sufficient speed strike a fluorescent screen a luminous spot will appear.

PROBLEMS

Note: Answers to problems are usually rounded off to two or three significant figures. Answers are given to all numerical problems except where giving it would defeat the purpose of the problem.

1. The plate current in a radio tube is 6 ma (milliamperes). How many electrons per second reach the anode? What is the total energy in joules with which the electrons arrive at the anode in a 10-second interval if the potential difference between cathode and anode is 100 volts?

Ans. 3.75×10^{16}; 6 joules.

2. Find the force in metric tons (1000 kg = 1 ton) between one milligram of electrons and another milligram 160.9 km (100 miles) distant. What would be the difficulty of assembling a milligram of electrons in a small region?

Ans. 1.09×10^{6} metric tons.

3. What is meant by an electron volt? Find the velocity of an electron possessing 1 ev of energy; 100 ev of energy.

Ans. 5.93×10^{5} m/sec; 59.3×10^{5} m/sec.

4. The electrons in a radio tube are accelerated toward the anode (plate) with 300 volts potential difference. With what velocity will they arrive at the anode? What will be the average velocity during flight from cathode to anode? What is the time of transit if the distance from cathode to anode is 2 mm?

Ans. $V_f = 10.3 \times 10^{6}$ m/sec;
$V_{av} = 5.14 \times 10^{6}$ m/sec;
3.88×10^{-10} sec.

5. In a cathode-ray tube electrons are shot into a field-free space from an electron gun having an accelerating potential of 3000 volts. How long will it take an electron to travel from the gun to the fluorescent screen 40 cm distant? (Neglect variation of mass with velocity.)

Ans. 1.23×10^{-8} sec.

6. Assuming that there are 10^{24} free electrons per cm^3 of a conductor, find their average drift velocity if a current density of 1000 amperes per cm^2 of cross section is maintained.

Ans. 6.25×10^{-3} cm/sec.

7. What magnetic flux density will bend the path of a 200-ev electron in the arc of a circle of 10 cm radius?

Ans. 4.77×10^{-4} weber/m^2 or 4.77 gauss.

8. An electron and a proton, each of 300 electron-volts energy pass through a uniform magnetic field of 50 gauss (50×10^{-4} weber/m^2). Find the radius of the arcs of the circles in which the paths of the particles are bent.

Ans. Electron, 1.17 cm; proton, 50.2 cm.

9. By means of the simple form of the Stokes law find the terminal velocity in air of a freely falling water droplet of diameter 10^{-3} cm and density 0.998 gm/cm^3. (Neglect buoyancy of air. Take viscosity of air at 20° = 1.81×10^{-4} poise.)

Ans. $V_t = 0.30$ cm/sec.

10. An oil droplet (density = 0.8 gm/cm^3) of 0.0005 cm diameter falls in air at what velocity? (Neglect buoyancy of air and other minor corrections.)

Ans. 0.060 cm/sec.

11. The horizontal plates for determining the charge of an electron by the oil-drop method are 1.5 cm apart and are kept at a potential difference of 1500 volts. What is the electric field intensity between the plates? What is the force on a droplet carrying a charge of 1 electron?

Ans. 3.33 dynes/statcoulomb or 10^5 newtons/coulomb; 1.6×10^{-9} dyne or 1.6×10^{-14} newton.

12. A droplet of 10^{-12} gm mass and charge e is held balanced in a vacuum between parallel plates by an electric field which opposes the pull of gravity. If the plates are 2 cm apart, what potential difference between the plates is required to just balance the pull of gravity?

Ans. 1225 volts.

13. What is the ratio of the mass of an electron, having a speed of 0.86 that of light, to its rest mass?

Ans. 2.

14. What is the mass of an electron having a speed 0.95 that of light?

Ans. 3.2 m_0 (m_0 = rest mass).

15. What is the speed of an electron with kinetic energy of 1 Mev? (1 Mev = 10^6 ev.)

Ans. 0.94c (c = speed of light).

16. What is the speed of an electron having an energy of 10 Mev?

Ans. 0.999c.

SUGGESTED READING

Note: At the end of each chapter a few selected references to other books are given for additional reading. These brief lists are intended to make it easy for the student in his own studies to supplement the material of this book. The first references in each list are usually the more elementary. Some are mentioned because of their historical interest, and a few references to periodicals are included. Occasionally more advanced books are mentioned because they have become standard and the student may desire at least to make their acquaintance. In all these the student will find further references to special subjects and to original articles in the journals should he desire to pursue a particular subject further.

R. A. Millikan, *Electrons, Protons, Photons, Neutrons and Cosmic Rays,* 2nd ed. (Chicago, Univ. of Chicago Press, 1947).

J. A. Crowther, *Ions, Electrons and Ionizing Radiations,* 8th ed. (New York, Longmans Green, 1949).

J. D. Stranathan, *The "Particles" of Modern Physics* (Philadelephia, Blakiston, 1942).

J. B. Hoag and S. A. Korff, *Electron and Nuclear Physics,* 3rd ed. (New York, Van Nostrand, 1948).

CHAPTER 2

POSITIVELY CHARGED PARTICLES

2-1. Motions of Particles in Electric and Magnetic Fields

When a positively charged particle passes through a magnetic field it is deflected in the same manner as an electron except that the deflection is in the opposite direction and the larger masses of the more common types of positive particles make them more difficult to deflect. If such a particle travels with constant speed at right angles to a uniform magnetic field of flux density B its path will be bent in the arc of a circle, and Eq. 1-4 may now be conveniently rewritten for a positive particle as

$$r = \frac{Mv}{Bq} = \frac{Mv}{Bne} \qquad [2\text{-}1]$$

where M now stands for the mass of the positive particle and q is the charge. Since such a particle may become positively charged by the loss of one or more electrons the charge q may be put equal to ne where n is a small integer.

Equation 2-1 may also be written in terms of the accelerating difference of potential V applied to the particle by making use of Eq. 1-10 with M instead of m for the mass and ne instead of e for the charge. The radius of curvature of the path is then given by

$$r = \frac{1}{B}\sqrt{\frac{2MV}{ne}} \qquad [2\text{-}1a]$$

From this it is seen that for the same accelerating potential the radii of curvature for particles of different mass are proportional to the square roots of their masses.

In an electric field the force on a singly charged positive ion is the same in magnitude as that on an electron though opposite in direction. The amount of the deflection produced by the field depends, as with electrons, on the time during which the particle is in the field. The deflection may be found if Eq. 1-5 is adapted for positive particles by the appropriate changes of mass and charge, giving

$$s = \frac{1}{2}\frac{neE}{M}\left(\frac{l}{v}\right)^2 \qquad [2\text{-}2]$$

Comparing Eqs. 1-5 and 2-2 it is apparent that for electrons and singly charged positive particles the deflections are inversely proportional to the masses only if both have the same velocity.

It is evident that positively and negatively charged particles may readily be separated by deflections in electric or magnetic fields, but of particular importance has been the separation by such deflections of positively charged particles of different masses. The measurement of the masses of these positive ions by various methods of deflection is known as **positive-ray analysis.** It has been one of the most rewarding fields of physical science, and will form the subject of much of the present chapter.

2-2. Positive Rays

The existence in an ordinary discharge tube of rapidly moving, positively charged particles known as positive rays was demonstrated in 1886 by Goldstein. These particles move in a direction opposite to that of the cathode rays, that is, from anode to cathode. Goldstein made a small hole in the cathode of such a tube and observed a faint glow on the opposite side of the cathode from the anode. This glow was caused by formation of excited atoms (§ 4-2) in the beam of positively charged rays that stream through the hole in the cathode (Fig. 2-1).

These rays were originally called *canal rays,* owing to their having passed through the small channel or canal in the cathode. Such positive rays lose their electric charge rapidly as they collide with the remaining gas molecules in the tube, but if the gas pressure in the tube is sufficiently low, in the neighborhood of a thousandth of a millimeter of mercury, the visible path of the rays extends far enough behind the cathode to be studied. To make these studies possible a pumping system was then arranged by means of which the gas pressure in the region behind the cathode was kept at a much lower value than in the region of the main discharge between the cathode and anode.

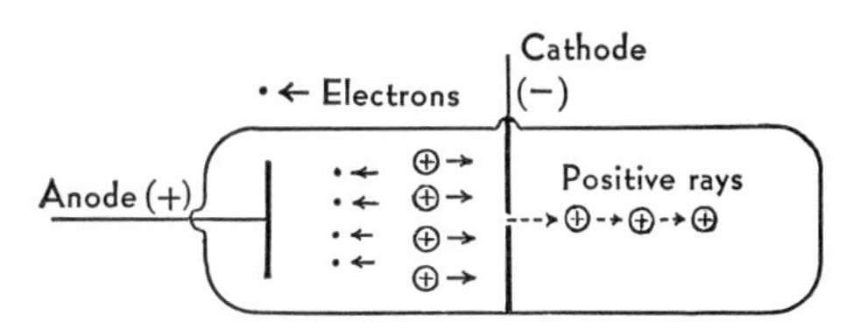

Fig. 2-1. Electric-discharge tube for separating positive rays from cathode rays (electrons) by allowing some positive rays to pass through a hole in the cathode.

As the positive rays move away from the cathode some of them emit light the frequencies of which are characteristic of the particular atoms of the gas in the tube. When this light is observed with a spectroscope the spectral lines appear in their usual position in the spectrum if the beam is observed at right angles to the direction of motion of the particles. However, if the rays are viewed end-on, that is, coming toward the observer, the lines are shifted toward the blue end of the spectrum in accordance with the **Doppler principle.** Such a shift in hydrogen of as much as 5 angstrom units (5×10^{-8} cm) has been observed, and the speeds of the particles may then be computed from the simple Doppler formula. It turns out that for an ordinary discharge tube the speeds may be in the neighborhood of 10^5 m/sec. These speeds are so small in comparison with maximum electron speeds in such a tube that it is evident that positive rays are far more massive than electrons and that they are most probably gas ions, that is, charged atoms or molecules.

If a study is made of the way in which the intensity of the light from the positive ion beam decays with increasing distance behind the cathode and if the speeds of the ions are known a result of much interest and importance is attained. The maximum duration of the process of light emission may be computed and is found to be not more than a few hundred millionths of a second. This quantity is of interest because of its relation to the question of the nature of light emission which has long been a major problem.

2-3. Protons and Other Positively Charged Particles

Ions Whereas the principal carrier of negative electricity is the electron, the positive carriers in a gas or vapor discharge are called ions, and they are formed by removal of one or more electrons from the atoms or molecules of gas in the tube. This process is called **ionization.** The atoms or molecules of any gas, or any substance which may be vaporized, may be ionized in an electric discharge, and when accelerated they are called positive rays. However, positively charged ions characteristic of the anode material are also commonly found under certain conditions such as in an arc discharge between metal or carbon electrodes at atmospheric pressure. When these ions or ion clusters are thrown off at the anode the process is called sputtering, and this is sometimes put to practical use in depositing thin films of anode material on a surface.

In an electric discharge in a diatomic gas in which each molecule is composed of two atoms, such as hydrogen (H_2), oxygen (O_2), or nitrogen (N_2), some molecules will be ionized and some will be dissociated, forming separate atoms which in turn may become ionized. Other ion clusters may occasionally form, and multiple as well as single ionization may occur; hence it is evident that the phenomenon of ionization in a gas discharge is more complex than it may at first seem, and a number of types of positive ions may occur even in a single gas.

The proton; mass number The positive gas ion of smallest known mass is found in a discharge tube containing hydrogen. From the vantage point of present knowledge we know that atoms consist of extremely small but relatively massive, positively charged nuclei surrounded by the same number of electrons as there are similar positive charges on the nucleus. According to this picture a hydrogen atom, the lightest of all, consists of a singly charged nuclear particle plus one external electron. Removal of the electron results in ionization of a hydrogen atom and leaves only a bare nucleus of hydrogen. This bare nucleus is called the proton. The proton not only is encountered in the hydrogen discharge; it is also one of the most important particles involved in the structure of the nuclei of all atoms. The mass of a proton is

$$m_p = 1.6724 \times 10^{-24} \text{ gm}$$

when referred to the customary atomic mass scale, for which the most common oxygen atom is chosen as standard and assigned the value 16; the proton then has a mass of 1.007593 (§ 2-7). On this scale the term **mass number** is given to the approximate mass represented by the nearest whole number. The mass number of the proton is consequently 1.

Since a proton is much more massive than an electron it moves much more slowly in an electric field. A proton of the same energy in electron volts as an electron moves with a speed inversely proportional to the square root of the mass ratio 1/1836 or approximately with a speed 1/43 that of an electron of the same energy. A still more massive particle such as, for instance, an ionized mercury atom would acquire a still smaller speed in falling through the same potential difference.

The deuteron The atomic nucleus of next smallest mass is called the deuteron. It is the nucleus of a heavy hydrogen atom, and it is what remains when an atom of heavy hydrogen (deuterium) is ionized by removal of its single electron. The mass of a heavy hydrogen atom (H^2 or D) is approximately twice that of an ordinary hydrogen atom; thus the nucleus has a mass number 2. The deuteron is not a single elementary particle but is composed of one proton plus one neutral particle of nearly the same mass, called the neutron, the nature of which is described later (§15-11).

Less than 1 in every 6000 ordinary hydrogen atoms is an atom of heavy hydrogen, and because of this rarity the deuteron would hardly be found in a gas discharge except when heavy hydrogen has been supplied for that purpose, as in positive-ray analysis. However, the deuteron is often used as the bombarding particle to produce nuclear transformations, and the study of the deuteron itself furnishes important information about the forces holding nuclear particles together.

The alpha particle The next most common nuclear particle in the scale of ascending masses is the alpha particle. It is the nucleus of a helium atom and has a mass number 4. It is composed of two protons and two neutrons. Since a helium atom has two electrons, loss of one of these would result in a singly charged helium atom. Loss of both electrons leaves only the doubly charged bare nucleus of helium, or an alpha particle. The alpha particle plays an important role in radioactivity and nuclear physics, as will be seen later, but it may be found in an electric discharge when helium is present.

The positron One of the most important positive particles is the positive electron or positron. It is the exact twin of an ordinary negative electron except that the charge is positive. This particle occurs most frequently in nuclear transformations and not at all in ordinary gas discharges. It is only mentioned at this time because of its general importance and because it was first detected by the method of magnetic deflection. In observing tracks of cosmic-ray electrons (Chap. 20) by means of a cloud chamber (§ 2-4), Anderson in

1932 noted one track bent by the magnetic field in exactly the opposite direction. It was obvious that the charge must be positive, and thus the world of physics acquired another "fundamental" particle of which much more will be said later.

2-4. The Wilson Cloud Chamber

One of the most beautifully simple yet amazingly effective physical instruments is the Wilson cloud chamber invented by C. T. R. Wilson in Cambridge, England (1907), under the stimulus of J. J. Thomson. It was originally designed to study the clouds of water droplets formed by condensation of water vapor on charged gas particles (ions), and early estimates of the charge of the electron were made by means of it. The silvery thread of droplets which condenses on ions left along the trail of a high-speed particle shows the path that the particle has followed, very much as, on a grander scale, the vapor trail in the sky shows the path of a jet airplane. With the addition of a magnetic field it became possible to distinguish visually between positive particles bent in one direction and negative particles bent in the opposite direction. It was thus that the positive electron or positron was discovered.

The cloud chamber has now become an invaluable means of studying the products of radioactive decay, or the rays from particle accelerators, or cosmic rays. Later discussion (§ 14-13) will deal with the many purposes served by the cloud chamber, but a brief description of the basic principle of its operation will be given here.

In its simplest form, a cloud chamber consists of an enclosed volume of air or gas saturated with water vapor and arranged so that by means of a piston or bellows or other method the pressure may be suddenly reduced, producing an expansion of the air or gas. This cools the water vapor which then tends to condense in the form of tiny droplets. Such condensation, as is well known, tends to occur about dust particles or gas ions. If dust has been carefully excluded from the cloud chamber the ions formed by the passage of a high-speed particle will act as centers of condensation about which droplets will form showing clearly the path of the particle. A piston form of cloud chamber suitable for use in the vertical position is represented in Fig. 2-2.

Different kinds of particles passing through the cloud chamber may usually be distinguished by the type of track produced. Because of its small size a high-speed electron in passing through a gas or vapor may make no more than a few hundred ionizing collisions per centimeter. Consequently the track is a long and thin one. A high-speed

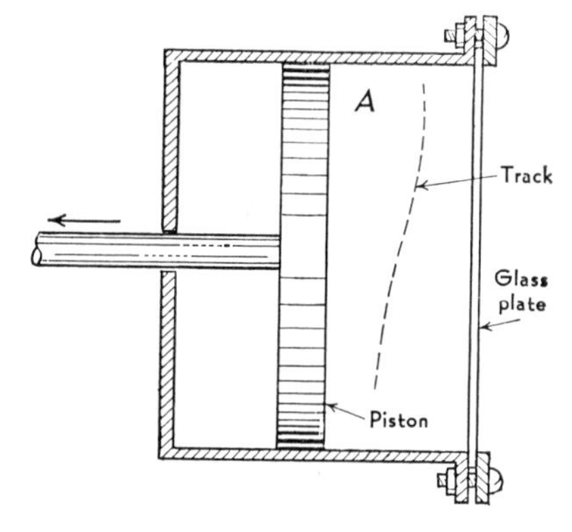

Fig. 2-2. Piston-type cloud chamber. When piston is moved rapidly to the left an expansion is produced in region *A*, where cloud tracks then form and may be observed directly or photographed.

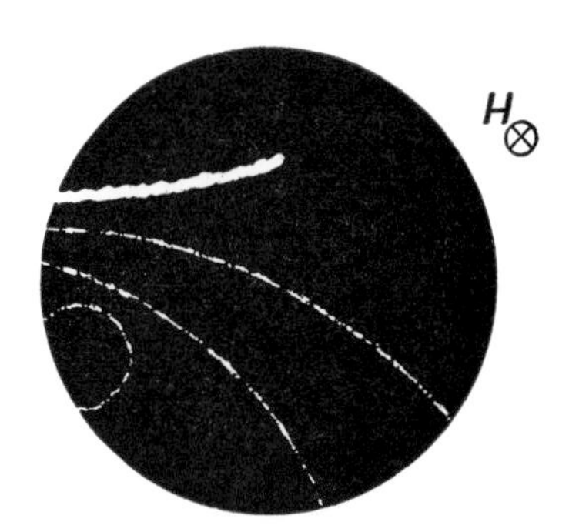

Fig. 2-3. Typical cloud-chamber tracks bent by a magnetic field, direction of which is indicated at *H*. Short heavy track is the kind left by an alpha particle or a proton; the thin tracks are the kind left by electrons of different speeds.

proton or alpha particle, on the other hand, makes many more ionizing collisions per centimeter and forms a shorter, heavier cloud track (Fig. 2-3). Since an alpha particle may make as many as 30,000 ionizing collisions per centimeter in air at atmospheric pressure, it loses energy rapidly and the range of the particle is much less than that of a high-speed electron.

2-5. Positive-Ray Analysis and Isotopes

The nature of positive rays was studied by J. J. Thomson in 1907 by means of electric and magnetic deflections, and he measured the ratio e/m in very much the same way as he had done with electrons. In his best-known experiment with positive rays, the rays were passed through superposed electric and magnetic fields parallel to one another (Fig. 2-4). Such a superposition of fields produces deflections by one field at right angles to those by the other. The deflection produced by an electric field may be seen from Eq. 2-2 to be inversely proportional to the square of the velocity of the particle, whereas the deflection produced by a magnetic field can be shown to be inversely proportional to the first power of the velocity.

If all the ions of a given mass also possessed the same speed they would reveal themselves by a single spot on a photographic plate, but since the ions in a discharge tube are formed at different distances from the cathode they acquire a wide range of velocities from zero to a maximum, and the erstwhile spot is stretched into a section of a parabola (Fig. 2-5). Consequently when ions of different masses are present a parabolic trace is found for each type of atom which is singly charged. Fainter parabolas were frequently found for doubly charged ions of the same atom. A most important result of this work was that the sharply defined parabolas Thomson obtained gave the first direct evidence that atoms of any element (or the atoms of any isotope if the

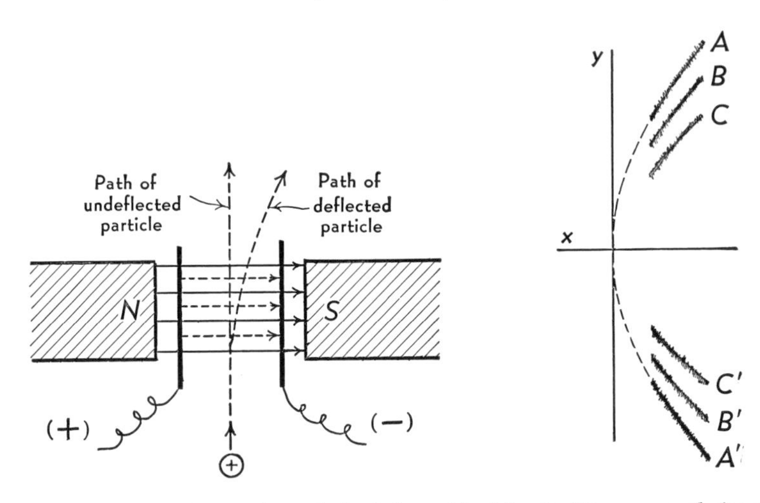

Fig. 2-4. **J. J. Thomson's method of deflecting positive rays by superposed and parallel electric and magnetic fields. Path of deflected particle is bent to right and also away from reader.**

Fig. 2-5. **Positive-ray parabolas obtained by method of Fig. 2-4, showing separation of ions of several elements. Ions of the same mass but different speeds form one trace such as *A* or *A'*. Lower half of curves were obtained by reversing the magnetic field.**

element possesses isotopes) all have exactly the same mass. This had been a questionable point.

In the pioneer experiment Thomson not only successfully separated ions of the same charge and different masses, but he also separated ions of the same mass and different charge. He studied ions in lighter gases in 1913 and found a distinct trace of a neon atom having a mass approximately 10 per cent larger than that of the recognized mass determined by chemical methods. This discovery opened up many new possibilities the investigation of which was delayed until after World War I.

Aston then followed Thomson and designed what is now called a mass spectrograph. With the new design he was able to distinguish between positive-ray particles the masses of which differed by only 1 part in 600. This was 30 times as sensitive as the original method of Thomson, and by the new method Aston made the definite discovery in 1919 of two kinds of neon atoms, one of atomic mass number 20 (Ne^{20}) and the other of mass number 22 (Ne^{22}). These two kinds of neon atoms were entirely indistinguishable chemically. Such atoms of any element, differing in mass though possessing the same general chemical properties, are called **isotopes** of that element. We now know that ordinary neon gas is composed of a mixture of three different kinds of stable atoms or isotopes, in the following proportions: Ne^{20}, 90.9 per cent; Ne^{22}, 8.8 per cent; and the rare Ne^{21}, 0.3 per cent.

The existence of isotopes of certain heavy atoms resulting from radioactive transformations was first recognized in 1905. After that, however, other experimenters entered the field, and the search for new isotopes among the atoms of other, lighter elements became intensified. Along with Aston in England, who investigated many gases, those most prominent in the development of the work in this country were Dempster, who investigated many solids, and later Nier and Bainbridge, who greatly increased the precision of such measurements.

2-6. The Mass Spectrograph

The mass spectrograph devised by Aston made use of successive electric and magnetic deflections (Fig. 2-6). From the diagram it will be observed that ions of somewhat different velocities, passing through the electric field between two plates at E, are spread into a divergent beam, the slower ions being deflected more because they remain in the field between the plates longer. The divergent beam then passes through the magnetic field H at right angles to the paper (represented by the circle). In this region the particles least deflected by the electric field

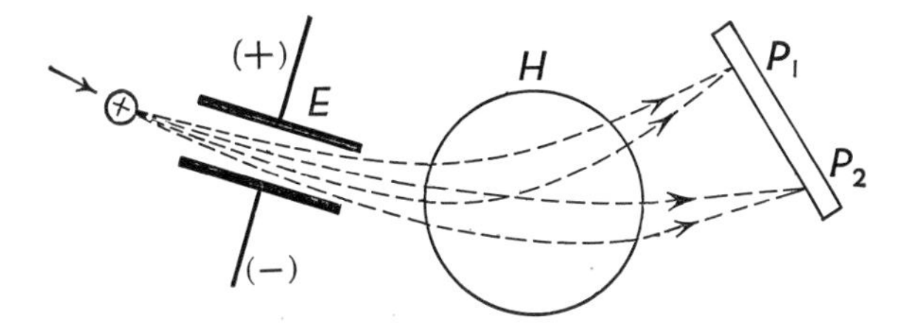

Fig. 2-6. Aston's mass spectrograph. Successive electric and magnetic deflections focus positive rays of the same mass at P_1 and of a different mass at P_2.

are also least deflected by the magnetic field but in the opposite direction. The slower particles of a given mass, being deflected more by both fields, converge again toward the faster particles.

By arranging the geometry and intensities of these fields properly Aston used the magnetic field to bring back to a focus the divergent rays emerging from the region of the electric field. Thus all rays of a given mass but differing in velocity were made to focus sharply at some point P_1 on a photographic plate. All rays of a different mass would focus at another point such as P_2, and so on. With oxygen as the standard of comparison, the masses of the atoms of various elements and of the isotopes of a given element could be obtained in terms of the mass of oxygen.

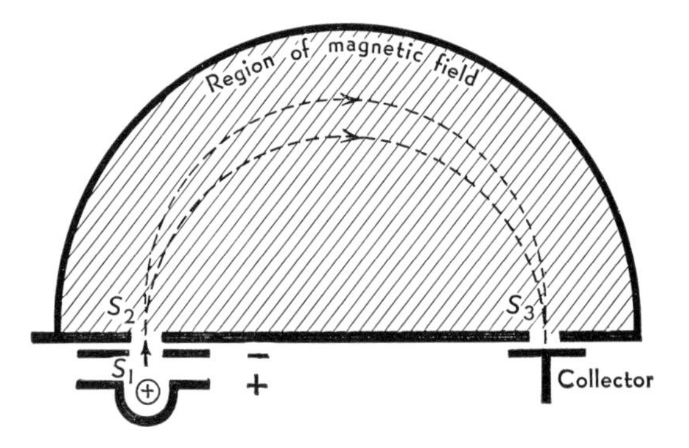

Fig. 2-7. Dempster's first mass spectrograph. Rays are first accelerated by electric field. After passing slit S_2 they are deflected by magnetic field so that rays of only one value of e/m reach collector.

Dempster devised a somewhat different type of mass spectrograph (Fig. 2-7) involving what is called direction focusing. Positive ions emerging from the slit S_2 may be traveling in slightly different directions. Upon entering the region of a uniform magnetic field (shaded region in diagram) their paths are bent into arcs of circles, and after moving through 180° they are again close together and form an approximate though not perfect focus. The early method of detection was to adjust the accelerating potential between S_1 and S_2 until the rays fell upon a slit S_3, behind which was a collecting electrode connected to a suitable detector.

With this apparatus peaks of electric current were measured, and these peaks indicated reception of beams of positive rays of a given mass. The higher the peak of the curve, the greater is the relative abundance of that particular isotope in any mixture. In Fig. 2-8 the results are shown for magnesium, indicating the existence of isotopes of mass numbers 24, 25, and 26. From this it is seen that ordinary magnesium is a mixture of isotopes with that of Mg^{24} strongly predominating. By measuring the abundances it was evident that the fractional atomic mass 24.34 obtained by the chemist for magnesium is the result of ordinary magnesium being the mixture of these isotopes of different masses.

To make more accurate measurements it was desirable to have sharper focusing of the rays. To detect rarer isotopes it was desirable to have more intense beams. The latter can be obtained by making the slit wider, but the ions now emerge from the wider slit with a larger range of directions. The direction focusing adopted by Dempster, though only approximate, improved the resolution of the lines con-

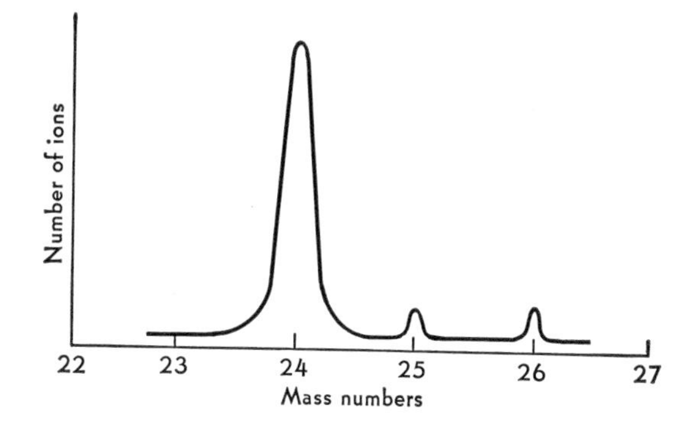

Fig. 2-8. Results of Dempster's measurements of magnesium, indicating three isotopes, with that of mass number 24 predominating.

siderably, but the peaks of the curve were also broadened because not all rays had the same speed. To sharpen the peaks a "velocity selector" (§ 1-8) was tried, but by thus limiting the beam to a narrow range of speeds the intensity was reduced too much for use with isotopes of low abundance.

Dempster now remodeled his mass spectrograph so as to obtain both direction and "velocity focusing." The rays were bent by the electric field E between curved plates (Fig. 2-9), and those of different speeds and directions were refocused by the magnetic field H. The ions were formed by a spark or arc near the anode and acquired more nearly the same speed in the accelerating field. With these improvements masses could be measured to 1 part in 4000. The race for high precision was now on. Bainbridge, following Dempster, used direction and "velocity focusing." Nier and others joined the race and reached new

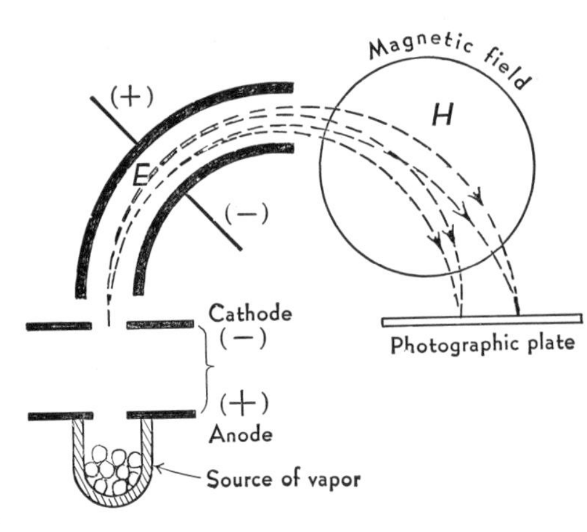

Fig. 2-9. Dempster's improved mass spectrograph.

heights of precision. It is now one of the wonders of science that isotopic masses can readily be determined accurately to a few parts in 100,000 and in some instances to as much as a few parts in 100 million. Dempster measured many of the heavy elements and discovered the rare isotope of uranium U^{235} destined to become so important in the field of atomic energy. Later Nier separated enough of it to show that it was the most important isotope in the fission of uranium.

2-7. Isotopic Masses, Physical Scale, and Atomic Mass Unit

Before the discovery of isotopes, chemists had been in the habit of measuring atomic weights in relation to the atomic weight of oxygen which they arbitrarily chose as 16 for reasons of convenience. Accordingly, unit weight was 1/16 the weight of an oxygen atom as then measured. When the atomic weight of chlorine, for instance, was stated as 35.46, the meaning was that the weight of a chlorine atom was 35.46 times 1/16 the weight of an oxygen atom. Long after the discovery of isotopes it was found that not all oxygen atoms have the same weight or mass, and it became clear that chemical atomic weights had been measured in terms of a hypothetical average oxygen atom which does not exist. Indeed, most other elements are likewise mixtures of stable isotopes. For instance, the fractional atomic weight of chlorine results from its being a mixture of two isotopes, Cl^{35} and Cl^{37}, in a ratio of nearly 3 to 1.

When ordinary oxygen gas was studied, it was found to be a mixture of three isotopes. As luck would have it the chief one of the three turned out to have a mass only slightly less than the hypothetical average, and to this is now assigned the mass 16.0000000. Ordinary oxygen, we now know, is composed of 99.76 per cent O^{16}, 0.2 per cent O^{18}, and 0.04 per cent of the much rarer isotope O^{17}. Such a mixture of the three isotopes gives an average mass of 16.00444. Measurements of mass made with reference to the latter value are said to be made on the **chemical scale.** Measurements made with respect to the one common isotope of oxygen as 16, that is, to O^{16} as 16.0000000, are made on what is called the **physical scale.** Since measurements made on the chemical scale are made with reference to "average oxygen," they are made in terms of a slightly more massive unit, and consequently the number obtained will be slightly smaller. Any atomic mass on the chemical scale must be multiplied by 1.00027 in order to give the correct value on the physical scale.

In the earlier days of chemical study of the atoms it was usually considered that the numbers representing atomic weights were only relative numbers representing ratios to the atomic weight of oxygen. Two important changes have taken place. Since mass is independent of gravity, the use of the concept of mass is preferable to that of weight, and the numbers representing relative masses are now commonly thought of as actual masses in terms of a new unit of mass. This new

TABLE 2-1. SOME PARTICLE AND ISOTOPIC MASSES

(Masses of the following bare nuclei are less than atoms by the total mass (0.000549*Z*) of the extranuclear electrons.)

Particle	Mass (amu)
Electron	0.000549
Proton	1.007593 (±3)
Neutron	1.008982 (±3)
Alpha particle	4.002775 (±15)
Isotope (atom)	
Hydrogen, H^1	1.008142 (±3)
Hydrogen, H^2	2.014732 (±4)
Helium, He^4	4.003860 (±12)
Carbon, C^{12}	12.0038167 (±8)
Oxygen, O^{16}	16.0000000 (standard)
Oxygen, O^{17}	17.004507 (±15)
Oxygen, O^{18}	18.004875 (±13)
Neon, Ne^{20}	19.998771 (±12)
Neon, Ne^{22}	21.998329 (±19)
Chlorine, Cl^{35}	34.980064 (±22)
Chlorine, Cl^{37}	36.977675 (±21)
Silver, Ag^{107}	106.950
Silver, Ag^{109}	108.949
Uranium, U^{238}	238.123

unit is called the *atomic mass unit* (amu) and is 1/16 the mass of 1 atom of O^{16}. In grams it has the value

$$1 \text{ amu} = 1.6595 \times 10^{-24} \text{ gm}$$

The masses of a number of light atoms are given in Table 2-1. There is a difference between the mass of an atom in the neutral state and the mass of an ionized atom. An ionized atom has lost one or more electrons, and although the mass of the electron is relatively very small it is by no means negligible in comparison to the atomic mass when measurements are made to a high degree of precision as they now frequently are. Consequently the mass of an electron which is 0.000549 amu must be added to the mass of any singly charged ion to get the mass of the neutral atom.

2-8. Nature of Isotopes and Nuclear Structure

The question of how isotopes of an element can exist, all having approximately the same general chemical properties yet possessing different masses, was not satisfactorily answered until the discovery of the neutron in 1932. It had been known that the general chemical properties and most of the physical properties of an atom are determined by the number of electrons surrounding the nucleus. All the atoms of any element regardless of mass have the same number of positive charges on the nucleus, and this determines that they must also have the same number of electrons surrounding the nucleus, but the nucleus may also contain neutrons possessing mass without resultant charge. Since an excess or deficit of neutrons does not change the nuclear charge it does not change the number of surrounding electrons or the general properties of the atom, aside from the change in mass. Consequently the *isotopes of any element may be defined as atoms all having the same characteristic nuclear charge but different numbers of neutrons in the nucleus.* Since we now believe that each positive charge of electron magnitude in the nucleus is associated with a proton we conclude that atomic nuclei are made up of protons and neutrons.

Present-day ideas about the nature of atoms were foreshadowed by Prout, who noticed more than a century ago that the weights of most of the atoms then known were close multiples of that of hydrogen. This led him to infer that perhaps all atoms were in some way built up from hydrogen, the lightest of all. When it was found that some atoms have fractional atomic weights nowhere near integral multiples of hydrogen the theory was abandoned. Today these exceptions are easily explained since the apparent fractional atomic weights result from mixtures of isotopes, but Prout's theory has to be revised to include neutrons in the nucleus.

2-9. Heavy Hydrogen (Deuterium)

When Aston first measured the atomic mass of hydrogen he found it to be in good agreement with the established value obtained by the chemists of 1.0078. Curiously enough the agreement which first looked so good was actually due to a small, unrecognized error made by Aston. This was before the discovery of the rarer isotopes of oxygen beginning in 1929. When the atomic mass of hydrogen was recomputed on the new physical scale in terms of the oxygen isotope O^{16}, it turned out to be appreciably smaller than the value obtained by the chemists. Here was a puzzle. The difference though small was too large to be assigned to experimental error.

It was suggested by Birge and Menzel in 1931 that the discrepancy might be due to the existence of one or more heavier isotopes of hydrogen, and in 1932 spectroscopic evidence was found (§ 8-9) of the existence of a rare isotope of hydrogen having a mass almost twice that of ordinary hydrogen. This is the isotope called heavy hydrogen or deuterium, H^2 or D, and its importance has grown rapidly. In combination with oxygen it forms "heavy water," one of the uses of which is as a moderator in nuclear reactors (§ 19-11); the importance of the heavy hydrogen nucleus or deuteron has already been noted (§ 2-3).

2-10. Avogadro's Number and the Faraday

Before the establishment of the accurate masses of atoms another extremely important atomic quantity had finally been determined with precision: the number of atoms in a gram-atomic weight of any substance, and also the number of molecules in a gram-molecular weight, also now called the gram-formula weight. In mks units it is the number in a kilogram-atomic weight. This important number is called Avogadro's number, after the great Italian scientist. In 1811, nine years after Dalton had introduced the concept of atoms into chemistry as a working hypothesis, Avogadro pointed out that current thinking led to the conclusion that equal volumes of different gases at the same temperature and pressure contain equal numbers of molecules. Although slow in gaining general acceptance, this principle has now been amply confirmed by many experiments.

The term *gram-atomic weight* (or gram-atom) has long served to represent the number of grams of any substance equal numerically to its atomic weight. This is a useful quantity because, if the atoms of one substance have twice the mass or atomic weight of the atoms of another substance, then a gram-atomic weight of the one will contain twice as many grams as the other, and it is evident that each will contain the same number of atoms as the other. In consequence we can say that a gram-atomic weight of any element contains the same number of atoms as a gram-atomic weight of any other element. The same rule applies to the molecules of a substance, where a *gram-molecular weight* is defined as the number of grams of a given molecule numerically equal to its molecular weight.

The term *molecular-formula weight* is now often used instead of molecular weight so as to emphasize that the atoms of a compound are associated in definite proportions even though, as in crystals, they do not form separate and individual molecules.

For a long time it was only possible to determine Avogadro's number by methods of more or less rough approximation. For instance, if some substance in crystalline form was studied the spacings of the atoms could be estimated if their sizes were known and their geometrical arrangement in the crystal were recognizable. From this it was possible to calculate the number of atoms in a gram-atomic or gram-molecular weight. Still, the sizes of atoms and molecules were only known to a rough degree of accuracy, and the value of Avogadro's number thus computed was likewise only approximate. However, with the precise measurement of the charge of the electron an alternate method presented itself by which Avogadro's number could be obtained with much accuracy in a very simple manner. For this story we must go back momentarily to Faraday's experiments on electrolysis.

Faraday made an experimental investigation of electrolysis in the earlier part of the nineteenth century. He found that, when copper, silver, or another metal was deposited upon an electrode by passage of an electric current through a solution containing the metal ions, the mass of the metal deposited is directly proportional to the atomic weight of that element and to the quantity of electricity passing through the solution.

The quantity of electricity required to deposit 1 gram-atomic weight of any monovalent element (an element forming singly charged ions) can be directly measured and is 96,522 coulombs. This quantity of electricity is now called the **faraday** and is the same for all elements. A related quantity, the *electrochemical equivalent*, is the number of grams of an element deposited by 1 coulomb of electricity (Table 2-2) and is different for different elements.

$$1 \text{ faraday} = 96{,}522 \text{ coulombs}$$

TABLE 2-2. SOME ELECTROCHEMICAL EQUIVALENTS

Element	Symbol	Number of Charges (valence)	Electrochemical Equivalent, gm/coulomb
Hydrogen	H	1	0.000010444
Copper	Cu	2	0.0003295
Zinc	Zn	2	0.0003387
Silver	Ag	1	0.0011183

For a bivalent element (one forming doubly charged ions) twice as much electricity is required as for the singly charged ions of a monovalent element. Experimental evidence early indicated that all singly charged ions must carry the same electric charge, and we now know that this is the same in magnitude as the charge of one electron. Ions with multiple charges would then carry charges which are integral multiples of the charge of one electron. In depositing 1 gram-atomic weight of any substance, Avogadro's number or N_0 atoms are deposited. If each carries a charge e, the total quantity of charge Q per gram-atomic weight is $N_0 e$. But this is the faraday F. Consequently,

$$N_0 e = F \quad [2\text{-}3]$$

Solving for N_0,

$$N_0 = \frac{F}{e} \quad [2\text{-}4]$$

Since the quantity of electricity F can be measured with much precision and since the charge e has also been determined with great precision, Avogadro's number is now known to a similar, high degree of precision. Its value is

$$\begin{aligned} N_0 &= 6.025 \times 10^{23} \text{ (per gram-atomic weight)} \\ &= 6.025 \times 10^{26} \text{ (per kilogram-atomic weight)} \end{aligned}$$

The uses of Avogadro's number are manifold, and it is one of the important constants of science. Since a gram-molecule of any gas occupies a volume of 22,415 cm^3 at 0° C and 76 cm mercury pressure, it is a simple matter to find the number of molecules per cm^3 of a gas under standard conditions. This is the prodigious number 2.68×10^{19}.

PROBLEMS

1. A particle 100 times the mass of a proton and possessing a positive charge twice the magnitude of that of an electron acquires what velocity in passing through a drop in potential of 1 volt? 100 volts?

Ans. 1.96×10^3 m/sec; 1.96×10^4 m/sec.

2. An alpha particle having a velocity 1/30 that of light and a mass of 6.65×10^{-24} gm will be deflected in the arc of a circle of what radius by a magnetic field of flux density 1 weber/m^2 (10,000 gauss)?

Ans. 0.208 meter.

3. Two particles move through a uniform magnetic field at right angles to it. If one of the particles has 24 times the mass, 6 times the charge, and 10 times the velocity of the other particle, what will be the ratio of the radii of curvature of their paths?

Ans. 40.

4. A singly ionized atom moves across a uniform magnetic field of flux density 1045 gauss (0.1045 weber/m^2) with a velocity of 10^6 m/sec. Its path is curved in the arc of a circle of 10 cm radius. Compute the mass of the atom.

Ans. 1.67×10^{-27} kg.

5. By application of Eq. 1-19 find the velocity acquired by a proton in an accelerating field of 10^6 volts and in one of 10^7 volts.

Ans. 0.046*c*; 0.15*c*.

6. Compute the velocities of an alpha particle accelerated by 100 Mev without the relativistic correction and with it.

Ans. 9.8×10^8 m/sec;
6.8×10^6 m/sec.

7. If the protons and deuterons accelerated by a potential difference of 100 volts pass through a small slit and are deflected by a magnetic field of 0.005 weber/m^2 (50 gauss), what will be the separation of the beams after traversing a semicircle?

Ans. 24 cm.

8. What is the approximate separation of the lines formed on a photographic film by the two isotopes of neon, of mass number 20 and 22, if the ions emerge from a narrow slit and travel a semicircular path in a magnetic field of flux density 0.01 weber/m^2 (100 gauss)? (Assume they have been accelerated by a difference of potential of 100 volts and are singly charged.)

Ans. 6.3 cm.

9. Two isotopes of a substance have atomic masses of 44 and 46, respectively. What percentage of each would give an apparent atomic mass of 45.8?

Ans. 10% of 44; 90% of 46.

10. The two isotopes of chlorine have masses of approximately 35 amu and 37 amu. Their relative abundances are 75.4 and 24.6 per cent, respectively. Find the chemical atomic weight.

Ans. 35.49.

11. Ordinary oxygen has an apparent atomic weight of 16.0044 on the physical scale. If composed chiefly of O^{16} and the rarer O^{18} isotope, what percentage of the atoms are the rare isotope?

Ans. 0.22%.

12. How many coulombs of electricity are required to deposit 10 gm of copper if each copper atom carries 2 charges (valence 2)?

Ans. 30,400 coulombs.

13. How many grams of silver will be deposited by 1 ampere of current flowing for 1 hour?

Ans. 4.03 gm.

14. From a knowledge of Avogadro's number, the atomic weight, and the known magnitude of the electronic charge, compute the number of grams of silver deposited by 1 coulomb of electricity (electrochemical equivalent).

Ans. 0.001118 gm/coul.

15. Compute the number of grams of copper (valence 2) deposited by 1 coulomb of electricity.

Ans. 0.000329 gm/coul.

16. If a gram-atomic weight of mercury is 200.5 grams, what volume will it occupy (density = 13.59 gm/cm^3)? How many atoms will there be per cm^3? What is the distance between centers of the atoms, assuming that they are packed directly on top of one another in parallel layers?

Ans. 2.92×10^{-8} cm or 2.92 A.

17. If the atoms in a cm^3 of silver are assumed to be arranged in regular layers on top of one another, what is the spacing of the layers if the density of silver is 10.5 gm/cm^3?

Ans. 2.58×10^{-8} cm or 2.58 A.

SUGGESTED READING

J. D. Stranathan, *The "Particles" of Modern Physics* (Philadelphia, Blakiston, 1942).

K. K. Darrow, *Introduction to Contemporary Physics,* 2nd ed. (New York, Van Nostrand, 1939).

J. B. Hoag and S. A. Korff, *Electron and Nuclear Physics,* 3rd ed. (New York, Van Nostrand, 1948).

F. W. Aston, *Mass Spectra and Isotopes* (New York, Longmans Green, 1933).

J. J. Thomson, *Rays of Positive Electricity and Their Application to Chemical Analysis,* 2nd ed. (London, Longmans Green, 1921).

CHAPTER 3

EMISSION OF ELECTRONS FROM METALS

3-1. Types of Emission

Electrons are most easily studied when they are removed as far as possible from surrounding matter. That is why many studies of electrons have been made in discharge tubes more or less highly evacuated. In the tubes it is necessary to obtain a supply of electrons in the space between the electrodes. This usually involves the emission of electrons by the cathode.

There are four common ways of getting electrons out of metals. These are thermionic emission, photoelectric emission, secondary emission, and field emission.

1. *Thermionic emission* is the emission of electrons from bodies at high temperatures by a process of evaporation.

2. *Photoelectric emission* is the ejection of electrons from a sensitive surface by the action of light (electromagnetic radiation) of the proper frequency falling on this surface.

3. *Secondary electron emission* is the emission of electrons from a surface that is being bombarded by other high-speed electrons. In an electric discharge in a gas, electrons may also be liberated at the cathode by positive ion bombardment.

4. *Field emission* is the emission of electrons from some portion of

a surface by an applied electric field intense enough to enable the electrons to escape from the metal.

These four methods have sometimes been rather lightheartedly referred to as "boil 'em out," "kick 'em out," "knock 'em out," and "pull 'em out." To understand the various processes of emission it is necessary to learn something of the state of the electrons in a metal before emission and the conditions under which they may escape from the metal.

3-2. Electrons in Metals

The problem of understanding how electricity flows through a conductor was long one of the great puzzles of science. With the discovery of the electron and the recognition of the electrical nature of the atom the problem became simpler but still presented many difficulties. In view of the extremely small size of the electron it was possible to qualitatively picture it as moving along a wire by passing through the spaces between atoms or in some fashion being handed on from atom to atom. There remained difficulties, however, in making the picture give quantitative results in agreement with experiment until the adoption of the more revolutionary methods of modern quantum mechanics (Chaps. 12 and 13). This involves treating the electron as a wave instead of a particle, a matter to be discussed in Chap. 6. Here we shall treat electrons as particles in the more classical tradition.

The differences between a conductor such as copper or silver and an insulator such as glass or sulfur depend upon the fact that in a conductor there are a large number of so-called "free" electrons, essentially the one or more valence electrons per atom. These are more or less free to move from atom to atom and from one part of a metal to another. In an insulator the electrons belonging to an atom are normally far more firmly bound to the atom and can be dislodged only with difficulty, if at all.

In 1903 Richardson in England proposed the theory that the free electrons in a metal possess a random motion similar to the molecules of a gas. They are presumed to be continually moving about with random motion, colliding with one another and with the atoms comprising the conductor, and colliding with the surface of the conductor much as the molecules of a gas in a room move about colliding with one another and with the walls of the room. By analogy these electrons are then often said to constitute an *electron gas*. When there is no difference of potential along a conductor, and no net transport of charge, as many electrons on the average are presumed to move in one direction as in the opposite direction. Based on this view a current of electricity in a solid conductor produced by a difference of potential consists of a drift of the electron gas in the direction in which a negative charge would move. The individual electrons are assumed to preserve their random motion as they drift along, just as molecules do in a current of air. Although this is an oversimplified view of an electric current in a solid conductor the main ideas are nearly correct enough for present purposes. Later we shall find that the most probable random speeds of electrons in a metal are different from the most probable speeds that the molecules of a gas possess (Chap. 13).

The free electrons in a conductor do not need to drift at a high speed through the conductor in order to constitute a considerable electric current because there are so many of them able to move. Whereas in a low-pressure gas discharge the velocities of electrons may be surprisingly high, amounting to hundreds or even thousands of miles per second, in a conductor the electrons progress at speeds on the average of only a small fracton of a centimeter per second. The reason why an electric current seems to flow almost instantly along a wire is that a wave of repulsion travels along a good conductor at a speed approaching that of light. This is an electromagnetic wave in which the field acts to set the electrons along the conductor in motion. Although the electrons themselves drift quite slowly the electromagnetic field which sets them in motion travels very fast. Since there is such a plentiful supply of free electrons in any conductor, the problem arises of how to get these electrons out of the conductor into a region where they can be studied or can serve some other purpose.

3-3. Thermionic Emission

One of the chief ways of getting electrons out of metal is by raising the temperature of the metal until the increased random motion of electrons is sufficient to enable an appreciable number to pass through the surface barrier of the metal. This process is known as thermionic emission. The surface of a metal does not present so solid a barrier as the walls of a room present to gas molecules. The barrier is an electric one, and electrons in passing the boundary surface must overcome a reverse electric field. This reverse field is the result of differences of potential, called a potential barrier. According to classical theory the electron can only escape when its energy in electron volts represents more volts than that of the barrier, thus enabling the electron to "pass over" the barrier. According to the more recently developed ideas of quantum or wave mechanics (Chap. 10) there is always a finite probability that an electron of lesser energy may "leak" through a barrier, but in the present chapter the complications involved in that possibility need not be included.

The discovery of thermionic emission goes back to a well-known experiment performed by Thomas A. Edison in 1884 while he was developing the incandescent lamp. He found that, if an additional electrode *P* (Fig. 3-1) was placed inside the bulb and if the filament was then made to glow, a strange effect was noted. When the extra electrode was made positive with respect to the filament, an electric current seemed to flow across the empty space between electrode and filament. The direction of the positive flow of current was always from electrode to filament. If the electrode was made negative with respect

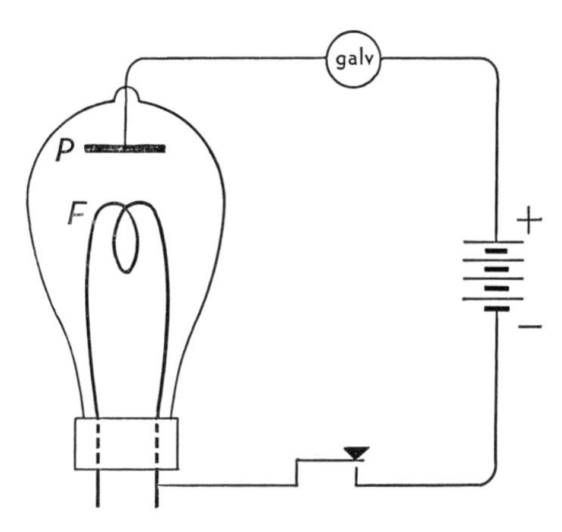

Fig. 3-1. Edison effect. Electric current flows across gap between filament *F* and plate *P* only when *P* is made positive with respect to *F*.

to the filament no current between the two could be detected. This effect, now called the *Edison effect,* could not be explained on the basis of the knowledge of that day. After the discovery of the electron the effect could be readily explained if the hot filament were assumed to emit electrons or other negatively charged particles. The emission was soon fully confirmed, and in 1899 J. J. Thomson and others determined the charge-to-mass ratio of the particles emitted by hot metals. The ratio was found to be the same as that for cathode rays, and thus the emitted particles were identified as electrons.

It was soon observed that thermionic emission increased very rapidly with a rise in temperature of the emitter. It was also found to depend upon the nature of the emitting surface. Since a tungsten wire filament could be heated to a very high temperature without melting, it soon became the standard filament for thermionic devices. The first practical device based on this effect was a simple two-electrode tube, now called a diode. This was used for rectifying alternating current by Fleming in England and was called the *Fleming valve.* In 1906 De Forest in this country had the brilliant idea of controlling the flow of electrons from filament to positive electrode, now called the anode or plate, by means of a wire mesh or grid. Thus was born the three-electrode tube or triode, which has led to such extraordinary developments in radio and long-distance telephony and in the more recent fields of television and radar. As is commonly known, the introduction of still more electrodes into various types of electronic tubes has led to many new applications.

3-4. The Thermionic-Emission Equation

Richardson in England made the most complete early study of thermionic emission. Building on the concept of the random motions of free electrons in a metal he showed that if a given electron should happen to acquire enough velocity it might be expected to pass the surface barrier and escape from the metal.

Richardson then made a mathematical analysis based on the theory of evaporation in order to deduce the number of electrons that would be expected to escape per second from unit area of a hot filament as a function of temperature. The accepted form of this equation is

$$i = AT^2\epsilon^{-(\varphi/kT)} = AT^2 \exp\left(-\frac{\varphi}{kT}\right) \qquad [3\text{-}1]$$

Richardson actually arrived at two equations on the basis of different theoretical assumptions. These equations differed in the exponent of the first T, but the one given here has been shown to agree with modern theory by Dushman and others. To understand this equation we must note that as T, the absolute temperature, increases the exponential term increases very rapidly, making it difficult to distinguish between T^2 and $T^{1/2}$ of the earlier equations. In the exponential term, φ is called the **work function** of the emitting surface, and k is the well-known Boltzmann constant of the kinetic theory of gases (§ 11-4).

$$k = 1.38 \times 10^{-23} \text{ joule/degree Kelvin}$$
$$= 1.38 \times 10^{-16} \text{ erg/degree Kelvin}$$

The work function φ of a surface is a measure of the barrier which the emitted electrons have to pass at the surface of the emitter. Work functions are often expressed in electron volts, but in Eq. 3-1 they must be reduced to joules or ergs since the denominator of the exponent will also be in joules or ergs. Values of the work function are characteristic of the particular material used and for the most part vary between 2 and 6 electron volts (Table 3-1).

TABLE 3-1. SOME WORK FUNCTIONS
(in electron volts)

Element	Thermionic Work Functions	Photoelectric Work Functions
Cesium	1.81	1.9
Sodium	—	2.28
Nickel	5.03	5.01
Mercury	—	4.53
Platinum	6.27	6.30
Tantalum	4.07	4.12
Tungsten	4.52	4.54
Zinc	—	4.3

According to theory the constant A should be independent of the particular metal used and should have a value of 60.2 for perfectly clean metals when the emitting surface area is 1 cm^2. Experimental difficulties in measuring both the work function and the constant A for clean metallic surfaces are very great, but the value of A found experimentally for several metals is close to this value and for most others lies between 60.2 and 120.4. The form of this equation, however, closely agrees with experimental observations, and in any actual circumstance the constant A for a given surface can be determined by experiment.

An experimental check of the general validity of the equation can be made by a plot of experimental values in the following manner. First, take natural logarithms of both sides of the equation.

$$\ln i = \ln A + \ln T^2 - \frac{\varphi}{kT} \qquad [3\text{-}2]$$

$$\ln\left(\frac{i}{T^2}\right) = \ln A - \left(\frac{\varphi}{k}\right)\frac{1}{T} \qquad [3\text{-}3]$$

If common logarithms are used the equation becomes

$$\log_{10}\frac{i}{T^2} = \log_{10} A - \left(\frac{0.434\varphi}{k}\right)\frac{1}{T} \qquad [3\text{-}3a]$$

Equation 3-3 (or 3-3*a*) is now of the form

$$y = b + mx$$

which is the equation of a straight line, and when values of ln (i/T^2) are plotted against $1/T$ the slope of the line is φ/k (or $-0.434\varphi/k$). From the known value of k, the thermionic work function φ may then be obtained. The fact that the plotted points actually lie on (or close to) a straight line indicates the validity of the equation.

Example Find the thermionic-emission current from the surface of a pure tungsten filament 0.1 mm in circumference and 1 cm long at a temperature of 2500° K.

Assume $A = 60.2$

Emission in amperes per cm² is given by Eq. 3-1.

$$\frac{\varphi}{kT} = \frac{4.52 \text{ ev} \times 1.6 \times 10^{-12} \text{ erg/ev}}{1.38 \times 10^{-16} \text{ erg/°K} \times 2500° \text{ K}}$$

$$= 21 \left(\frac{\text{ergs}}{\text{ergs}}\right)$$

$$\exp(-21) = 7.58 \times 10^{-10}$$

$$i = 60.2 \times (2500)^2 \exp(-21) = 0.28 \text{ amp/cm}^2$$

$$I = \text{amp/cm}^2 \times \text{area}$$

$$= 0.28 \times 0.01 = 0.0028 \text{ amp} = 2.8 \text{ ma}$$

3-5. Space Charge and Space Current

The electrons emitted from a hot filament if slowed down in their escape may seem to collect around the filament in what is called a

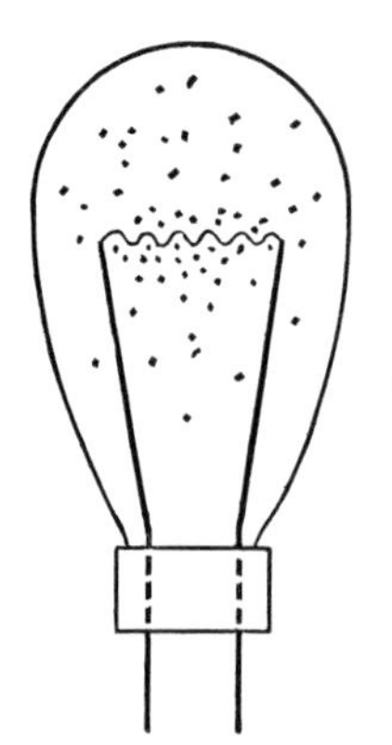

Fig. 3-2. Electron space charge in tube such as an incandescent lamp or any tube with a hot filament. Some electrons diffuse to walls of tube and charge them negatively.

space charge (Fig. 3-2). Since there is mutual repulsion between electrons those at the outer edge of the space-charge cloud may drift as far as the walls of the containing vessel. The cloud has a marked effect upon the further emission of electrons. Because of mutual repulsion the cloud tends to make it more difficult for electrons to successfully get away from the filament. An equilibrium state is reached when as many electrons are returned to the filament by repulsion and random motion as are emitted per unit time.

If another electrode is now placed within the tube, and if it is made positive with respect to the filament, the space charge will tend to be dissipated by moving toward the anode under the action of the field. This disturbs the equilibrium condition and permits more electrons to escape successfully from the filament (cathode). Thus an electron current is set up from filament to anode. In a highly evacuated tube there are no appreciable gas ions formed, and only the electrons move, although according to the usual convention we say that positive current flows from anode to filament or cathode. If the potential of the anode is increased with respect to the cathode, more of the space-charge electrons will be drawn to it and the current is thereby increased.

In this experiment we see that there are three important variables, the current through the tube, the difference of potential between anode and cathode, and the temperature of the cathode which is determined by a separate heating current. Variations of current with voltage for different fixed temperatures in one experiment are shown in Fig. 3-3. The temperature T_3 is higher than T_2 (which in turn is higher than T_1), and it is seen that the maximum current is also larger. For a given temperature the current reaches a maximum when the anode voltage is sufficiently high with respect to the cathode and thereafter does not increase with voltage. This is called the *saturation current* for a particular temperature and represents the state in which electrons are removed to the plate or anode as fast as they are emitted by the cathode. In the portion of the curve where the current is increasing with increasing anode voltage the current is said to be *limited by space charge.* In the horizontal portion of the curve the saturation current is said to be *limited by emission.* If the temperature is increased the emission is also increased and the saturation current is likewise larger.

It should be noted that in Fig. 3-3 current and voltage are not directly proportional. Doubling the voltage does not double the current. This is contrary to Ohm's law for a metallic conductor where, for a given temperature, current and voltage are directly proportional, that is, the relation between them is *linear.* In an electronic tube with two

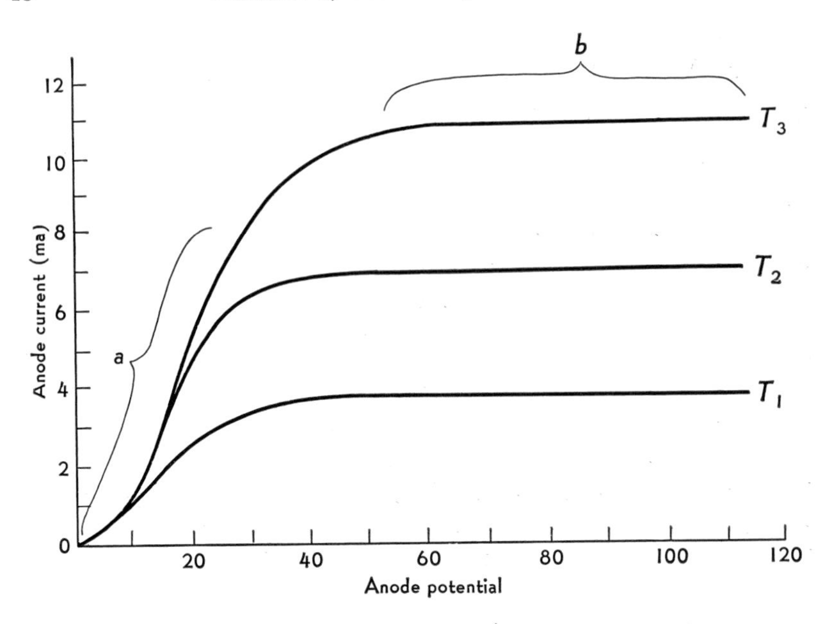

Fig. 3-3. Anode currents in a diode for different filament temperatures; *a*, current limited by space charge, *b*, saturation current, current limited by emission.

or more electrodes the current-voltage curve as indicated is *nonlinear*, and such a device is commonly said to be a *nonlinear conductor*. Since current can flow in one direction only it is also said to be a *unilateral nonlinear conductor*.

It is of interest to compare the equations for these two types of conduction. The familiar equation for a linear conductor is Ohm's law, $I = V/R$. For the simplest case of nonlinear electron conduction in a vacuum between extended parallel-plane electrodes, the current per unit area or current density J is given by the following equation:

$$J = \frac{1}{9\pi}\sqrt{\frac{2e}{m}}\frac{V^{3/2}}{x^2} = A\,\frac{V^{3/2}}{x^2} \qquad [3\text{-}4]$$

This becomes

$$\mathrm{J}\,\frac{(\mathrm{amp})}{(\mathrm{cm}^2)} = 2.33 \times 10^{-6}\,\frac{V^{3/2}}{x^2} \qquad [3\text{-}5]$$

where V is in volts and x the separation of the electrodes is in cm.

This law is known as Child's law, or the "three-halves-power law," and it can be made to apply by suitable modification to concentric cylinders and generally to the electrodes found in most radio tubes of this type. The derivation of the equation can be found in more advanced texts but is based on the following important simplifying assumptions:

1. The electrodes are infinite parallel planes.
2. A plentiful supply of electrons of zero velocity is maintained at the cathode.
3. The current is limited only by space charge and not by emission or other processes.
4. There is no gas between the electrodes that might retard electrons or produce ions.
5. Electrodes are of the same metal to eliminate contact potentials (§ 3-6).

For concentric cylindrical electrodes in the ideal case, where the radius of the outer cylinder is r and the inner cylinder is small, as for instance, the cathode of a radio tube, r enters to the first power and

$$J\left(\frac{\text{amp}}{\text{cm}^2}\right) = 14.65 \times 10^{-6}\frac{V^{3/2}}{r} \qquad [3\text{-}6]$$

where V is in volts and r is in cm.

For a three-electrode radio tube the addition of the third electrode or grid involves still another variable. If the temperature of the filament is kept constant, the current through the tube is determined both by the grid potential with respect to the cathode and by the plate potential with respect to the cathode.

3-6. Contact Potential

When two solid conductors of different material at the same temperature are in contact there is always a difference of potential between their outer surfaces or between the terminals of any conductors connected to them. This difference of potential, called the contact potential, cannot be measured by an ordinary voltmeter, no matter how sensitive, since connecting the voltmeter across the terminals completes the circuit and opposes the contact potential of the inner surfaces by that of the outer surfaces.

Such contact potentials can by no means be neglected in many types of experimental work especially where the differences of potential between two electrodes of different material are involved, and they must be added to (or subtracted from) normal voltage readings. Contact potentials arise because the conduction electrons in different metals are in different energy states. When two such metals are in contact and are at the same temperature the electrons tend to flow from the metal in which their normal energy level is higher to the metal in which their normal energy level is lower. This flow is only momentary since the metal toward which they flow becomes charged negatively by the transfer of charge and its potential drops until the flow is stopped and the two metals are then at different potentials. This is the contact difference of potential, and for any two metals A and B it is the difference of their work functions.

$$\text{Contact difference of potential} = \varphi_A - \varphi_B$$

where φ_A and φ_B are the work functions, respectively, of the two metals. This is apparent if one considers that the work function of a metal represents a barrier above the upper energy levels of the conduction electrons in that metal. When two metals are in contact the difference between these two barriers is the difference between their work functions and is also the same as the difference between the upper energy levels of their conduction electrons. Similar conditions give rise to thermoelectric emf's. When the junctions of two or more metals are not at the same temperature, the differences in potential at these junctions when summed up around a closed circuit do not cancel. More complex explanations based on quantum mechanics can be found in more advanced texts.

3-7. Thoriated and Oxide-Coated Surfaces

It has been found possible to greatly reduce the effective work function of a tungsten surface by coating the filament as nearly as possible with a *monatomic layer* of thorium (a layer 1 atom thick). The emission may then be hundreds or thousands of times greater than for pure tungsten at the same temperature. The explanation of how the work function of the surface is thus apparently reduced has been the subject of intensive research but is far from complete. In practice a small amount of thorium is added to the tungsten, and when the temperature of such a thoriated tungsten filament is raised, some thorium atoms migrate to the surface.

Wehnelt in Germany in 1904 found that if a coating of certain oxides of rare earths is put on a platinum filament copious emission may be obtained at temperatures far lower than those needed for tungsten. Whereas tungsten filaments are usually heated to between

2000° C and 2600° C, oxide-coated filaments give good emission at temperatures around 1000° C where they are barely red-hot. It is now known that the most effective agent for such oxide-coated filaments is barium oxide and the filament may be a suitable alloy.

Filaments of these two types, because of their much higher efficiency, are now used almost exclusively in low-power radio and similar electronic tubes.

3-8. Secondary Electron Emission

If electrons hit a target electrode with sufficient speeds they may dislodge electrons from the target. These electrons which are "splashed" out of the target are called secondary electrons, and the phenomenon is known as secondary electron emission.

As the energy of the bombarding electrons is increased up to values of a hundred or so electron volts, the chances of the bombarding electrons each knocking out one or more electrons from the surface of the target increase rapidly. This emission occurs more readily with some surfaces than with others, but on the average not more than 1 to 10 secondaries are produced by 1 primary. Such emission may be a blessing or a curse. In the newer type of amplifying device, called a **multiplier tube,** electrons emitted from the cathode (Fig. 3-4) are drawn successively to a series of anodes, and one electron from the cathode may be amplified to several million electrons by the time the last electrode is reached. For example, assume that each electron in striking a target or anode (called a *dynode*) produces secondary emission of 5 electrons. Then at the first dynode 5 electrons are emitted, and at the second there would be 5 times 5 (5^2), at the third 5^3 or 125, and

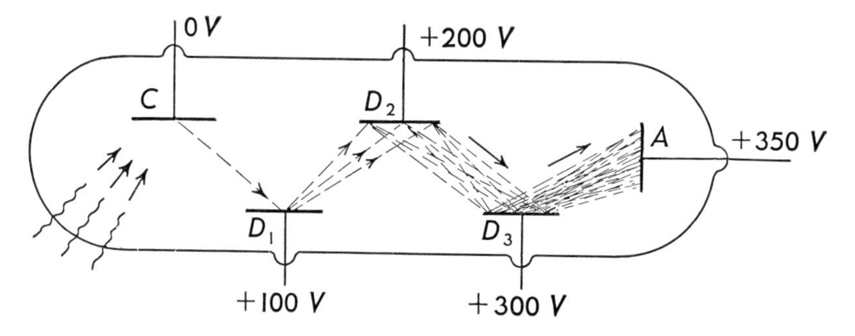

Fig. 3-4. Principle of photomultiplier tube. Electron current from photosensitive cathode C is drawn successively to dynodes D_1, D_2, D_3. Secondary emission from each dynode multiplies current to anode A.

so on. By such means in 9 steps an amplification of more than a million could be reached. Tubes with as many as 10 or 12 dynodes are common. This type of multiplier is now in use in television cameras and in many experimental arrangements where an extremely small electric current must be amplified a very large amount.

Such a multiplier-amplifying device far outreaches the possibilities of ordinary electronic tubes, and if the cathode C (Fig. 3-4) is a photosensitive surface it can be made directly sensitive to extremely small amounts of light. In this form, known as a **photomultiplier,** it has been used to study the stars and to count the otherwise invisible scintillations produced on a screen or in a crystal by high-speed rays from nuclear transformations. The latter may be readily counted electronically at rates as high as billions per day.

In a multigrid radio tube, secondary electron emission by electron bombardment of the anode is usually unwanted and would prevent normal operation of the tube. In the common type of triple-grid (pentode) tube the third grid near the anode, called the suppressor grid, is held at a relatively negative potential to repel secondary electrons and return them to the anode. In a beam-power tube (tetrode) a similar effect is achieved by so concentrating the electrons into a beam that the beam itself repels secondaries.

3-9. Field Emission

With smooth parallel-plate electrodes no electric field obtainable is sufficient to produce appreciable direct emission of electrons. However, for a pointed cathode or for a very fine wire surrounded by a cylindrical anode the electric field at the point or close to the wire may reach a very high value. The effect of such a field in pulling electrons out of the cathode may be considerable. Such emission is called field emission, and it was put to practical use in the early emission form of electron microscope. Lauritsen applied the principle to obtain large currents of brief duration (up to 2000 amp for 10^{-5} sec) in the first million-volt x-ray tube. Field emission may occur from corners or edges or even from the microscopic roughnesses of any apparently smooth surface, and the possibility of such emission must always be considered; however, in what follows it will usually be negligible.

3-10. Photoelectric Emission

The ejection of electrons by the direct action of electromagnetic radiation is called the photoelectric effect. The electromagnetic nature of light waves and the existence of other electromagnetic waves or radiation were inferred by Maxwell from the theory which he developed, and the existence of the waves was experimentally confirmed by Hertz in 1887. In the same year Hertz also observed that the light from an electric spark falling on the electrodes of another spark gap produced a lower breakdown voltage of that gap. This observation was quickly followed in 1888 by Hallwachs' discovery that ultraviolet light falling on a zinc plate causes a loss of negative charge from the zinc plate connected to an electroscope.

This was the beginning of a long series of experiments confirming the idea that electrons may be liberated from a metal by the direct action of light of sufficiently high frequency. Aluminum shows an effect similar to that of zinc but less intense. Certain metals, such as the alkali, possess this property to a marked degree although all substances show some effect. With aluminum it was found that light of higher frequency was required to produce emission than for zinc. These and other observations have led to the formulation of the conditions of photoelectric emission.

The conditions listed below are sometimes called the "laws" of photoelectric emission. They are uniformities derived from many experimental observations. Foremost among those who established their validity was R. A. Millikan.

1. The number of photoelectrons emitted per second varies directly as the intensity of the incident light.
2. Emission from a given surface does not occur unless the frequency of the incident light is equal to, or greater than, a particular minimum value, known as the threshold value.
3. The maximum energy of the photoelectrons after emission from a surface does not depend upon the intensity of the light.
4. The maximum energy of the photoelectrons after emission increases with increase in frequency of the light.
5. Emission of photoelectrons occurs at once, regardless of the intensity of the light.

Certain questions presented by these observations cannot be explained on the basis of the classical electromagnetic theory of light but require the newer concepts of the quantum theory of radiation.

3-11. Quantum Theory and the Einstein Photoelectric Equation

One of the greatest difficulties in explaining photoelectric emission lay in the observation that emission occurs almost instantly in light so weak in intensity that according to classical theory it would be impossible for an electron to absorb sufficient energy to cause its emission. Another difficulty was how to explain, on the basis of classical theory, why emission only occurs for frequencies of incident light larger than a certain minimum, the minimum being different for different metals.

No reasonable explanation of the photoelectric effect was possible until after Einstein with great insight seized upon the basic principle of the quantum theory of radiation proposed by Max Planck in Berlin in 1900 to explain certain discrepancies in the study of thermal radiation. The quantum theory will form much of the basis of the interpretation of the atomic world as we study it in this book; however, at this point we shall confine ourselves to a preliminary statement. Planck found it necessary to assume that radiation is not continuously radiated or absorbed, as had been previously believed, but that the process occurs discontinuously in definite indivisible energy units. These energy units are called ***quanta,*** and the energy E_q of a quantum for any given frequency f of light depends on the frequency and is given by the relation

$$E_q = hf \qquad [3\text{-}7]$$

where h is known as the Planck constant and its value in cgs units is

$$h = 6.625 \times 10^{-27} \text{ erg sec}$$

The units in which h is usually measured are ergs *times* seconds. The name *action* has been given to any such units in which energy is multiplied by time.

Einstein in 1905 borrowed the new concept of quanta to explain photoelectric emission. Good experimental confirmation did not come for seven years, but in 1921 he was awarded the Nobel Prize for his work. Einstein assumed that electrons are only emitted when they have absorbed a quantum of energy large enough to enable them to pass through the potential barrier at the surface of the emitter. If in going through this surface the photoelectron loses an energy w_0, the kinetic energy that it retains on leaving the surface equals the energy of the absorbed quantum minus w_0, or

$$\frac{1}{2} mv^2 = hf - w_0 \qquad [3\text{-}8]$$

where w_0 is usually measured in ergs or electron volts.

The quantity w_0 is called the photoelectric work function of the substance. It is a quantity so apparently similar to the thermionic work function that at once the question arose as to whether or not for any given substance both work functions are identical. Theory indicated that they should be the same. Much experimental work has been done in this field, and though the experimental difficulties are formidable measured values of the photoelectric work function are usually in good agreement with measurements of the thermionic work function (Table 3-1). The chief difficulty in such experimental work is that the slightest contamination of the surface affects the results. One of the first to make careful and accurate comparative measurements to settle the question was DuBridge, who in 1927 and 1928 obtained the same values within the limit of experimental error for platinum (Table 3-1) and confirmed their identity.

The Einstein photoelectric equation agrees with the experimental observation that emission can only occur at frequencies equal to or above a certain minimum called the threshold frequency. Also it predicts that the maximum energy of emitted electrons increases linearly with the frequency of the light and is directly proportional to the energy excess of the quantum over that required to pass the surface barrier. Since a quantum of light is indivisible an electron either absorbs a quantum or none at all, and hence if absorption occurs the electron may escape almost instantly.

Thus the quantum theory served to explain photoelectric emission, and also the phenomenon of photoemission is now seen to be one of the important experimental confirmations of the quantum theory and makes possible an experimental determination of the Planck constant (§ 3-13).

Example Find the lowest frequency of light (threshold frequency) which will just release electrons from a surface the photoelectric work function for which is 3.3 volts.

$$3.3 \text{ volts} = \frac{3.3}{300} \text{ statvolts} = \frac{3.3}{300} \text{ ergs per statcoulomb}$$

$$\begin{aligned} \text{ergs/electron} &= \frac{3.3}{300} \times 4.80 \times 10^{-10} \\ &= 5.28 \times 10^{-12} = hf \\ &= 6.62 \times 10^{-27} f \\ f &= 7.98 \times 10^{14} \text{ sec}^{-1} \end{aligned}$$

Although cgs units are as yet more common in dealing with atomic quantities, mks units may just as well be used in this and in all similar problems. For this example the frequency is just beyond the usual visual limit at the violet end of the visible spectrum. For some substances the threshold frequency is in the visible region or in the infrared.

3-12. Measuring Energies of Photoelectrons

Since it has been observed that the maximum energies of emitted photoelectrons increase with increasing frequency of the incident light, it may be asked how these energies can be measured. In the simplest form of such an experiment a stopping electrode (Fig. 3-5) is placed

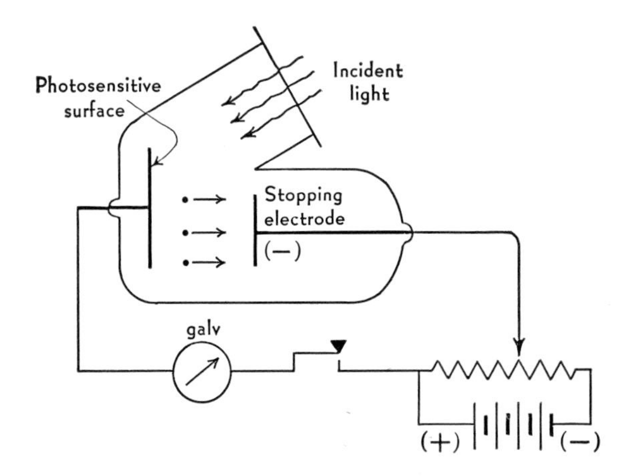

Fig. 3-5. Photoelectric tube with stopping electrode to measure energies of photoelectrons emitted by photosensitive surface.

near a photosensitive surface and is connected with a variable source of potential so that the electrode potential may be made increasingly negative with respect to the photosensitive surface. All electrodes should be of the same material to avoid contact potentials (§ 3-6). The speeds that the electrons possess after emission enable them to travel to this electrode unless they are sufficiently repelled by the retarding field. If the electrode is made negative enough, photoelectrons of maximum speed will just fail to reach this electrode. Under this condition the opposing field has done an amount of work eV on the electron exactly equal to the kinetic energy of the electron and has brought it to rest just before reaching the stopping electrode. By the Einstein photoelectric equation

$$eV = \frac{1}{2}mv^2 = hf - w_0 \qquad [3\text{-}9]$$

The energies thus measured are usually expressed in terms of electron volts.

3-13. Determination of the Planck Constant

If the maximum energies of photoelectrons from a given photosensitive surface are measured for different frequencies of light a graph such as that shown in Fig. 3-6 may be obtained in which stopping potentials are plotted against frequency. Setting the right-hand side of Eq. 3-8 equal to the energy eV and dividing both sides by e gives the result

$$V = \left(\frac{h}{e}\right)f - \frac{w_0}{e} \qquad [3\text{-}10]$$

This is the equation of a straight line in terms of V and f, with h/e as the slope of the line and $-w_0/e$ as the intercept on the y axis in the figure.

From the slope of the experimental graph and the known charge e of the electron the value of h is readily obtained. The experiment, however, is by no means as simple as this description makes it seem. To secure correct values for h and w_0 and also for the threshold frequency of a given metal, the surface of the metal should be perfectly clean.

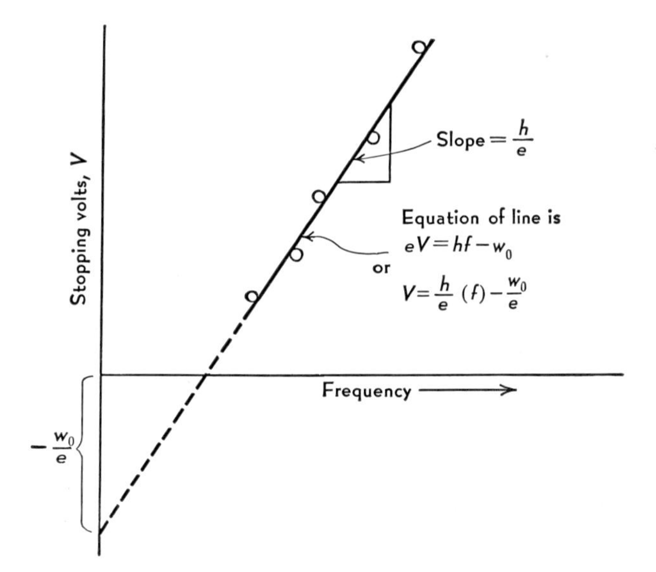

Fig. 3-6. A graph of experimental values obtained by an apparatus similar to that of Fig. 3-5 enables one to determine the Planck constant *h*.

a positive ion sheath forms about the grid, and it becomes inoperative until the discharge is quenched by some other method involving the accompanying circuitry. Such a sheath about a probe or control electrode carries only a small amount of current. Sheaths of a somewhat different character form about the anode and cathode, the main electrodes in a discharge, and are called current-carrying sheaths. The general appearance of the glow discharge is complicated, depending on many factors chief of which are the formation of these sheaths, the mean free paths of the electrons emitted at the cathode, and the formation of regions of maximum and minimum ionization and excitation.

PROBLEMS

1. In an electron avalanche, how many electrons are liberated after 10 ionizing collisions by 1 electron and the electrons it produces, assuming that none are lost.

Ans. 1023.

2. Compute the mean free path of a molecule of a gas at 1 mm pressure if there are 3×10^{19} molecules per cm^3 at 76 cm pressure and if the effective diameter of a molecule is 3×10^{-8} cm. What is the mean free path of an electron in the same gas?

Ans. 0.0063 cm; 0.036 cm.

3. Compute the mean free path of a mercury atom in mercury vapor at 0° C if the number of atoms of a standard gas is 2.7×10^{19} per cm^3 at 76 cm pressure, and if the diameter of a mercury atom is 2.5×10^{-8} cm. What is the computed mean free path of an electron in mercury vapor at this temperature? (See Table 4-2.)

Ans. 56 cm; 318 cm.

4. What is the computed mean free path of an electron in mercury vapor at 20° C? (Assume the diameter of the mercury atom is 2.5×10^{-8} cm.)

Ans. 48 cm.

5. A discharge tube is connected to a mercury pump, and the air pressure is reduced to a negligible value. If the tube is kept at a temperature of −20° C, what will the mercury vapor pressure be in the tube, and what will the mean free path of an electron be? (Assume the diameter of the mercury atom d is 2.5×10^{-8} cm.)

Ans. 180 m.

6. If there are 10^{12} ion pairs per cm^3 in the plasma of a low-pressure arc in which there is a current of 1 ma per cm^2, what is the average drift velocity of the electrons, assuming that 98 per cent of the current is carried by electrons?

Ans. 6.1×10^3 cm/sec.

7. If there are 3×10^{15} atoms of mercury vapor per cm^3 in an electric-discharge tube and if 2 per cent of the atoms are singly ionized, what is the average drift velocity of the electrons when 1 ma of current per cm^2 flows through the tube? (Assume the current carried by positive ions is negligible.)

Ans. 104 cm/sec.

8. At a point in the plasma of an arc discharge in hydrogen, the currents carried by positive ions and electrons are in inverse proportion to the square roots of their masses. If there are 10^{15} ions of each sign per cm^3, what are the average drift velocities of positive ions and electrons when the current density is 0.1 ampere per cm^2?

Ans. 14.2 cm/sec; 610 cm/sec.

9. Design a tube and circuit for the measurement of resonance potentials in a gas or vapor. Would the apparatus of Fig. 4-1 be suitable for this purpose?

10. If the mobility of a gas ion is 20 cm/sec per volt/cm (0.002 m/sec per volt/m), what is the average velocity of the ions in a field of 100 volts/m?

Ans. 20 cm/sec.

11. If 10^{12} electrons per cm^3 in a gas discharge move so as to produce a current of 10 ma/cm^2, what is their mobility when the difference of potential is 100 volts over a length of discharge of 10 cm?

Ans. 6.25×10^3 cm/sec per volt/cm.

SUGGESTED READING

J. D. STRANATHAN, *The "Particles" of Modern Physics* (Philadelphia, Blakiston, 1942).

K. G. Emeléus, *The Conduction of Electricity Through Gases* (London, Methuen, 1929).

K. K. DARROW, *Electrical Phenomena in Gases* (Baltimore, Williams & Wilkins, 1932).

L. B. LOEB, *Fundamental Processes of Electrical Discharge in Gases* (New York, Wiley, 1939).

J. J. THOMSON and G. P. Thomson, *Conduction of Electricity Through Gases,* 3rd ed. (London, Cambridge Univ. Press, 1933).

CHAPTER 5

X-RAYS AND CRYSTAL STRUCTURE

5-1. Radiant Energy and Photons

Many aspects of the intellectual development of man are illustrated by the changing concepts concerning the nature of light. In early Greek times vision was vaguely thought of as an emanation from objects seen or from the eye itself. The emanation was thought of chiefly in terms of invisible particles, and of course there was no adequate concept of wave motion. Centuries later Newton leaned toward a more sophisticated particle theory largely because he thought no waves could possibly be small enough to account for observed effects. Huygens opposed Newton and held to a wave theory, but he supposed the waves to be longitudinal. When in the early nineteenth century polarization and diffraction effects seemed to prove conclusively that light was a form of transverse wave motion, it was conceived to be a mechanical wave in some all-pervasive medium having the character of a solid, yet indetectable. Such irrational properties of this hypothetical medium, called the ether, presented one of the great problems in science.

When Maxwell laid the foundation for the electromagnetic theory of light in the 1860's, an intellectual revolution was in the making which has continued to this day. Not only visible light but radiation of shorter and longer wavelengths, including thermal radiation and what are now called radio waves, were found to fall into the same category. The old mechanical ether of space was supplanted by a more highly intellectualized electromagnetic ether, but many difficulties still remained. However, generally a satisfactory pattern seemed to be forming which would not need further revolutionary changes.

Then came the discovery of x-rays, and a few years later at the turn of the century Planck's idea of the quantization of radiation. The process of conceptual development was again upset by sweeping changes. In 1921 Arthur H. Compton showed that an x-ray quantum has such sharply defined particle-like characteristics as to warrant a new name. The term **photon** was coined. The interpretation and harmonization of the apparently contradictory wave-like and particle-like aspects of radiant energy has been one of the chief concerns of science since that time, and the degree of success has been notable. For this chapter, however, the wave aspect of the x-ray will be found to be most useful. The particle-like aspect of radiation will be dealt with in the next chapter.

5-2. Discovery of X-rays

X-rays were discovered by Roentgen in 1895 at the University of Würzburg, and the announcement was made during Christmas week of that year. The rays were so named because of their unknown nature. Within the short space of a few weeks Roentgen's discovery was confirmed by other scientists, and the new rays were quickly introduced into laboratories and hospitals throughout the world. Their value in locating foreign objects within the body and in the diagnosis of broken bones was obvious, and the procedures soon became an everyday matter. They are now so commonplace that the term *x-ray* is almost immediately associated with them in the minds of most people.

However, the study of x-rays has led to scientific advances of extraordinary importance. By their use it has been possible to determine quickly and accurately the structure of crystalline substances and the spacing of atoms in a crystal. In the study of metals and alloys they are important both industrially and scientifically. In the testing of finished parts they are used to detect faults, and x-rays can now be generated that are of sufficient penetration to pass through a foot or more of steel. High-speed x-ray photographs may even serve for the study of the motion of a projectile in the barrel of a large-caliber gun. Along more purely scientific lines studies of x-ray spectra have furnished some of the most important information concerning the structure of atoms themselves and the relations of the elements to each other (Chap. 9).

Roentgen was one of a number of physicists who were carefully studying electric discharges in gases at low pressures. The existence of cathode rays, whose nature was as yet not clearly defined, had been definitely shown by the extensive experiments of Sir William Crookes and others. It was known that these rays produced fluorescence in the glass of the tube when the air was sufficiently exhausted. Roentgen was working in his laboratory with an electric-discharge tube of this general type. He noticed that a paper screen which had been painted with a fluorescent solution of platinum-barium-cyanide glowed with a greenish light at a distance of as much as two meters from the discharge tube. It glowed even when black cardboard was interposed between the tube and the screen, and Roentgen soon found that the new kind of radiation could penetrate other substances of low density but that denser materials would cast a more or less dark shadow.

5-3. Properties and Nature of X-rays

The nature of the x-ray was at first vigorously debated. Some thought x-rays consisted of particles of extremely small dimensions. Others thought them to be a form of extremely penetrating wave motion. The properties listed below were soon confirmed by Roentgen and others.

1. X-rays make a fluorescent screen glow with visible light.
2. They blacken a photographic plate.
3. In passing through air or any gas they make the gas a conductor by producing ions in the gas.
4. They are strongly absorbed by dense substances such as iron or lead.
5. They cast shadows of dense objects on a fluorescent screen and hence must travel in straight lines.
6. They produce a reddening of the skin which may become a serious and even fatal burn.
7. They are not deflected by either electric or magnetic fields.

Before the discovery of x-rays it was well known that there are light waves too short to affect the eye (ultraviolet) and light waves too long to affect the eye (infrared). It had also become generally accepted that light is a form of electromagnetic wave motion having the property of passing through what is now called empty space with a speed of 186,299 mi/sec or very nearly 3×10^8 m/sec. In order to determine whether x-rays showed the common properties of light waves Roentgen tried to produce reflection, refraction, polarization, and diffraction. From these experiments he obtained only negative results. However, later experimenters by means of much more refined methods have detected all these effects.

By 1902 Brunhes and Blondlot in a series of experiments had shown that x-rays travel at approximately the speed of light, and this result was further substantiated by later investigators. The method was to show that the rays travel near a wire at a speed comparable to that of an electromagnetic wave along the wire. The speed of the electromagnetic wave under favorable conditions was known to approximate the speed of light in free space.

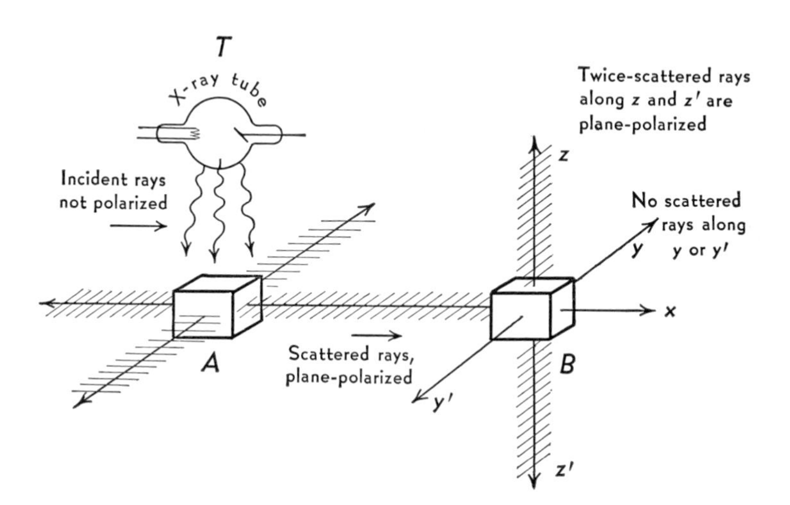

Fig. 5-1. Barkla's experiment to show that x-rays can be polarized. Rays scattered from carbon block *A* are scattered again from second carbon block *B*. Absence of scattered rays along *yy′* and presence along *zz′* indicate that vibrations are transverse and that rays incident on *B* are plane-polarized.

The fact that x-rays could not be deflected by electric or magnetic fields was taken to indicate that they do not consist of charged particles such as the cathode rays or positive rays found in a discharge tube, but there remained the possibility that they might be uncharged particles. In 1905 Barkla in England found that the rays could be polarized.

Barkla's experiment is illustrated in Fig. 5-1. X-rays from the tube T are scattered in all directions from the block A when the rays presumably cause electrons in the carbon to vibrate. The rays scattered in a direction x must be approximately plane-polarized if the incident x-ray is a transverse wave. They can only be formed by electrons vibrating at right angles to the direction x since electrons vibrating in the direction y do not produce waves in that direction. Such waves would have to be longitudinal waves, and longitudinal electromagnetic waves do not exist. To show that the waves in direction x were plane-polarized Barkla scattered them again from another block of carbon at B. A transverse wave could only produce transverse scattered waves along z or z' and not along y or y' since vibrations of electrons in the second carbon block at B could only be along yy', and no radiation in that direction should result. Barkla's experiment demonstrated the existence of scattered waves along z and z' but none along y and y'. Thus it was demonstrated that, whatever the nature of the x-ray was, it could be polarized in the same way as light, and hence behaves like a transverse electromagnetic wave.

It was still conceivable that particles might show some kind of polarization effect, but several inconclusive experiments had seemed to show that when x-rays were passed through a narrow V-shaped slit the point of the image formed was broadened by apparent diffraction more than could be explained if the rays consisted of particles. Up to this time experimenters had no inkling of how short the x-ray wavelengths really were, and their apparatus was entirely too clumsy to give definite results.

It remained for Max von Laue in Germany in 1911 to show that diffraction effects involving interference and reinforcement could be obtained. This was the critical experiment which tipped the scales in favor of the wave theory of the ray (§ 5-9). In 1924 it was found that the rays could, after all, be bent slightly by a glass prism but were bent in the opposite direction from that of ordinary light, the index of refraction being slightly less than 1.0 whereas for visible light the index of refraction is considerably greater than 1. Actual values of the index of refraction vary with the x-ray wavelength selected, but for glass they range from 0.999995 to 0.999990. As this indicates, the bending is found to be extremely small but is sufficient to be measured when the rays strike the prism at a very small glancing angle. These experiments gave generally accepted evidence that the x-ray is a form of electromagnetic wave similar to light waves but with wavelengths a thousandth or less than that of visible light.

5-4. The Production of X-rays and Million-Volt X-rays

X-rays are produced whenever high-speed electrons (cathode rays) strike a dense target and are suddenly stopped. The higher the speed of an electron at the moment it is stopped, and the more suddenly it is stopped, the more penetrating is the x-ray produced. The larger the number of electrons per second being stopped, the more intense is the x-ray beam. Tungsten targets are frequently used although less penetrating x-rays can be produced with less dense targets. An x-ray tube contains two electrodes, the cathode which is the source of electrons, and the anode or target upon which they strike. X-rays radiate from the portion of the target being bombarded.

The older-style x-ray tube was a cold cathode discharge tube (Fig. 5-2) to which a high voltage was applied. Since electrons are ejected from a metal electrode along the field lines perpendicular to the surface the cathode was made with a concave surface which focused the

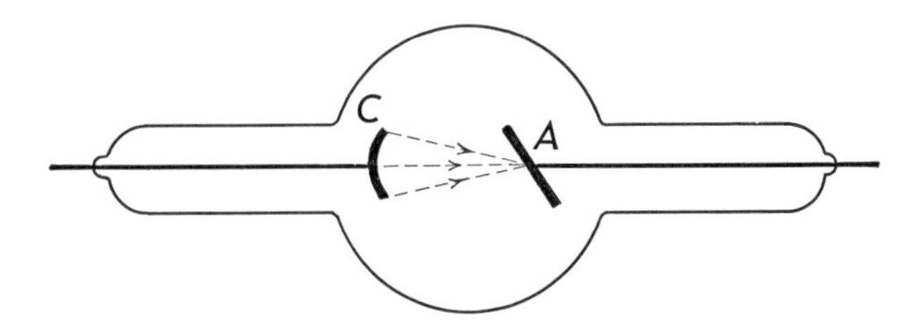

Fig. 5-2. Early-type cold cathode x-ray tube with anode *A* and cathode *C*.

electrons at a small spot on the target. The presence of an appreciable amount of gas in the older-style tubes, although slowing down many electrons by collision, was desirable because positive ion bombardment of the cathode released more electrons and hence produced a more intense beam.

The newer type of x-ray tube originated with W. D. Coolidge's idea of using a heated filament for a cathode, thereby obtaining a more liberal supply of electrons by means of thermionic emission. Such a tube is represented in Fig. 5-3. Since positive ion bombardment of the

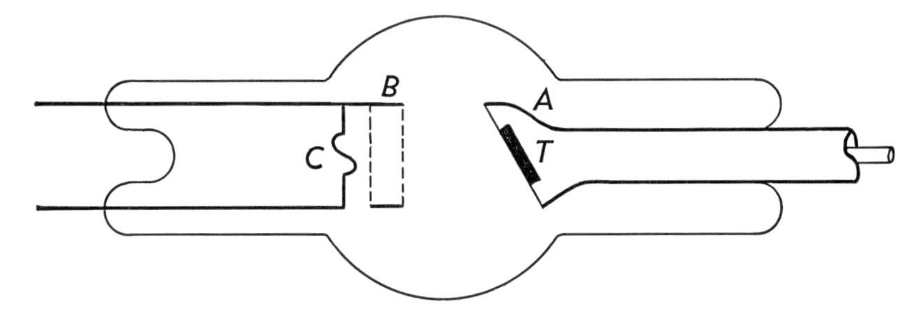

Fig. 5-3. Hot-cathode or Coolidge-type x-ray tube with anode *A*, focusing electrode *B*, and hot filament cathode *C*. Anode is usually arranged for air or water cooling, and a target *T* of dense metal such as tungsten is set into copper electrode.

cathode is not required the tube may be so highly evacuated that an inappreciable number of gas ions is produced, and it is then possible to apply higher voltages to the tube. Accelerating potentials as high as 100,000 volts are common, and much higher voltages are used for special purposes. The electron current through the tube, and in consequence the intensity of the x-rays, can readily be controlled by adjusting the temperature of the cathode. A subsidiary electrode surrounding the cathode provides an electric field which focuses the electrons at a small spot on the target. The penetration (sometimes called hardness) of the x-rays can easily be changed by varying the potential across the tube. The efficiency of production of x-rays is not high, 1 per cent or less of the energy of the current to the anode being transformed into energy of x-rays.

Figure 5-4 shows the required electrical connections for operation of an ordinary hot-cathode tube. The heating current for the filament is obtained from a small step-down transformer, and the high voltage for the anode is obtained from a step-up transformer. Though in some experiments it might be desirable to have continuous, high, positive potential on the anode it is common practice to operate present-day x-ray tubes with alternating potential between cathode and anode because of the ease of stepping up the voltage by means of a transformer. Hence, during each negative half cycle the tube is inoperative, and

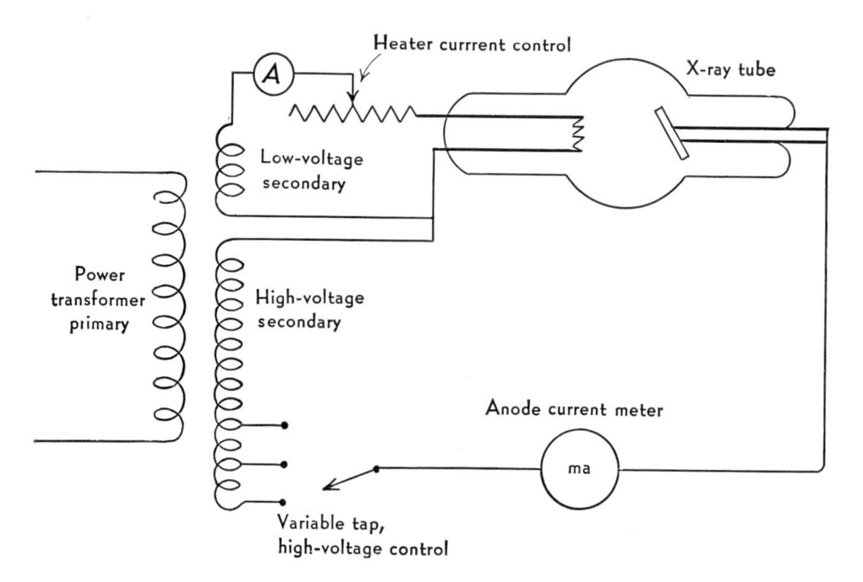

Fig. 5-4. Schematic diagram of electrical connections for operating x-ray tube from alternating current circuit.

x-rays are produced only during each half cycle for which the anode is positive. The Coolidge-type tube lends itself to this manner of operation because of its high vacuum and dearth of gas ions. There is in consequence no reverse discharge when the voltage on the tube is reversed, and the tube is said to be self-rectifying.

In taking an x-ray picture the object to be photographed is usually placed as near the photographic plate as possible. In photographing, for instance, the bones of the hand, a current of 3 or 4 milliamperes through the tube at 50,000 volts may suffice with an exposure of a few seconds. That a shadow picture of the bones in the hands results is due to the fact that the bones contain denser material, which absorbs more of the rays than the fleshy part of the hand. To take a shadowgraph of a thicker portion of the body, such as the chest or head, would require more penetrating x-rays and a higher voltage on the tube. To make it possible to observe portions of the body such as the intestinal tract, a "meal" is swallowed containing a considerable amount of harmless dense material which is a good absorber. To distinguish the heart and lungs, the intensity and penetration of the rays must be carefully adjusted.

Operation of x-ray tubes in the million-volt range has been accomplished in recent years by the design of special tubes for the purpose. Ordinary tubes could not operate at such high voltages, as collection of electric charge on the glass would cause puncture or cracking of the glass. These electric stresses on the glass may be relieved by sealing together successive sections of glass with flat metal rings between, as shown in Fig. 5-5.

By a quite different method of accelerating electrons the upper limit of x-ray energies has now been raised to a new level. This in-

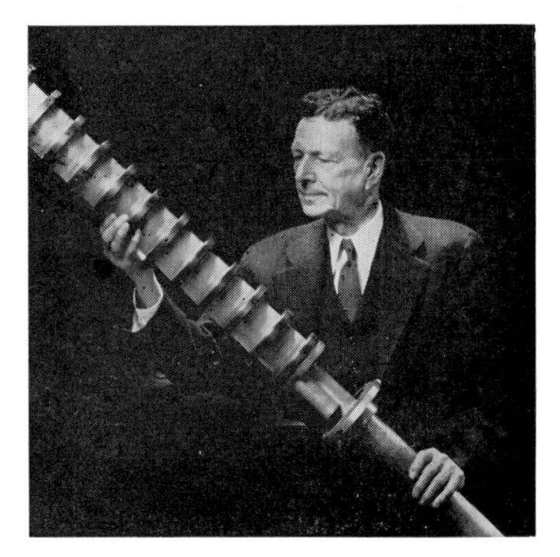

Fig. 5-5. A million-volt x-ray tube showing laminated construction. The tube is in the hands of W. D. Coolidge. (Courtesy, General Electric Co.)

volves a recently developed electron accelerator called the betatron, which is described in Chap. 18. The betatron enables electrons to be accelerated until they reach energies of as much as several hundred million electron volts. When these electrons are allowed to hit a target, x-rays of this maximum energy are produced; they are of the highest frequency and the most penetrating produced by man. Although the cost and the weight of such a machine prevent its common use it has proved to be a tool of extraordinary value in nuclear research and certain other applications.

5-5. Origin of X-rays

The production of x-rays from the stoppage of moving electrons is a kind of inverse photoelectric effect. In the latter, a quantum of energy must be absorbed for an electron to be ejected, and in the production of x-rays a quantum of radiation is produced by a moving electron which is suddenly stopped. In one instance the energy of a photon is transferred to the electron whereas in the other the energy of the moving electron is transferred to the photon. Each process evidently embodies the idea of a quantum. We may write, for the most favorable condition where all the energy eV of the moving electron goes into producing a quantum of radiation of energy hf,

$$eV = hf \qquad [5\text{-}1]$$

This is the Duane and Hunt law. It is also the photoelectric equation when V is so large that the work function is negligible. Since the frequency of a wave is the velocity divided by the wavelength, the quantity c/λ may be substituted in Eq. 5-1 giving

$$eV = \frac{hc}{\lambda} \qquad [5\text{-}2]$$

where c is the velocity of light. From this the minimum wavelength of the x-ray is

$$\lambda_{\text{min}} = \frac{hc}{eV} \qquad [5\text{-}3]$$

Since many electrons are not suddenly stopped in a single collision at the target not all quanta have maximum energy and frequency. There is a distribution of frequencies (and wavelengths) even if all electrons were to have exactly the same energy before stoppage, which is unlikely. Typical curves for the distribution of intensity of x-rays for different frequencies at a particular voltage are given in Fig. 5-6. For a given voltage on the tube the minimum wavelength (or maximum frequency as represented on the graph) is given by Eq. 5-4.

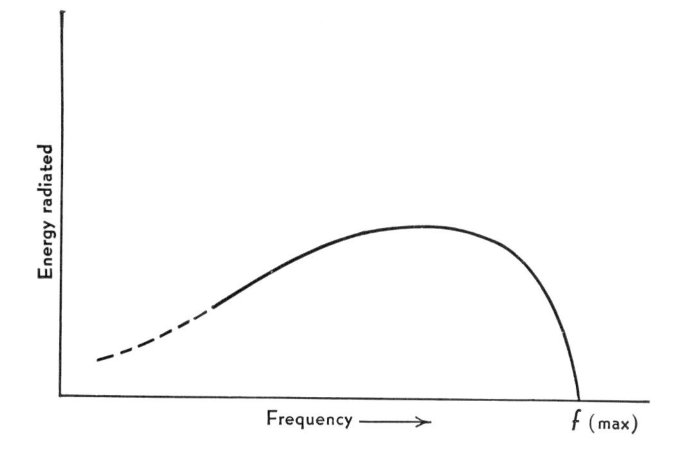

Fig. 5-6. Energy radiated at different frequencies in the continuous radiation from an x-ray tube. For the maximum-energy x-ray quantum the frequency is a maximum and the wavelength is a minimum.

Putting into Eq. 5-3 the numerical values of the Planck constant, the velocity of light, and the charge of the electron, there results

$$\lambda_{\text{min}} = \frac{12395}{V\ (\text{volts})} \times 10^{-8}\ \text{cm} \qquad [5\text{-}4]$$

or

$$= \frac{12395}{V\ (\text{volts})}\ \text{angstrom units} \qquad [5\text{-}4a]$$

(As a memory device the numerical constant in the latter equation may be remembered with an error of less than 1 per cent as 12345.) The angstrom unit is the common unit in which to measure small lengths such as the wavelengths of light or x-rays.

$$1\ \text{A} = 10^{-8}\ \text{cm}$$

For very short x-ray wavelengths a still smaller unit is sometimes employed, called the *X* unit. For practical purposes it may be defined as a thousandth of an angstrom unit.

$$1\ X\ \text{unit} = \frac{1}{1000}\ \text{A}$$

The exact definition is given in § 5-12.

5-6. Absorption of X-rays and Absorption Coefficients

All substances absorb x-rays to a greater or lesser degree. The more dense the substance and the thicker the absorbing layer are, the greater will be the absorption for a given wavelength. Even in a gas there is some absorption of x-rays caused by energy losses in ionizing some of the gas molecules, but because of the low density of matter in a gas the absorption is slight.

The decrease in intensity of a monochromatic x-ray beam when it passes through an absorbing medium is very closely represented by a logarithmic decay curve, and the formula for the intensity at any distance x is given by

$$I = I_0\, \epsilon^{-\mu x} \qquad [5\text{-}5]$$

where I_0 is the intensity of the incident beam, ϵ is the base of the natural system of logarithms, and μ is a coefficient characteristic of the absorber. This type of equation involving exponential decrease of a variable is of great importance in physics and is of similar form to the one to be encountered later for decay of a radioactive substance. In its application to x-rays it may be readily obtained by the following method, which involves the integration of a simple equation.

Let ΔI be the decrease in intensity of the beam when passing through a thin layer of absorbing material the thickness of which is Δx. The decrease in intensity is represented by a negative sign, and it may be assumed to be proportional to the thickness Δx, to the intensity of the beam I, and to a constant μ, representing the absorbing ability of the material.

$$-\Delta I = \mu I\, \Delta x$$

In the limit this becomes

$$-dI = \mu I\, dx \qquad [5\text{-}6]$$

which, being integrated readily, gives the previous equation (5-5), the constant of integration being the value of the intensity at $x = 0$ or I_0. (The method of solving Eq. 5-6 is given for the mathematically similar equation for radioactive decay in § 14-4.)

If I is taken to represent the intensity of the x-ray beam in terms of energy per second per square centimeter falling on the absorber, μ is called the linear coefficient of absorption. Dividing this by the density ρ of the absorbing material the quantity μ_m is obtained where $\mu = \mu_m \rho$, and μ_m is known as the mass absorption coefficient of the substance. Equation 5-5 may now be written

$$I = I_0 \epsilon^{-\mu_m \rho x} \qquad [5\text{-}7]$$

for a given value x of the thickness of the absorbing layer. The mass absorption coefficient makes it simpler to compare the absorption of samples of different substances regardless of thickness.

When two absorbers of different material and thickness are found to give the same absorption the exponential terms for each must be equal, and

$$\mu_{m1}\rho_1 x_1 = \mu_{m2}\rho_2 x_2 \qquad [5\text{-}8]$$

from which

$$\mu_{m1} = \mu_{m2}\frac{\rho_2 x_2}{\rho_1 x_1} \qquad [5\text{-}9]$$

and an unknown mass absorption coefficient μ_{m1} can be computed from the known value of a standard μ_{m2} when the relative densities and thicknesses are known. Carbon is usually taken as the standard reference material because its absorption is more nearly constant for different wavelengths than that of most substances.

Example To what fraction of its original intensity will an x-ray be reduced by a lead shield of 2-mm thickness if the mass absorption coefficient of the lead for the particular wavelength of x-ray used is $\mu_m = 3$. The density ρ of the lead is 11.3 gm/cm³.

$$\frac{I}{I_0} = \epsilon^{-\mu_m \rho x} = \epsilon^{-3(11.3)0.2}$$

$$= \epsilon^{-6.78} = \frac{1}{880}$$

and the intensity has been reduced to $I = 0.00114\, I_0$.

5-7. Means of Detecting X-rays

The most common methods of detecting x-rays are by means of a *fluorescent screen*, a *photographic film*, an *ionization chamber*, or an *electroscope*.

A number of fluorescent materials may be used to coat a screen; a common one is calcium tungstate. If the radiation is not too weak the visible glow will be seen on the screen where the x-rays strike, and the brightness of the glow indicates the intensity of the radiation.

A photographic emulsion is affected by x-rays in a manner similar to that for ordinary light. Upon the development of the film the blackening due to the formation of grains of free silver is observed. One advantage of the photographic film is that low intensities of radiation may be detected by making a proportionally longer exposure.

A charged electroscope irradiated by x-rays loses its charge at a rate depending on the intensity of the radiation. Loss of charge is due to neutralization of charge by ions formed in the gas by the radiation. A simple form of electroscope will show the effect, but more sensitive types are desirable where accurate measurements are intended.

A more sensitive device based on the ionizing capacity of x-rays is the ionization chamber. It consists of an enclosed volume of gas with a thin window through which the rays can readily pass. An electrode in the ionization chamber is kept at positive potential with respect to the walls of the chamber by means of a battery or other source of emf. When ions are formed in the gas in the chamber, current will flow and may be measured by some sensitive detecting device. The ionization chamber is more useful for some purposes than photographic film because the ionization produced is directly proportional to the intensity of the radiation producing it. With photographic film the blackening is not necessarily so.

Scintillation and Geiger-Müller detectors such as are common in nuclear and cosmic-ray study (Chap. 14) are also sometimes used for detecting x-rays, especially to measure beams of low intensity as in x-ray spectroscopy.

5-8. Dangers of X-rays and the Roentgen

All workers with x-rays must take proper precautions to avoid burns or overexposure. X-ray equipment must be properly shielded with some good absorber. Lead is commonly used and is easy to manipulate. The safety of any shielding system may be tested by photographic test film exposed for considerable periods of time or carried by the operator. Radiation meters are also effective. Any unnecessary exposure to x-rays should be scrupulously avoided.

A common unit for measuring the possible physiological effects of x-rays is the roentgen. It is defined as the amount of x-radiation (or the amount of gamma radiation from a radioactive source) that will produce 2.08×10^9 ion pairs or 1 statcoulomb of electricity of each sign by ionization in 1 cm^3 of air at standard conditions. Exposures of less than 0.3 roentgen per week are considered fairly safe for most people as far as short-range ill effects are concerned (§ 14-14).

5-9. X-ray Crystal Diffraction—von Laue's Method

When Newton years ago was concerned with the problem of the nature of visible light he leaned toward the corpuscular theory, as previously mentioned, because he felt that to describe light in terms of wave motion required unbelievably short wavelengths. A similar difficulty arose in the study of the nature of x-rays, where wavelengths are so very much smaller even than those we now recognize as belonging to visible light. However, by 1911, increased evidence had begun to indicate that x-ray wavelengths might be as short as a few hundred millionths of a centimeter or a few angstrom units. This led Max von Laue in Germany to the brilliant idea that, since atomic layers in a crystal usually have spacings of a few angstrom units, they might act to give an effect somewhat similar to crossed diffraction gratings closely ruled with very fine lines and thus afford the means for a critical test.

Fig. 5-7. X-ray diffraction. Von Laue spot pattern obtained by passing narrow beam of x-rays through crystal of rock salt.

Von Laue predicted that if x-rays were passed through such a crystal a pattern of reinforcement spots would be found, the geometrical arrangement of which would depend on the arrangement and spacing of the atoms in the crystal. The prediction was complicated by the fact that a crystal could not act as a two-dimensional grating, but would constitute a kind of three-dimensional grating and furthermore that atomic layers could be thought of as existing in many planes. However, at von Laue's suggestion the experiment was tried by two of his students, Friedrich and Knipping, and it was a notable success.

A typical photograph of von Laue spots is shown in Fig. 5-7. The large central spot is merely the result of the direct beam of x-rays from which only a relatively small fraction of the rays are diffracted by the crystal. The positions of the spots were close to where von Laue had calculated they would be. Here was direct evidence of the wave character of x-rays.

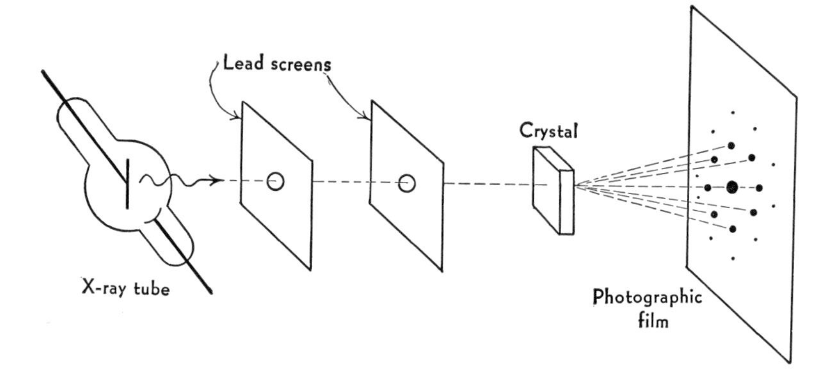

Fig. 5-8. Schematic diagram of apparatus for producing von Laue spots.

The experimental arrangement to secure a spot pattern is shown in Fig. 5-8. X-rays are confined to a narrow beam by means of blocks of lead through which a small hole is drilled. This pencil of x-rays is allowed to pass through a crystal of some substance such as potassium chloride. The spots are obtained on a photographic film, in the position shown, after an exposure of as much as 30 minutes or more.

5-10. X-ray Crystal Diffraction—Bragg's Method

The way in which the diffraction of x-rays depends upon the wavelength and the crystal spacing is more simply seen from the work of W. H. Bragg in England, in which his son, W. L. Bragg, took part.

Whereas von Laue passed the x-rays through a crystal to obtain diffraction, the Braggs reflected the x-rays from the successive planes parallel to the face of a crystal and also obtained a diffraction pattern. Such a pattern is much simpler to analyze than the one obtained by von Laue. For one thing, in von Laue's method a large number of directions may be chosen to represent the crystal planes. For another he did not use x-rays of a single wavelength, since the radiation from an x-ray tube has a distribution of wavelengths, as previously shown in Fig. 5-6.

The geometrical arrangement of atoms in a crystal is represented by a pattern of lines called a **crystal lattice,** the intersections of the lines representing the locations of the atoms. In Fig. 5-9 a two-dimensional representation of atoms arranged on a cubic lattice is shown.

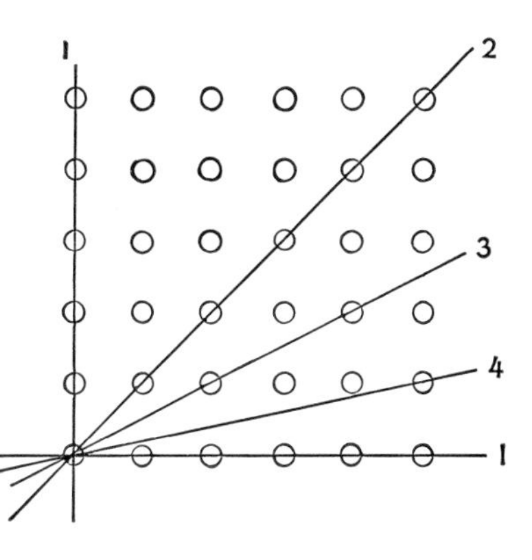

Fig. 5-9. One face of a cubic crystal lattice. The lines represent traces of planes through lattice points. Line 1 represents the greatest population density of points and line 4 the least.

Lines are drawn to indicate the traces of planes in different directions, any one of which may be considered a crystal plane. Note that the rectangular axes represent planes with the greatest population of atoms. The main diagonal axis represents the direction of planes with almost as much population, but other directions may be taken in which the populations are less and less. These account for the weak "reflections" which produce the fainter spots in a von Laue photograph.

In order to simplify the description of various crystal planes, certain numbers known as **Miller indices** are used. If a rectangular crystal is set with its axes parallel to the x, y, and z axes of Fig. 5-10a, the direction of the perpendicular line from the origin to any plane in the crystal serves to specify that plane. The term *plane* is taken to mean not an individual plane but any plane parallel to a given plane. The direction of the perpendicular to a given plane could be specified by the directional cosines of the line, but it is simpler to specify it in terms of its intercepts on the x, y, and z axes. This is particularly true since the spacing of planes may be different in the three directions, and furthermore the crystal axes may not even be at right angles to one another.

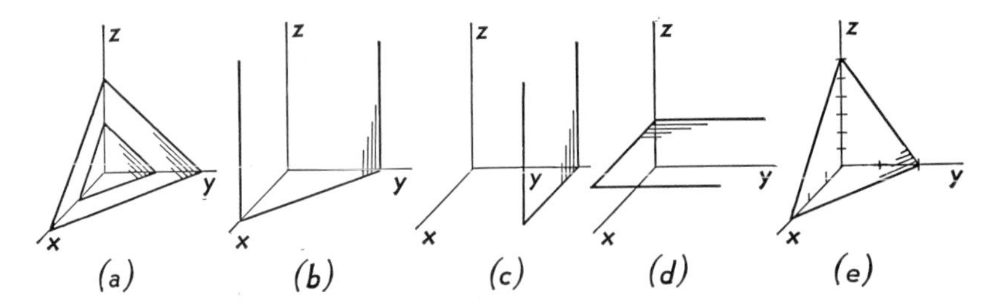

Fig. 5-10. Representation of some planes of a crystal by Miller indices: *a*, 111; *b*, 110; *c*, 010; *d*, 001; *e*, 231.

Referring to Fig. 5-10*e*, let a be the lattice spacing in the x direction, and b and c be the spacings in the y and z directions. For example, let the plane for which it is now desired to obtain the Miller indices cut the x axis at $3a$, the y axis at $2b$, and the z axis at $6c$. Write the reciprocals of the numerical values as

$$\frac{1}{3}, \frac{1}{2}, \frac{1}{6}$$

Reducing these to a least common denominator we have

$$\frac{2}{6}, \frac{3}{6}, \frac{1}{6}$$

The numerators 2, 3, 1 are the Miller indices. For the plane in Fig. 5-10*a* intersecting the axes at equal numbers of units the Miller indices are 111. When a plane is parallel to an axis the intercept is at infinity, and the index is $1/\infty = 0$. The indices 110 for the plane at b indicate that the plane is parallel to the z axis. At c it is parallel to both x and z axes, and at d it is parallel to the x and y axes.

Let us consider how x-rays would be reflected from the planes of such a crystal lattice according to Bragg's method. Figure 5-11 represents an x-ray beam incident upon the crystal plane at an angle θ, called the grazing angle. Rays reflected at the same angle θ are also indicated. The term *reflection* in a general sense embodies the idea that each atom with its electrons acts as a center of scattering of x-rays from which wavelets spread out in all directions. These wavelets add to form a clearly defined wave front in the direction of ordinary reflection so that the angle of incidence equals the angle of reflection and the complementary or grazing angles are also equal.

From the diagram it is seen that the difference in path between rays from successive planes is $2d \sin \theta$, where d is the spacing between the crystal planes. Reinforcement occurs for the emerging beam if the waves are in phase. This occurs only at those angles for which the path difference is a whole wavelength or an integral number of wavelengths

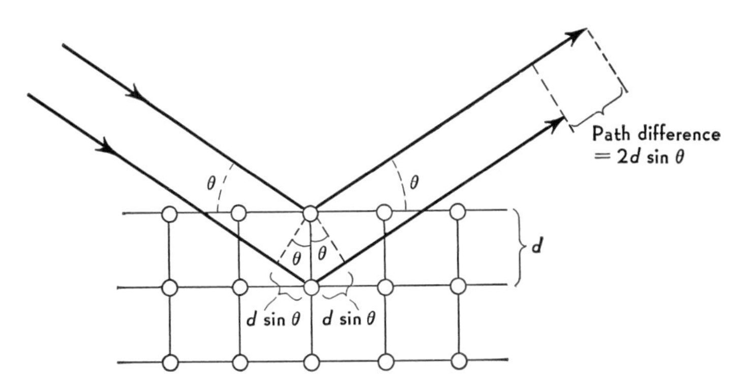

Fig. 5-11. Diagram for derivation of the Bragg equation for x-ray diffraction by reflection of x-rays from face of a crystal. For reinforcement, path difference $2d \sin \theta$ must equal an integral number n of whole wavelengths λ.

and if the angles of incidence and reflection are equal. A reinforcement spot then occurs when

$$n\lambda = 2d \sin \theta \qquad [5\text{-}10]$$

where n may have integral values 1, 2, 3, · · · . The smallest angle θ for a reinforcement spot would be given when n has the value 1, called first-order reinforcement. At a larger angle reinforcement would occur again for $n = 2$, called second-order reinforcement, and so on. It is now possible to set up a **crystal x-ray spectrometer** in such a way that angles for reinforcement positions can be measured with suitable detectors such as an ionization chamber or photographic film. The experimental arrangement is shown in Fig. 5-12. With such a crystal x-ray spectrometer the wavelength of x-rays can be computed if the spacing of the crystal planes is known and if the angle to the proper reinforcement spot is measured.

Instead of its serving to determine wavelengths when the crystal spacing is known, the x-ray spectrometer may be used to determine the crystal spacing if the wavelength of the x-ray is known. W. H. Bragg and his son, now Sir Lawrence Bragg, made many such measurements, and the crystal spacings have now been accurately measured for many crystals. This is one of the great achievements in the field of x-rays. Whereas by older methods crystallographers could only estimate approximate positions and spacings of atoms in the crystal, precise information can now be obtained in a relatively short space of time.

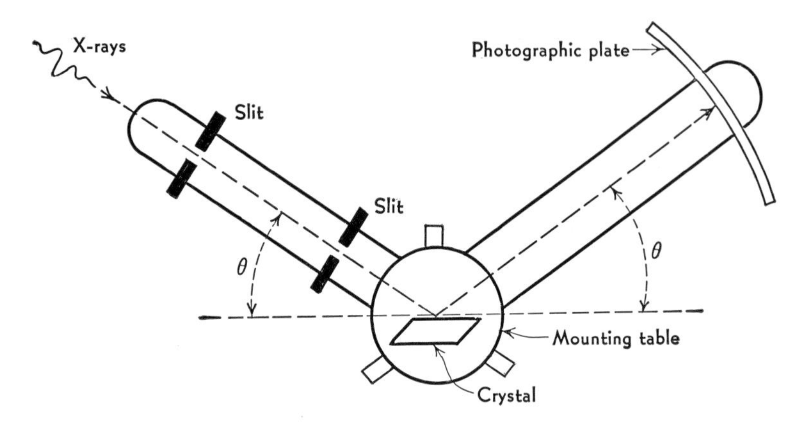

Fig. 5-12. Essential elements of a Bragg x-ray crystal spectrometer (top view).

Since, however, it is required to know either the wavelength of the x-rays or the spacing of the atomic planes in the crystal in order to compute the other by the Bragg formula, the question arises as to how either one can ever be obtained. The answer is that a start was made by computing the atomic spacing as nearly as possible by means of data obtained from other experimental sources, and in particular by the accurate value of Avogadro's number, as in the following example.

Example To find the distance between adjacent atoms in a sodium chloride (NaCl) crystal.

Atomic weight of Na	= 23.00
Atomic weight of Cl	= 35.46
Molecular-formula weight of NaCl	= 58.46

One gram-formula weight of NaCl = 58.46 gm

The number of molecules in 1 gram-formula weight would be

$$N_0 = \text{Avogadro's number} = 6.025 \times 10^{23}$$

Since there are equal numbers of atoms of each kind

$2N_0$ = number of atoms of both kinds in 58.46 gm NaCl
Mass per unit volume = density
Density of NaCl = 2.163 gm/cm^3

Hence the number of atoms in 1 cm^3 is

$$2N_0 = 2(6.025 \times 10^{23})\frac{2.163}{58.46} = 2 \times 22.3 \times 10^{21}$$

If the number of atoms along 1 centimeter of edge of the crystal is n, then

$$n^3 = 44.6 \times 10^{21}$$

from which

$$n = 3.55 \times 10^7$$

The spacing between atoms d is consequently $1/n$, and

$$d = \frac{1}{n} = 2.82 \times 10^{-8} \text{ cm} = 2.82 \text{ A}$$

From such values as those of the preceding example put into the Bragg formula it was possible to compute x-ray wavelengths from experimental measurements of the angle θ. However, an independent method of measuring such wavelengths was greatly desired. Independent measurements were finally obtained with great accuracy by means of ruled gratings (§ 5-12).

5-11. X-ray Crystal Diffraction—the Powder Method

Later, a diffraction method of analyzing crystals was developed by Hull and by Debye and Scherrer, in which it is not necessary to use a large single crystal, as in the original Bragg method. Crystal fragments such as those of which a metal wire is composed, or fragments in the form of a powder, are effective since they are actually large compared to the x-ray wavelengths. These fragments present relatively large crystal planes to the incident rays, just as the single crystal does in the Bragg method, but they are oriented in nearly all possible directions.

Instead of reinforcement lines or spots being produced on a photographic film, circles are obtained. The random orientation of crystal fragments causes the reinforcement spots from a given set of crystal planes (that is, for a given grazing angle) to fall on the arc of a circle about the central spot formed by the original beam (Fig. 5-13). For

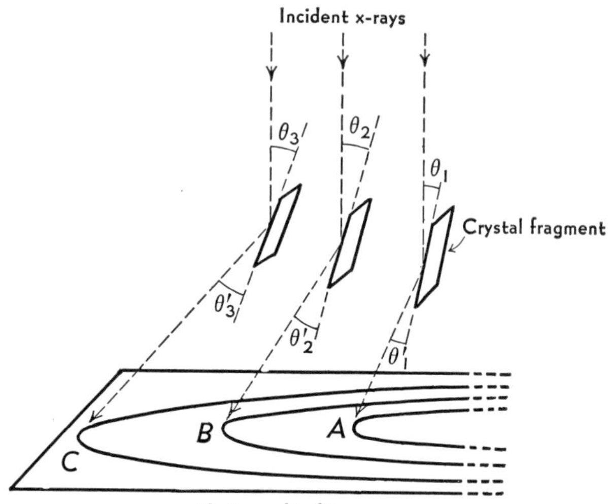

Fig. 5-13. X-ray powder diffraction. Reinforcement occurs at points such as *A*, *B*, *C* only when $\theta = \theta'$ and if $n\lambda = 2d \sin \theta$. Some crystal fragments will always be found at the proper angle. Rotation of a crystal about an axis parallel to the incident rays does not affect the relations for reinforcement but causes these points to fall on a circle.

different grazing angles and for different sets of atomic planes there would be reinforcement at other circles concentric with the first. If a strip of photographic film is not wide enough to show the complete circles, it will show the reinforcement regions as arcs of circles, as in Fig. 5-14. From the radii of the reinforcement circles and the angles at

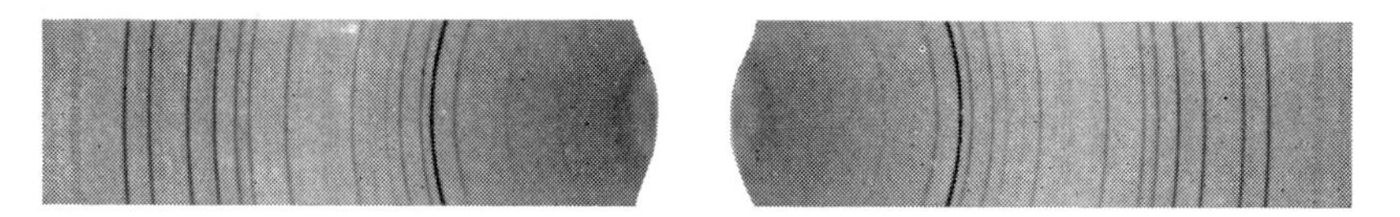

Fig. 5-14. Powder-diffraction x-ray photograph of crystals of lead oxide. The lines would form complete circles, but for convenience only a strip is usually taken with central dark spot blocked off. (Courtesy, General Electric Co.)

which they are formed the crystal spacings can be readily determined. The convenience of this method has led to its widespread scientific and industrial adoption in the study of metals and alloys.

5-12. X-ray Wavelengths Determined with Ruled Gratings

X-rays are so penetrating that no appreciable reflection is observed from an ordinary mirror surface, and early attempts to detect such reflections were unsuccessful. In 1922 A. H. Compton found that there was considerable reflection for an x-ray beam falling on a surface at a very small glancing angle, that is, almost parallel to the surface. Applying this to a high-grade, ruled diffraction grating such as that used for visible light, Compton and Doan found in 1925 that it was possible to obtain diffraction of x-rays with this grating and thus independently to determine the wavelength of x-rays with precision.

It is evident that the grating, if observed at a very small glancing angle, appears to have lines ruled far more closely together than could actually be accomplished by direct ruling. This apparent close spacing for any such angle can be readily computed. X-rays reflected from the flat spaces between the rulings were found to form a diffraction pattern of reinforcement and interference regions, just as with visible light. By this method the wavelength of incident x-rays could then be determined. This was exactly what was needed to make certain of the accuracy of previous values of atomic spacings in crystals.

With the Bragg method of crystal analysis, and x-ray wavelengths determined by means of a ruled grating, Bearden was able to obtain precise values for the atomic spacing of calcite ($CaCO_3$), sodium chloride, and other crystals. These values in turn could now be applied in the Bragg formula when it was desired to measure unknown x-ray wavelengths. The X unit is then defined in such a way as to make the atomic spacing of sodium chloride exactly 2814.00 X units. It was this work by Bearden which led to the question of the accuracy of the measurement by Millikan of the charge of the electron and to the correction of that value (§ 1-9).

5-13. Characteristic X-rays

So far, in the subject of x-rays, we have discussed the production of x-rays by sudden stoppage of electrons upon hitting a target and the distribution of wavelengths produced by the various ways in which electrons are stopped. These x-rays are known as the **general** or **continuous x-rays** (Fig. 5-6), but another process occurring at the target leads to what are called **characteristic x-rays,** discovered in 1908 by Barkla and Sadler. General x-rays are relatively independent of the material of the target. Characteristic x-rays depend upon the material of the target. Production of both kinds of x-rays occurs in a tube at the same time. When the intensity of x-rays is measured for the full range of frequencies given off by an x-ray tube, these characteristic x-rays appear as lines of considerable intensity superposed on the continuous background of radiation (Fig. 9-9).

Characteristic x-rays are produced when the bombarding electrons cause disturbances in the atoms of the target which lead to the emission of x-rays having wavelengths characteristic of those atoms. In the study of different kinds of atoms these characteristic x-rays are of great importance. They will be discussed more completely in Chap. 9 (§ 9-11), after a fuller treatment of atomic theory, when their manner of production will be better understood.

5-14. Complete Spectrum of Electromagnetic Radiation

The recognition that the x-ray is fundamentally an electromagnetic wave of very short wavelength filled another gap in the extensive range of known electromagnetic waves (Fig. 5-15). From the longest radio waves to the shortest waves produced by electrical methods there is now a continuous stretch from 20,000 meters to less than 1 millimeter. From the shortest of these up through those waves classed as thermal radiation and infrared to the visible red, a little less than a ten-thousandth of a centimeter in wavelength, there is no gap. Beyond the visible violet, in the ultraviolet, the wavelengths become still shorter and shorter, merging with the longer and less penetrating x-rays known as soft x-rays of a few angstroms in length. Then on they continue to the more penetrating (hard) x-rays and to the realm of gamma rays from radioactive substances and finally to the similar but even shorter gamma-ray component of cosmic rays, with wavelengths as short as a millionth of an angstrom or even less.

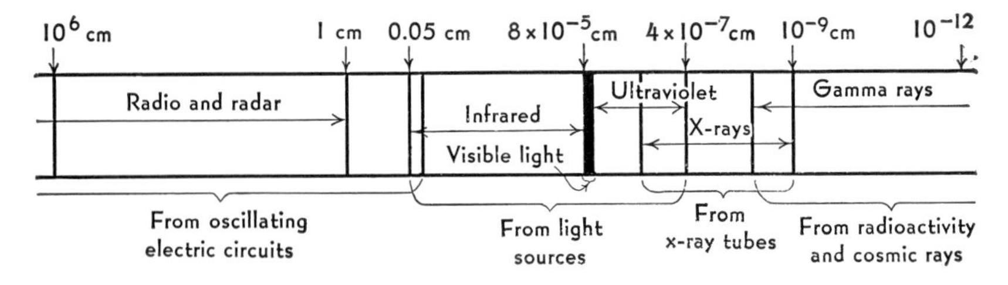

Fig. 5-15. A complete spectrum of electromagnetic radiations.

The tremendous range of wavelengths is most impressive; the chart (Fig. 5-15) is worth careful study and provides a striking illustration of how science has brought relatedness and uniformity out of what at first appeared to be quite separate phenomena.

5-15. Structure of Metals

Much of present civilization depends upon various kinds of metals in the forms to which man has adapted them. The word *metal* has a definite meaning for most people. They think of a hard, bright, shiny substance which conducts both heat and electricity and may take a high polish. They sometimes forget that mercury, one of the common metals, is not a solid at ordinary temperatures but a liquid. They may momentarily overlook the fact that aluminum and magnesium are not relatively heavy but quite light. They may forget that some metals are not strong but very brittle, and that some metals may even burn under proper conditions with an intense flame.

One characteristic that metals have in common is that all are crystalline in the solid state. All substances known to man may be classified as crystalline or noncrystalline. A substance such as paraffin or glass is noncrystalline. The atoms or molecules of a noncrystalline substance are not fixed in a regular geometrical order. They often more closely resemble the relation between molecules of a substance dissolved in a liquid, and for this reason glass is sometimes spoken of as a solid solution. On the other hand, the atoms of a metal preserve the characteristic geometrical order described as a crystal lattice. Crystal x-ray analysis of the metals has led to interesting results. Of the 32 known geometrical forms of crystal structure, the great majority of metals crystallize in one of three forms.

The simplest geometrical arrangement of atoms would be a cubic

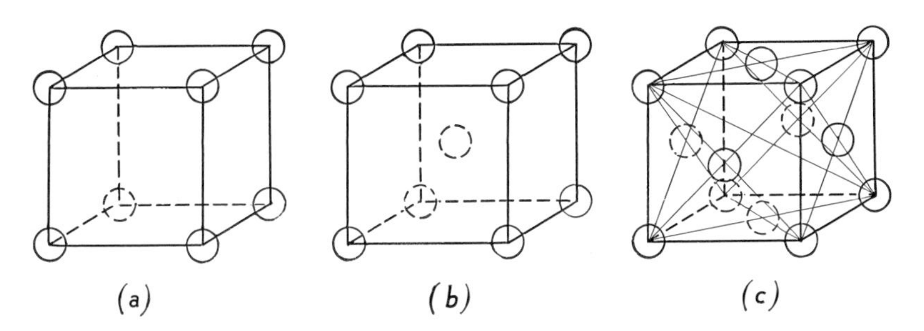

Fig. 5-16. The three types of cubic crystal lattice structure: *a*, simple cubic; *b*, body-centered cubic; *c*, face-centered cubic.

arrangement, the atoms being related to each other as the eight corners of a cube. This simple cubic structure does not quite exist in nature, but two modifications of the cubic structure are common. These are known as the **body-centered cubic** and the **face-centered cubic.** In Fig. 5-16*a* a simple cubic structure is shown; at *b* a body-centered cubic is indicated; and *c* represents a face-centered cubic. The body-centered cubic is one in which, in addition to eight atoms at the corners of each cube, there is one atom at the center of each cube. In the face-centered cubic arrangement, in addition to the eight atoms at the corners of each cube, there is one atom at the center of each of the six faces of the cube.

Potassium chloride and sodium chloride (table salt) crystallize on

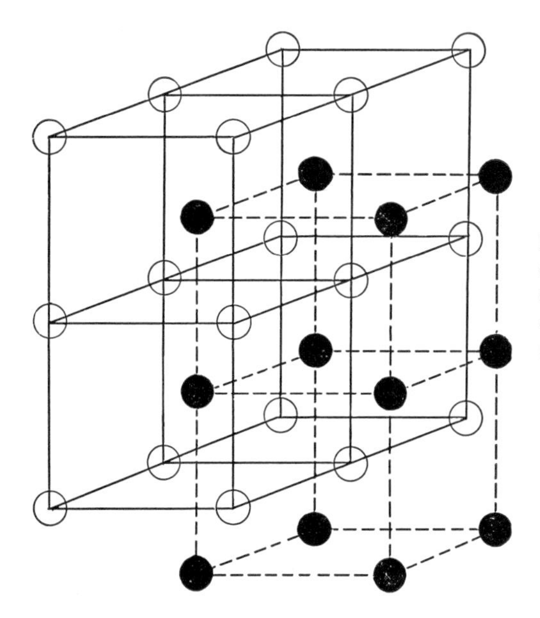

Fig. 5-17. A body-centered crystal lattice is equivalent to two interpenetrating simple cubics. The atoms at the centers of the cubes are shaded for easy identification.

a cubic lattice in what is the nearest to simple cubic to be found in nature. Potassium and chlorine atoms (or sodium and chlorine) are found alternately at the corners of the cubes, but the arrangement is not quite pure cubic, because the atoms are not quite the same size and the cubes are thus not perfectly symmetrical.

Examples of metals that crystallize on a body-centered cubic lattice are iron, tungsten, vanadium, sodium, potassium, and molybdenum. In Fig. 5-17 a body-centered cubic lattice is shown to be the equivalent of two interpenetrating cubic lattices. This interlocking arrangement is thought to explain in part the fact that the metals, iron and tungsten and others of this type, are very tough and not very ductile. Examples of metals that crystallize on a face-centered cubic lattice are copper, gold, nickel, silver, aluminum, and lead. For the most part these are ductile metals, and they are not particularly tough.

The third common type of metal structure is known as **hexagonal close-packed.** The arrangement is indicated in Fig. 5-18 and is recognized as the manner in which oranges are often packed in a crate. Examples of metals that crystallize in this fashion are beryllium, cobalt, cadmium, zinc, titanium, and zirconium.

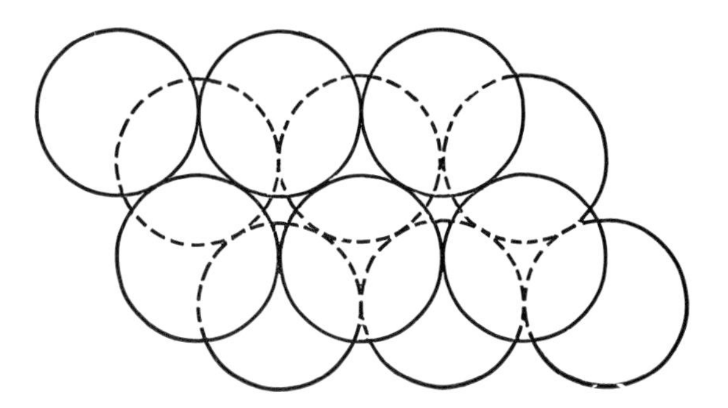

Fig. 5-18. Hexagonal close-packed ("orange-crate") pattern of a crystal lattice, showing two layers superposed.

The study of the alloys formed by combining various metals is of great importance but represents further complications, and many alloys are found to have properties quite different from their constituent metals.

One of the most interesting of all metals because of its great industrial use is iron. At ordinary temperatures iron forms a body-centered structure known as *alpha iron.* At higher temperatures (around 900° C) the iron changes to the face-centered state in which it is called *gamma iron.* Alpha iron is strongly magnetic. Gamma iron has lost this magnetic property. The temperature at which it loses its characteristic magnetic properties is called the Curie point.

Steel is an alloy of iron with carbon and frequently with other components. These elements modify the crystal structure. The iron may form different arrangements with the carbon, some of which are analogous to chemical combinations, whereas in other circumstances the carbon atoms may displace iron atoms on the crystal lattice. The size and character of the crystal grains formed when steel cools determine the hardness and other properties.

PROBLEMS

1. Prove the validity of the equation

$$\lambda \text{ (angstrom units)} = \frac{12395}{V \text{ (volts)}}$$

2. Derive Eq. 5-4 from Eq. 5-3, using mks units.

3. Derive Eq. 5-4 from Eq. 5-3, using cgs units.

4. What difference of potential across an x-ray tube will produce x-rays having a minimum wavelength of 1 A? Of 0.01 A?

Ans. 12395 volts; 1,239,500 volts.

5. What is the maximum frequency of the x-rays produced by electrons accelerated by a potential difference of 50,000 volts?

Ans. 1.208×10^{19} sec^{-1}.

6. If the electrons arriving at the anode of an x-ray tube have fallen through a potential difference of 100,000 volts, and if 10 ma of current flows through the tube, how much power in the form of heat must be dissipated at the anode, assuming that 0.3 per cent of the electrons are effective in producing x-rays? How can this much power be dissipated?

Ans. 997 watts.

7. The mass absorption coefficient of iron for x-rays of wavelength 0.2 A is 1. If the density of iron is 7.8 gm/cm^3, how much will the intensity I_0 of such an x-ray beam be reduced by 1 cm of thickness of iron?

Ans. To 0.00041 I_0.

8. How much lead shielding is required to reduce the intensity of a penetrating x-ray beam to 1/1000 of its value if the mass absorption coefficient of lead for the wavelength in question is 6 (density of lead = 11.3 gm/cm^3)?

Ans. 0.1 cm.

9. A ruled diffraction grating has 20,000 lines/cm. What is the effective number of lines per cm if the grating is viewed at a glancing angle of 4°? Of 1°?

Ans. 286,700 cm^{-1}; 1,146,000 cm^{-1}.

10. A plane cuts across a crystal so as to intersect the x axis at $5a$, the y axis at $3b$, and the z axis at $1c$, where a, b, and c are the separations of the planes along the respective axes. What are the Miller indices?

Ans. 3; 5; 15.

11. A plane intersects the axes of a crystal at $2a$, $5b$, and ∞, where a and b are the intervals between planes along the x and y axes. What are the Miller indices?

Ans. 5; 2; 0.

12. For a simple cubic crystal find the ratios of the spacings of the 111, 110, and 100 planes.

Ans. 0.578; 0.707; 1.

13. The spacing of the 111 planes of a simple cubic crystal is found to be 1.80 A. What is the spacing of the 100 planes?

Ans. 3.12 A.

14. The distance between planes of a crystal is 3 A. Compute the smallest angle for which a reinforcement line will be formed if the wavelength of the x-ray is 0.7 A.

Ans. 6.7°.

15. If the spacing of certain planes in calcite is 3.14 A, find the angles at which first- and third-order reinforcements are found for x-rays of wavelength 0.8 A.

Ans. 7.3°; 22.5°.

SUGGESTED READING

J. D. Stranathan, *The "Particles" of Modern Physics* (Philadelphia, Blakiston, 1942).

A. H. Compton and S. K. Allison, *X-Rays in Theory and Experiment,* 2nd ed. (New York, Van Nostrand, 1935).

W. H. Bragg and W. L. Bragg, *X-Rays and Crystal Structure* (London, G. Bell, 1915).

G. L. Clark, *Applied X-Rays,* 3rd ed. (New York, McGraw-Hill, 1940).

CHAPTER 6

QUANTUM PROPERTIES OF WAVES AND PARTICLES

6-1. Introduction

The quantum theory originated in 1900 when Max Planck advanced the hypothesis that radiant energy is absorbed or emitted in definite units called quanta. Planck had been forced to this conclusion when he attempted to reconcile conflicting theories of thermal radiation (Chap. 12). On this new assumption radiation and absorption processes instead of being continuous, as had been supposed, were presumed to be discontinuous. This discontinuous or "atomic" character of radiation is in many ways similar to the atomic character of matter and of electricity. Ordinary matter exists in "quanta," which we call atoms. Electricity is "quantized" in the form of electrons. With the acceptance of the quantum theory we see that not only matter and electricity but also radiant energy (at least in its interactions with atoms and electrons) are all essentially discontinuous in nature.

In man's attempt to understand nature and describe it, he has had to supplement the classical wave picture of radiation with the quantum theory, and we may therefore say that the wave theory does not provide a complete description of the nature of radiant energy. In a similar manner we shall find that the particle concept, as applied to the electron (and to other elementary particles), also does not afford a complete description of these particles. It is necessary under certain circumstances to supplement this description with ideas borrowed from the classical wave theory; consequently we may say that the particle picture of the electron is not a complete description. In short, under certain conditions radiant energy in the form of quanta may exhibit a particle-like behavior, and similarly particles under certain conditions may exhibit a wave-like behavior.

It will be the object of this chapter to reveal more clearly the particle and wave characteristics of radiant energy and the electron, especially as evidenced by the experimental observations on which the quantum theory is now so firmly based. It is these ideas which have led to new viewpoints regarding the world of atoms, electrons, and quanta, and it is by such new viewpoints that we have learned to unravel many secrets of the structure of the atom and more recently of the nature of the nucleus.

6-2. The Compton Effect and Photons

One of the most revolutionary experiments concerning radiation was performed by A. H. Compton in 1921. When he studied the scattering of x-rays by matter he found that observed effects could be satisfactorily described only if the radiation was assumed to consist of individual quanta, each quantum possessing a definite amount of momentum just as a moving mechanical object does. He then found that when a quantum collides with a particle of matter the quantum itself behaves like a particle and transfers momentum to the particle hit, according to the fundamental laws of mechanics. To emphasize this particle-like character a quantum of radiation is now frequently called a photon.

Compton was studying the ways in which x-rays are scattered in various directions when a beam of x-rays falls upon a slab of some material such as carbon. It was well known that ordinary light is scattered in all directions by dust particles and small water droplets without appreciable change in wavelength. According to classical theory any loss of energy in the scattering process is at the expense of the amplitude of the incident wave. From this it might be expected that scattered x-rays would have the same wavelength (or frequency) as the rays of the incident beam. Compton did find such scattering, but he also detected a new and different kind of scattering in which the scattered x-rays were found to have a longer wavelength (lower frequency) than that possessed by the rays of the original beam.

This shift in wavelength, sometimes called the *Compton shift*, presented an obstacle to any simple explanation of the scattering on the basis of the classical wave theory of radiation. Such a shift is, however, implicit in the definition of the energy E_q of the quantum where $E_q = hf$. Since h is the Planck constant any loss of energy can only be at the expense of the frequency f. To compute the energy loss in the collision, Compton applied the familiar laws of collision of ordinary objects, and thus with the aid of the quantum concept he was able to obtain a simple explanation of the observed effect. Some of the electrons in a block of carbon are so loosely bound as to be considered free electrons. An x-ray quantum or photon striking one of these electrons bounces back from the collision much as if the collision had occurred between two perfectly elastic spheres. Although billiard balls are by no means perfectly elastic, collisions of billiard balls are familiar and well understood, and they represent many aspects of the collision between an x-ray quantum and an electron.

According to familiar mechanical principles, when two objects such as billiard balls collide, both momentum and energy are conserved. Momentum and energy may be transferred from one billiard ball to the other, but the total momentum of the two balls after collision will be the same as the total momentum of the two balls before the collision. In the ideal case of perfectly elastic billiard balls no energy will be lost in the form of heat, and the total kinetic energy of the balls after collision will be the same as the total kinetic energy before (Fig. 6-1*a*). Compton suggested that exactly such a transfer of energy and momentum occurs in the collision between a photon and an electron as occurs in the collision of ideal billiard balls. This suggestion violated classical wave theory and seemed radical at the time, but its experimental confirmation has now become one of the cornerstones of the quantum theory. Assuming that an x-ray photon of energy hf loses energy in a collision, just as a particle would, it is evident that it must suffer a decrease in frequency (increase in wavelength) as in Fig. 6-1*b*. Comp-

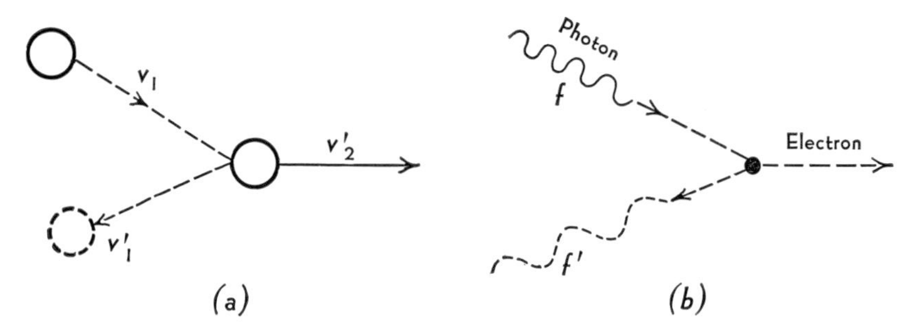

Fig. 6-1. *a*, **Ideal billiard ball recoils from collision with change in velocity;** *b*, **photon recoils from collision with electron with change in frequency.**

ton found that, with the aid of this assumption plus the laws of conservation of energy and momentum, he could describe exactly the observed wavelength shift of the scattered x-rays no matter at what angle the collision took place.

Consider the simplest possible collision, a head-on collision in which the quantum bounces directly back from the electron, exactly reversing its path. In addition to the classical laws of conservation of energy and momentum two basic relations are involved.

1. By the Planck hypothesis the energy E_q of a quantum is

$$E_q = hf \qquad [6\text{-}1]$$

2. From classical electromagnetic theory it had been known that radiation could exert a pressure and could be thought of as possessing momentum p represented by

$$p = \frac{E}{c} \qquad [6\text{-}2]$$

where E is the energy of the radiation and c is the velocity of light This equation implies that if the energy of a photon is hf it should possess momentum p where

$$p = \frac{hf}{c} = \frac{h}{\lambda} \qquad [6\text{-}3]$$

where λ is c/f. Applying the law of conservation of energy

$$\begin{pmatrix}\text{Energy of}\\ \text{incident photon}\end{pmatrix} = \begin{pmatrix}\text{Energy of}\\ \text{scattered photon}\end{pmatrix} + \begin{pmatrix}\text{Energy given}\\ \text{to electron}\end{pmatrix}$$

$$hf = hf' + \frac{1}{2}mv^2 \qquad [6\text{-}4]$$

where f' is the new and lower frequency of the scattered photon. Applying the law of conservation of momentum

$$\begin{pmatrix}\text{Momentum of}\\ \text{incident photon}\end{pmatrix} = \begin{pmatrix}\text{Momentum of}\\ \text{scattered photon}\end{pmatrix} + \begin{pmatrix}\text{Momentum given}\\ \text{to electron}\end{pmatrix}$$

$$\frac{h}{\lambda} = \frac{-h}{\lambda'} + mv \qquad [6\text{-}5]$$

where λ' is the wavelength of the scattered photon corresponding to its frequency f' and the sign of the momentum associated with the momentum of the scattered photon is negative because the direction is reversed. Equation 6-4 expresses the fact that when, at the time of collision, the incident photon of energy hf transfers kinetic energy $\frac{1}{2}mv^2$ to the electron, the resulting energy of the photon becomes hf' where $hf' = hf - \frac{1}{2}mv^2$. Equation 6-5 represents a similar transfer of momentum and may be written

$$\frac{h}{\lambda} + \frac{h}{\lambda'} = mv = \frac{2h}{\lambda} \text{ (approximately)} \qquad [6\text{-}6]$$

since for a small change in wavelength the product $\lambda\lambda'$ is approximately equal to λ^2 and $\lambda + \lambda'$ is approximately 2λ. Now by squaring Eq. 6-6 and eliminating mv^2 between it and Eq. 6-4, there results

$$f - f' = \frac{2h}{m\lambda^2} \qquad [6\text{-}7]$$

This gives the frequency shift or difference in frequency between the incident and scattered photons. To convert this to a change in wavelength, divide both sides of the equation by c, the velocity of light, and substitute $1/\lambda$ for f/c. This gives

$$\lambda' - \lambda = \frac{2h}{mc} = 0.048 \times 10^{-8} \text{ cm} = 0.048 \text{ A} \qquad [6\text{-}8]$$

This is the change in wavelength (Compton shift) for direct rebound of the photon. It can be shown that for scattering at any angle θ, with respect to the direction of the incident photon,

$$\lambda' - \lambda = \frac{h}{mc}(1 - \cos\theta) \qquad [6\text{-}9]$$

$$= 0.024\,(1 - \cos\theta) \text{ angstrom units} \qquad [6\text{-}10]$$

With ordinary light these shifts would be too small to be detectable, but with x-rays the frequency is so high that each photon possesses sufficient energy and momentum to produce a shift which can be measured with a good x-ray crystal spectrometer. At very high energies, however, the simple mathematical treatment must be modified by relativistic corrections.

When the experiment is performed scattered photons that have not undergone change in frequency and wavelength are also detected and present a problem. It is well known that a small object in elastic collision with a more massive object or with an object that is fixed in position does not lose appreciable energy by transfer to the second object. Since many electrons in a block of carbon are more firmly bound to the parent atom, photons in collision with them lose little energy, and the scattering occurs with no appreciable shift in wavelength.

Compton's measurements confirmed his hypothesis completely. Nevertheless, with characteristic scientific thoroughness he made measurements with a cloud chamber in which the directions of the recoil electrons could be observed and measured. Again the measurements confirmed the theory. Since the classical wave theory of light cannot explain this phenomenon, the more revolutionary photon aspect of radiant energy has now become well established, and in all experiments of this type we must recognize the particle-like behavior of the photons.

6-3. The de Broglie Hypothesis

The particle-like behavior of radiant energy under such conditions as given in the preceding section raised a question in the mind of Louis de Broglie in France. If waves might sometimes act as particles, perhaps particles might sometimes act as waves. This thought, that under appropriate conditions particles might exhibit wave-like behavior, did not come entirely from a clear sky. De Broglie derived it in 1922 from an analysis of the requirements of the theory of relativity, combined with Planck's idea of the quantum of energy hf. In Eq. 6-3, where p, the momentum of the photon, is found to be h/λ, a possible duality of particles and waves appears. If for the momentum p of the photon there is substituted the momentum mv of a particle of mass m and velocity v

$$mv = \frac{h}{\lambda} \qquad [6\text{-}11]$$

and

$$\lambda = \frac{h}{mv} \qquad [6\text{-}12]$$

The wavelength λ may then be considered the equivalent wavelength of a particle of momentum mv.

This is the now famous de Broglie wavelength equation, which not only implies that a particle may exhibit a wave-like character but that the equivalent wavelength is dependent upon h, the basic constant of the quantum theory, and that it is inversely proportional to the momentum of the particle. A question now arises as to what degree of reality may be attached to this wavelength. Is it an equivalent wavelength, an associated wavelength, a convenient mathematical fiction, or what? Much can be said in reply to such questions, but if an electron of momentum mv, for example, can be caught in the act of exhibiting any properties of the wavelength indicated by the de Broglie equation, this wavelength must be considered to possess some degree of reality.

6-4. Electron Diffraction

Three years after the suggestion by de Broglie that electrons might sometimes act as waves, experimental confirmation was obtained first by Davisson and Germer in this country (1925), and shortly after by G. P. Thomson in England, son of J. J. Thomson. Davisson and Germer used electrons accelerated by only a few volts, since according to the de Broglie formula they would then have wavelengths approximating those of ordinary x-rays. The electron beam was directed toward the face of a single crystal of pure nickel. The experimenters found that electrons were most strongly reflected at a certain favored angle (Fig. 6-2). This angle corresponded almost exactly to the angle which would have been observed for reinforcement of x-rays of the same wavelength as that of the electrons given by the de Broglie formula.

G. P. Thomson applied electrons of higher speed in an experiment similar to the x-ray experiment of von Laue. Instead of passing a

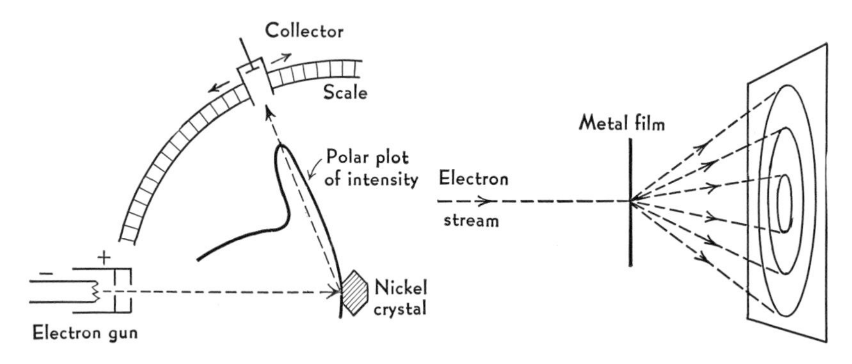

Fig. 6-2. In the Davisson and Germer experiment electrons of a particular speed were reflected from a certain plane in a nickel crystal, giving a maximum at that angle for which the de Broglie wavelength would give reinforcement.

Fig. 6-3. Method by which G. P. Thomson obtained electron diffraction. Owing to the random orientation of the small crystals, or fragments, of which the metal film is composed the regions of reinforcement become circles.

narrow beam of x-rays through a crystal as von Laue did, Thomson passed a narrow beam of electrons through a metal film (Fig. 6-3), but in order to get penetration he had to use a quite thin film. Since even the thin film of metal contains many small broken crystals in all possible positions the pattern obtained consists of circles instead of spots. These circles are similar to those obtained by the x-ray powder diffraction process. Indeed, the diffraction pattern produced by electrons passing through a thin metal film may be so similar to the diffraction of a beam of x-rays as to be practically indistinguishable (Fig. 6-4). The experiments afford striking confirmation of de Broglie's suggestion and further indicate the complementary nature of photons and particles. Such experiments also lead us to believe as firmly in electron waves as in x-ray photons.

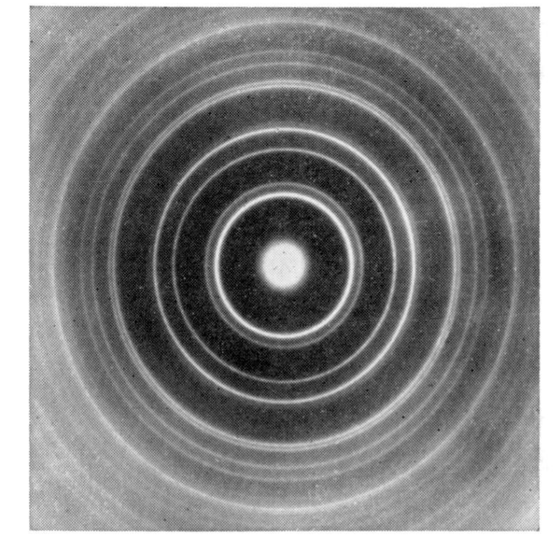

Fig. 6-4. Diffraction rings formed by passing narrow beam of electrons through thin silver foil, following the method of G. P. Thomson. (Courtesy, L. H. Germer, Bell Telephone Laboratories.)

It is of added interest to note that the wave-like character of a particle not only appears in the behavior of an electron but has been more recently verified in the behavior of protons and other atomic or subatomic particles. That the de Broglie equation would lose its customary significance if applied to large objects such as those of everyday life is fairly evident. Since the objects would be relatively enormous and the wavelengths would be almost vanishingly small, diffraction experiments would be impossible. In the quantum mechanical treatment of large-scale phenomena quantum effects become "smoothed out" and gradually merge into those of classical mechanics. This is an expression of the Bohr **correspondence principle.**

6-5. Waves and Particles; Complementarity

The Compton effect and the nature of photoelectric emission clearly indicate the particle-like behavior of light quanta (photons). Similarly the experiments of Davisson and Germer and of G. P. Thomson clearly indicate the wave-like behavior of electrons. If wave and particle concepts are both used in the description of photons and electrons it might at first seem that all sharpness of distinction between waves and particles had been lost. This is by no means true. Photons travel through empty space at the speed of light and are not known to be affected by collisions with other photons. Particles, on the other hand, such as electrons, can never travel as fast as the speed of light in empty space and can only approach that speed. Moreover, the velocity of such particles is affected by collisions with other particles.

It is further true that, as far as any detecting device is concerned, electrons do not act as both particles and waves at the same time. Neither do photons act simultaneously as waves and particles. Under one set of circumstances the experimental arrangement may reveal the particle-like character of radiation, but a different experimental arrangement may reveal the wave-like character. The same is true of electrons. We must remember these fundamental distinctions between radiant energy and matter, and we may help preserve these distinctions by being careful to say that radiant energy *may* exhibit particle-like characteristics and that electrons and other particles *may* exhibit wave-like characteristics. Thus we avoid the apparent contradiction of saying that an electron is both a particle and a wave and that a photon is also both a wave and a particle.

Resolution of the apparent particle-wave difficulty has been carried further by a statement of Niels Bohr, called the **principle of complementarity.** This statement asserts that wave and particle aspects in the atomic world are not so much contradictory as they are complementary. This implies that we have reached a limit in attempting to give a complete description of the elements of either matter or radiation by means of a single term. The terms *wave* and *particle,* borrowed from everyday life, cannot be applied in the atomic realm with such assurance and mutual exclusion as in the realm of everyday affairs. To adequately describe phenomena involving photons and electrons and other elementary particles we must resort to both concepts of wave and particle in a complementary manner, not in a contradictory manner, and each mode of description has its sphere of usefulness.

6-6. The Heisenberg Principle of Indeterminacy

The duality of the wave and particle concepts has been given a more quantitative meaning by Heisenberg in what is called the principle of indeterminacy. Heisenberg, formulating it, called it the principle of "Unbestimmtheit." This word has also been translated as "indefiniteness" and "uncertainty." Neither name expresses the complementary nature of the quantities involved, and the word *uncertainty* has very objectionable connotations. The principle expresses a fundamental limitation inherent in the nature of things. In dealing with ordinary mechanical phenomena we can determine both the velocity (or momentum) of an object and its position at any instant by making two successive measurements of time at different positions. Any disturbance of an ordinary object by the act of measuring it is inappreciable, but in the atomic realm the very act of measuring the momentum of an electron disturbs the position, and vice versa.

Heisenberg's principle states that in the atomic realm it is impossible to simultaneously measure both position and momentum with equally high precision. There is no "uncertainty" about individual measurements. It is possible to measure either momentum or position with any desired degree of precision within the limits of experimental equipment, but in general both may not be determined simultaneously with equally high precision. Let us consider an electron in motion. Even the most ideal case would require that at least one or more photons of light be reflected from the electron in order for it to be observed. However, when a photon is reflected from an electron, the electron also rebounds and hence does not follow the same path as it did before the observation. Thus, while making an observation on the path of the electron the path is changed in a manner that cannot be predicted with precision. The more precisely the momentum is measured the less precisely can the position be measured, and, conversely, the more precisely the position is measured the less precisely can the momentum be measured.

Heisenberg determined from basic theory that the product of the indeterminacy Δx of the position of a particle by the indeterminacy Δp in the measurement of its momentum will be of the order of magnitude of $h/2\pi$ where h is the Planck constant.

$$\Delta x \, \Delta p = \frac{h}{2\pi} \qquad [6\text{-}13]$$

Since the product is equal to a constant, increase in determinateness of one of the factors means decrease in the determinateness of the other.

Because the customary causal relations of classical mechanics depend upon the precise simultaneous knowledge of both positions and momenta of objects at any instant, this kind of causality breaks down completely when applied to atomic affairs. In no way does it mean that science has given up causality, for causality as understood today is largely an expression of the uniformity of nature, without which no science of any kind would be possible. When it is found impossible to apply strict causality to individual processes in the atomic realm, the scientist falls back on the statistics of large groups and applies causal principles to predict the probability of various states of these aggregates; thus the concept of the uniformity of nature is preserved (§ 12-6).

An interesting example of the necessity for acceptance of Heisenberg's principle in the atomic realm is given by Heisenberg himself. With very sensitive apparatus we could perform the following experiment and measure the velocity (or momentum) of an electron by timing its flight between two points. The electron could presumably be located at these points by two extremely sensitive microscopes (Fig. 6-5). The minimum amount of light that could be reflected from an electron would, of course, be one photon. From the small quantities involved it may be seen that this is an idealized experiment, not one which could actually be realized. By referring to the figure it is seen that an electron moving along the line *AB* could have a photon of light reflected from it into the microscope M_1, by which it is detected at position *B*. If the time of observation were noted and if the time of observation at a second position *C* by means of microscope M_2 could be noted, the velocity of the electron could be obtained. However,

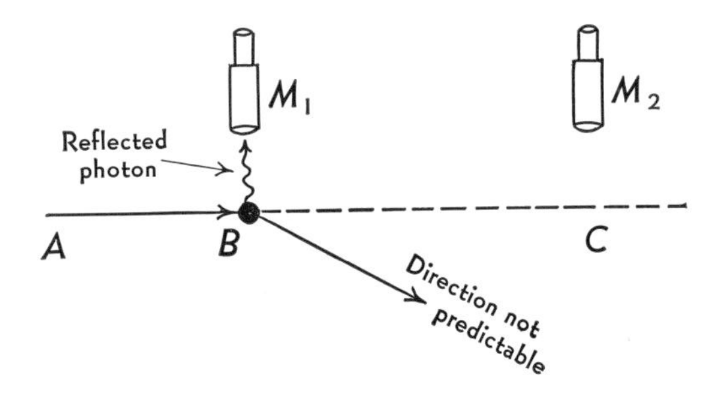

Fig. 6-5. Hypothetical experiment to measure electron velocity between *B* and *C*. Recoil of electron from photon collision at *B* sends it off in an unpredictable direction and prevents the measurement at *C* from being made.

we know from Compton's experiment that the photon reflected into the microscope at B in its collision with the electron gives the electron momentum and diverts it in some unpredictable direction D from its original path. The location of the electron at position D by the microscope M_2 is thereby defeated, and the velocity measurement becomes indeterminate. In this experiment the precise location of the electron at point B prevents the making of a precise measurement of the velocity.

Let us try again by another method. We may locate the position of the electron by observing the point at which it strikes a fluorescent screen. The tiny flash of light given by the screen may with considerable precision locate the position of the electron but only at the expense of knowledge of its velocity (or momentum). When the electron strikes the screen and produces a scintillation it either loses its velocity completely or has its velocity greatly changed in a way that cannot be directly measured. Thus again, in localizing the position of the electron, we sacrifice the capacity to measure its velocity or momentum.

From the converse viewpoint an attempt to measure the velocity of the electron can only be made at the expense of an attempt to locate its position accurately. Take, for instance, the determination of the velocity of an electron by deflecting it in a uniform magnetic field. From the radius of path and the strength of magnetic field, together with the value of e/m, the velocity can be determined with precision, but the location of the electron in its path is now indeterminate.

From such considerations Heisenberg arrived at his principle of indeterminacy. Although in any physical measurement there must always be a degree of indeterminacy, owing to limitations of the measuring apparatus, the limitation discussed in this section is of a different kind. It is fundamental in the nature of things. The quantum of light cannot be cut in two to provide a more precise means of observation, and so long as we rely on light quanta for observation there must always be a complementary relation between experimental measurements of position and momentum. This complementarity is more fully displayed in attempts to represent both the position and the momentum of the electron simultaneously by the wave picture.

6-7. Wave Description of the Electron

Let us first approach the description of the electron from the wave viewpoint in an elementary manner. For an electron traveling with a definite velocity the de Broglie equation gives a sharply defined wavelength $\lambda = h/mv$. For a wave train to represent a sharply defined wavelength, that is, to be a truly "monochromatic" wave, it must be infinite in extent. Consequently when the velocity of an electron is precisely described by an infinite wave train, as in Fig. 6-6*a*, the possibility of locating the electron has been lost.

On the other hand, if we desire to locate the electron more definitely we can represent it by means of a shorter wave train or wave group. It is a common phenomenon of wave motion, readily observed when a pebble is dropped into water, that a series of ripples travels outward. This series of ripples is not a single wave train of infinite length but is called a **wave group** or packet. The amplitude rises to a maximum in the middle, as shown in Fig. 6-6*b*, and decreases to zero in a finite region. The Fourier analysis of such a wave group shows it to be the summation of a set of different infinite wave trains, each having a different frequency or wavelength and consequently each representing a different velocity. These component wave trains add together constructively to give the wave group as indicated but at all other points add up destructively to zero. The shorter the wave group is, the larger will be the number of component wave trains and the wider will be the spread of velocities represented.

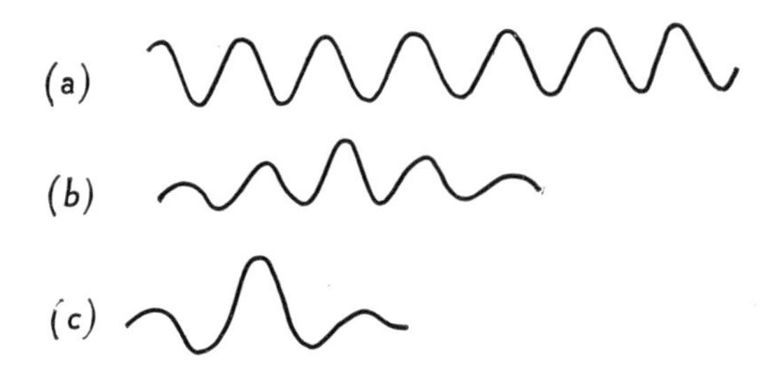

Fig. 6-6. ***a*, An infinite train of de Broglie waves represents the velocity of an electron exactly, but its position is then completely indeterminate; *b*, a wave packet represents the position of an electron more definitely, but the velocity is then less sharply defined; *c*, a shorter wave packet increases the precision of location of position but decreases the definiteness in velocity.**

If we now seek to represent an electron by a wave group, we can increase the precision of locating the electron in the region occupied by the wave group by choosing a shorter group. However, the shorter the group is, as in Fig. 6-6*c*, the larger is the range of wavelengths involved, and by the de Broglie formula the larger is the range of velocities involved. Thus in making the location of position more precise the velocity becomes less precise, and vice versa, and the wave description of the particle has led us directly to the complementary relation of the wave and particle descriptions.

To obtain the velocity of a component de Broglie wave we may multiply the wavelength by the frequency. The wavelength is

$$\lambda = \frac{h}{mv} \qquad [6\text{-}14]$$

To get the frequency we consider the usual quantum relation where the energy E of the quantum equals hf. To represent the equivalent energy of an electron of mass m we borrow a fundamental relation from the theory of relativity $E = mc^2$, where c is the velocity of light (§ 7-10). Then

$$f = \frac{E}{h} = \frac{mc^2}{h} \qquad [6\text{-}15]$$

and the velocity u of the "monochromatic" de Broglie wave is

$$u = \lambda f = \left(\frac{h}{mv}\right)\left(\frac{mc^2}{h}\right) \qquad [6\text{-}16]$$

and

$$u = \frac{c^2}{v} \qquad [6\text{-}17]$$

This presents a surprising answer. If the electron travels with a speed v less than c, the speed of light, as any material particle must do, then the speed u of the de Broglie wave by which the electron is described must be greater than the speed of light. According to this result it would seem that the de Broglie wave train representing the electron would travel faster than the electron and would leave it far behind. At this point the wave description again appears somewhat unsatisfactory, and the waves evidently cannot be physical waves in real space since a speed greater than that of light would violate a basic principle of the theory of relativity (Chap. 7). They must then be only mathematical waves in some kind of mathematical space.

However, the wave picture is greatly improved by using the idea of a wave group instead of a single de Broglie wave train. It is well known that the velocity of a wave group (group velocity) may be entirely different from the velocity of the component waves making up the group, and the group velocity may be much less than the phase velocity of the components. The way in which the phase waves in water travel faster than the group and seem to move through the group can be seen by anybody observing closely. Such a wave group, with a velocity different from the component waves, can only be formed when the component waves of the group themselves have different velocities, that is, when the waves occur in a dispersive medium. This is true for waves in water, but light waves in empty space all travel with the same velocity and cannot form a group which travels at a different velocity. In air, light waves can form such a group, and though the effect is small it must often be taken into consideration in measurements of the velocity of light.

The way in which the group velocity is affected by the dispersive qualities of the medium is well known and is given by the equation

$$v(\text{group}) = u - \lambda \frac{du}{d\lambda} \qquad [6\text{-}18]$$

where u is the velocity of the individual waves in the group. If there is no dispersion $du/d\lambda = 0$ and $v = u$; that is, the group and individual wave velocities or *phase velocities* are the same.

The new description of the electron in terms of a wave group chosen to have its group velocity the same as the velocity of the electron now much better represents the complementary character of its wave and particle aspects. Furthermore, the student is perhaps comforted to have the wave and particle aspects of the electron travel together at the same speed.

6-8. Wave Mechanics

The wave description of the electron is of far greater value than merely (a) predicting the distributions of electrons reflected from a crystal, or (b) predicting the energies that an electron can acquire from interaction with radiant energy. It now lies at the basis of the present-day, more complete quantum mechanical theory known as wave mechanics, which has been found to be particularly effective throughout the entire range of atomic and subatomic phenomena.

The fundamental relations of wave mechanics were formulated by Heisenberg, and also by Schrödinger who gave them the form known as the Schrödinger wave equation. This is a differential equation, and for a single particle moving in one dimension only it is

$$\frac{d^2\psi}{dx^2} + \frac{8\pi^2 m}{h^2}(E - V)\,\psi = 0 \qquad [6\text{-}19]$$

where E is the total energy of a particle of mass m such as an electron, V is its potential energy, and h is the Planck constant. The quantity ψ

is the amplitude the variation of which constitutes the wave, and the physical significance of ψ is to be determined (Chap. 10). The usefulness of this equation and its effectiveness in dealing with many atomic problems have been outstanding and will form the subject of Chap. 10. For students who have not become acquainted with the notation of the calculus the Schrödinger equation may appear formidable, and they may wish to omit Chap. 10 or skim through it. However, the importance of the equation is so great that the general student should at least know what it looks like.

The analysis of atomic problems by means of the Schrödinger wave equation or by related methods has led to what is sometimes called the new quantum theory, to distinguish it from the old quantum theory. The latter began with Planck's original assumption and reached a climax with the Compton experiment with photons, and with the experiments of Davisson and Germer and of G. P. Thomson with electrons.

6-9. Electron Optics and Electron Lenses

In previous chapters the electron has been treated as a particle or tiny bullet (electron ballistics), but we now have an alternate way of treating the electron, from the wave viewpoint.

The subject of electron optics is chiefly concerned with the formation of images by electron beams. Just as in geometrical optics the formation of images is studied by the use of light rays, so in electron optics such image formation may be studied by means of electron paths ("rays"). However, just as in physical optics the wave nature of light provides the fundamental mode of description, so also in electron optics the de Broglie wave concept may serve a similar purpose. Indeed, just as in ordinary optics the ray picture is an approximation when diffraction effects are ignored, so also in electron optics the particle-path or ray method is the short-wavelength approximation to the wave picture. When diffraction effects are negligible the particle picture is satisfactory, but frequently in electron optics the wave picture is required to give more complete information. For instance, the limit of useful operation of any optical device is given in terms of its resolving power, and this depends upon the wavelength involved.

Electrons may be reflected, refracted, and focused just as light may be. In Fig. 6-7, an electron is represented as approaching a negatively charged plate. If the field in front of the plate is sufficiently intense the direction of motion of the electron will be reversed, and *reflection*

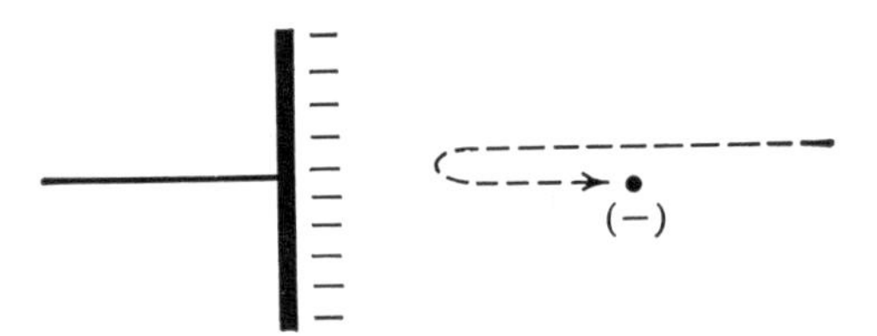

Fig. 6-7. Reflection of electron from negatively charged plate.

occurs. The path of an electron on passing into an electric or magnetic field may be bent, and *refraction* occurs.

If a divergent beam of electrons is passed through a properly shaped electric or magnetic field it may be brought to a focus in much the same way as divergent light rays are brought to a focus by means of a lens. The electric or magnetic field, so shaped as to accomplish this, is called an **electrostatic** or **magnetic lens,** or simply an electron lens. Such lenses suffer from defects similar to those of optical lenses. In "chromatic aberration" electrons of different wavelengths (different velocities) may fail to focus at the same point. In a defect similar to spherical aberration the electrons may not all be bent so as to focus sharply. The sharpness of the focus ultimately depends on the resolving power, which in turn depends on the wavelength associated with the electrons.

An electrostatic electron lens, formed by arranging electrodes so as to give a symmetrical field that will focus a diverging beam of electrons, is called a converging lens. If the lines are drawn to represent points of equal potential in the electric field, these lines make the appearance of the field more like that of an optical lens. Actually electrons moving through this field are so affected by it as to tend to move in a direction at right angles to the equipotential line. For instance, in the electrostatic field between metal-ring electrodes (Fig. 6-8) elec-

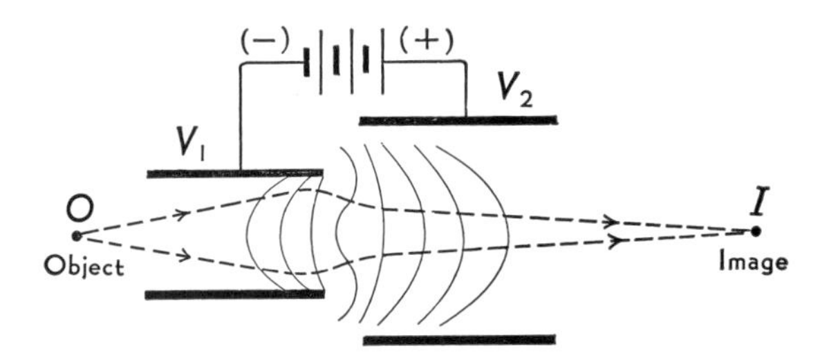

Fig. 6-8. Electrostatic electron lens formed by electric field between two coaxial cylinders. Fine lines are equipotential lines (at right angles to the electric field). This is a long focus lens, equivalent to a strong converging lens plus a weak diverging lens.

trons from point O may be focused at point I. The analogy between electron lenses and optical lenses may be pushed further, and an expression may be obtained for the focal length of an electron lens and for the index of refraction for electrons considered as waves.

A divergent electron beam may also be focused by a properly shaped magnetic field (magnetic lens). A coil of wire A (Fig. 6-9), in which a current is flowing, has a magnetic field, as indicated by the dashed lines H. Electrons in passing through this coil are deflected in such a way as to focus at point I. The actual motion of electrons in such a magnetic field is more complicated than is indicated in Fig. 6-9. Instead of traveling along a line curved in a single plane, an electron possessing a component of velocity at right angles to the field tends to spiral about the lines representing the magnetic field. However, mathe-

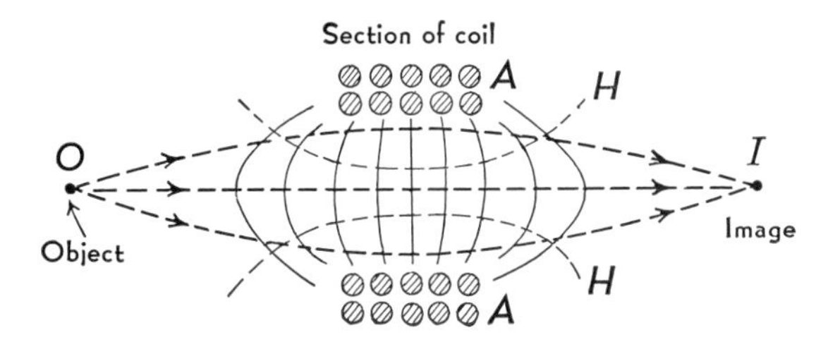

Fig. 6-9. Magnetic electron lens. Nine fine vertical lines are lines of equal magnetic potential (at right angles to the magnetic field *H*, *H*). Electron paths are actually spirals which cannot easily be represented in two dimensions.

matical analysis shows that a divergent beam of electrons can still be made to focus at the point I. Such electron lenses have many applications, one of the most important of which is the electron microscope.

6-10. The Electron Microscope

From classical theory it has long been known that the useful magnification by an optical instrument is limited by the resolving power of that instrument. The resolving power of any optical instrument is inversely proportional to the wavelength of light. The shorter the waves are the more distinct will be the magnified image, and hence the larger will be the magnification that is effective. The limit of magnification of an ordinary microscope using visible light is in the neighborhood of 2000 diameters. This extreme limit is independent of the degree of perfection of the lenses and depends only upon the wavelength of the light when the other optical dimensions are unchanged. Enlargement of the image beyond this point merely produces a fuzzy and less distinct image. Since x-rays have far shorter wavelengths than ordinary light, a microscope using x-rays could give much greater magnification. Owing to the difficulty of bending or refracting x-rays such applications have only been possible in extremely limited cases.

Electrons of sufficient speeds, however, may have wavelengths much smaller even than those of x-rays, and consequently they present the possibility for far greater magnification provided that they can be made to produce detectable images. Since electrons, like x-rays, produce fluorescence on a suitable screen, an electron image falling on such a screen can be transformed into a visible image to be observed directly or photographed. Either the electrons forming the image must be emitted by the specimen to be observed, or else the specimen must be thin enough for electrons from another source to be able to pass through it. The latter method has been adopted for commercial instruments, many of which are now in use.

The nonrelativistic formula for the de Broglie wavelength (Eq. 6-12) of an electron accelerated by a potential of V volts is

$$\lambda = \frac{12.3}{\sqrt{V}}\,10^{-8}\ \text{cm} = \frac{12.3}{\sqrt{V}}\ \text{A} \qquad [6\text{-}20]$$

For a 50,000-volt electron $\lambda = 0.055$ A, and if the relativistic correction is made it will be a few per cent less than this. The customary formula for the resolving power of a light microscope is

$$d = \frac{0.61\ \lambda}{\sin\alpha} \qquad [6\text{-}21]$$

where d is the least distance between two points that can be resolved and α is half the angle at the object subtended by the objective lens. Applying this formula to the electron microscope the limit of its resolving power should be nearly 100,000 times better than that of the best optical microscope, since the de Broglie wavelength just stated is approximately 1/100,000 that of visible light. If this upper limit to the resolution were possible, objects far smaller in size than atoms could be seen. Unfortunately the magnetic and electric lenses of an electron microscope have inherent limitations and cannot be shaped anywhere near so accurately as optical lenses. Consequently electron beams may only be permitted to diverge through angles a hundredth or less of those for light beams. This reduction in α decreases the practical upper limit of resolving power proportionately, but even this has not been reached, and the best to be expected at present is something like a thousandth of the ideal limit or a hundred times better than an optical microscope. This would mean magnifications of 200,000 diameters, and since an optical microscope may be able to resolve an object of 1000 A (10^5 cm) diameter an electron microscope would then have a resolving power of about 10 A, and very large molecules would be within its range. Some of these have already been observed.

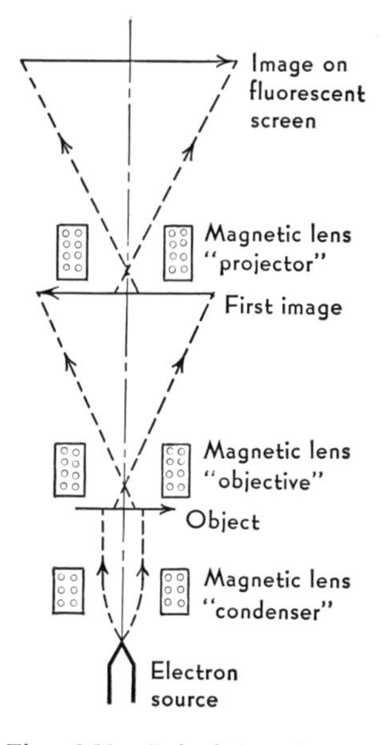

Fig. 6-10. Principle of two-stage electron microscope with magnetic lenses. Unlike an optical microscope, the second lens projects a magnified image on a fluorescent screen.

Fig. 6-11. Electron-microscope photo of influenza virus A and B vaccine, magnification 11,500. The white squares are small crystals of magnesium oxide. (Courtesy, Dr. F. Heinmetz, University of Pennsylvania.)

The principle of the electron microscope is shown in Fig. 6-10. Electrons from a hot cathode are accelerated by a positive potential on an anode and are focused so as to form a beam of high-speed electrons which fall upon a sample to be observed. Electrons emerging from this sample are focused by another electron lens and may form a magnified image on a fluorescent screen. In a compound electron microscope, a second lens is placed in the path of the electron beam so that electrons diverging from the plane of the first image will focus at a second plane in such a way as to magnify the already magnified image. The fluorescent screen is now placed at the plane of the second image, and the image may be observed directly or photographed. Examples of photographs so obtained are shown in Fig. 6-11, together with a typical electron microscope, Fig. 6-12.

Some of the practical limitations of the electron microscope should be mentioned. The specimen to be examined must be quite thin so as to permit the passage of the electron beam through the less dense portions of the sample. Specimens such as bacilli that are alive may be quickly killed and perhaps disintegrated by the electron beam.

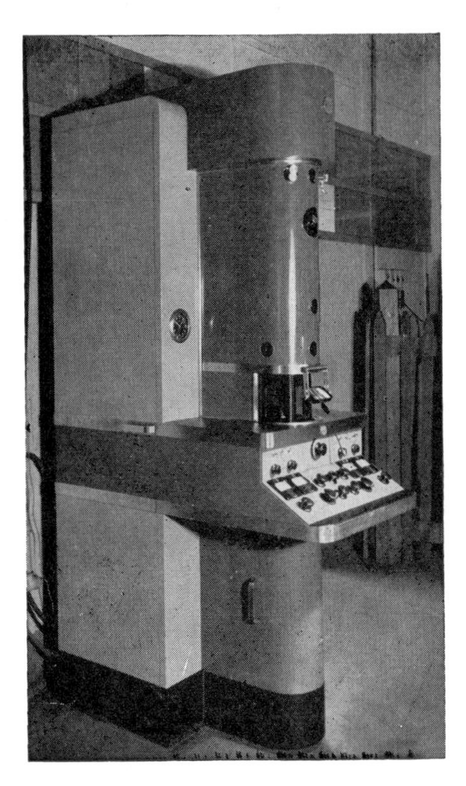

Fig. 6-12. Two-stage electron microscope. (Courtesy, Radio Corporation of America.)

The interior of the microscope must be at a very high vacuum. To obviate the need of letting air into the whole region when changing samples, the sample is usually placed in a small drawer-like chamber with an air lock between it and the other compartment. In problems such as the study of the crystalline character of the surface of a metal, a casting of the surface may be made in a thin film of some plastic material, and the observations may be made on this thin film. In spite of many limitations tremendous advances have already been made along many lines, industrial as well as medical, physiological, and more purely scientific.

PROBLEMS

1. Compute the energy of a photon of sodium light for $\lambda = 5890$ A. How many of these photons/sec equal 1 watt?

Ans. 3.38×10^{-12} erg; 2.98×10^{18} photons/sec.

2. A faint star is just visible if 2000 photons/sec enter the eye. What energy per second does this represent in terms of sodium light? ($\lambda = 5890$ A)

Ans. 6.76×10^{-16} watt.

3. Find the nonrelativistic de Broglie wavelength for an electron of 100,000-ev energy.

Ans. 0.039 A.

4. Find the de Broglie wavelength (nonrelativistic) for a slow neutron of velocity 10^5 cm/sec and of mass 1.675×10^{-24} gm.

Ans. 3.96 A.

5. Find the de Broglie wavelength (nonrelativistic) for a proton of mass 1.672×10^{-24} gm accelerated by a field of 100 volts.

Ans. 0.0286 A.

6. If the maximum magnification of an ordinary microscope is 2000 using light of average wavelength 5000 A, what would be the upper limit of magnification with an electron microscope using 10,000-volt electrons? (Neglect relativistic corrections.)

Ans. 8.1×10^7.

7. Find the resolving power of an electron microscope in the ideal case of $\alpha = 1°$ if 40,000-volt electrons are used (§ 6-10).

Ans. 2.15×10^{-8} cm.

8. Electrons of 16-ev energy are reflected from a crystal the planes of which are 2 A apart. At what glancing angle will the first-order reinforcement occur?

Ans. 50.2°.

9. An electron initially at rest is hit "head-on" by an x-ray photon of wavelength 0.5 A. What are the energy and the momentum given to the electron?

Ans. 37×10^{-10} erg;
2.6×10^{-18} gm cm/sec.

10. An x-ray photon has a wavelength of 0.2 A. Compute its equivalent mass and momentum.

Ans. Momentum $= 3.31 \times 10^{-18}$ gm cm/sec;
mass $= 1.10 \times 10^{-28}$ gm.

11. An x-ray photon of wavelength 0.2 A is reflected at an angle of 135° with its original direction after colliding with an electron at rest. What is the Compton shift in wavelength and what is the wavelength of the reflected photon?

Ans. Shift $= 0.0414$ A; $\lambda = 0.241$ A.

12. An x-ray photon of wavelength 0.1 A is reflected at an angle of 90° with its original direction after colliding with an electron at rest. What energy in ergs does it lose and what is the frequency change of the photon?

Ans. Energy loss $= 3.98 \times 10^{-8}$ erg;
$\Delta f = 6 \times 10^{18}$ sec^{-1}.

13. If waves in deep water travel with a phase velocity $u = (g\lambda/2\pi)^{1/2}$ where g is the acceleration of gravity, find the group velocity of the waves.

$$Ans.\ v = \frac{u}{2} = \left(\frac{g\lambda}{8\pi}\right)^{1/2}.$$

SUGGESTED READING

M. Born, *Atomic Physics*, 5th ed. (New York, Steckert-Haffner, 1951).
W. Heisenberg, *The Physical Principles of the Quantum Theory* (Chicago, Univ. of Chicago Press, 1930).
K. K. Darrow, *Introduction to Contemporary Physics*, 2nd ed. (New York, Van Nostrand, 1939).
A. H. Compton and S. K. Allison, *X-rays in Theory and Experiment*, 2nd ed. (New York, Van Nostrand, 1935).
L. Jacob, *An Introduction to Electron Optics* (New York, Wiley, 1951).
E. F. Burton and W. H. Kohl, *The Electron Microscope* (New York, Reinhold, 1942).
A. S. Eddington, *The Nature of the Physical World* (New York, Macmillan, 1928).
P. Franck, *Between Physics and Philosophy* (Cambridge, Harvard Univ. Press, 1941).

CHAPTER 7

THEORY OF RELATIVITY

7-1. Introduction

Einstein developed his theory of relativity in an attempt to solve what had become one of the greatest dilemmas of all physical science. This dilemma arose from apparent contradictions both in theory and in experiment. Popular emphasis on the mathematical intricacies of Einstein's theory has sometimes obscured the fact that much of the basic theory can be stated without the use of advanced mathematics. Furthermore, an understanding of the nature of the problem and its chief results is essential to much in modern science.

7-2. Galilean-Newtonian Relativity

Some idea of the relativity of all motion may be traced back to ancient times, but since the ancients had no precise working concepts for the analysis of motion the relativity was not sharply defined. With the development of fundamental mechanical concepts by Galileo and Newton the phenomena of motion could be clearly defined, including the way in which the measured velocity of an object depends upon the state of rest or motion of an observer.

The fact that all motion is relative to a frame of reference is implied in the very definition of velocity, where velocity in the x direction is defined as dx/dt. The x is a measurement of distance from some reference point. From the same reference point measurements could also be made in the y and z directions. The x, y, z axes assumed to exist at the reference point form the frame of reference. *All measurements are made in some frame of reference.* Usually it is simplest to choose a frame of reference at rest with respect to the observer. However, the frame of reference may be in motion with respect to the observer, and the basic problem to be discussed is how measurements made in a moving system are related to those made by an observer in his own rest system.

According to Newton's first law of motion, whenever an object is accelerated the acceleration is assumed to be the result of some applied force. According to the second law of motion, the assumed force is proportional to the rate of change of momentum of the object. If the rate of change of momentum is zero no force is assumed to act. Indeed, force in the Newtonian sense is that which produces change in momentum. For an object at rest with respect to an observer, or moving with respect to him with a constant velocity, there is no observed change of momentum, and he assumes that there is no force acting upon it. A second observer moving with constant velocity with respect to the first, that is, moving in a nonaccelerated system, would observe the body in a state of relative motion with a constant velocity, and so to him also there would be no implied force acting on the body.

If, however, the object is seen by one of these observers to be accelerated it will be seen to have the same acceleration by any other observer moving with constant velocity with respect to the first observer. In other words, all observers will obtain the same acceleration from their measurements of a given body if the observers are moving with constant velocities with respect to one another.

For instance, observer A notes at time t_1 that the object is moving with velocity v_1, and at time t_2 he notes that it is moving with velocity v_2. If observer B is moving with constant velocity k with respect to observer A he notes at the same moments that the velocities are $v'_1 = v_1 + k$ and $v'_2 = v_2 + k$, respectively. The observed accelerations a are then equal since

$$a \text{ (observed by A)} = \frac{v_2 - v_1}{t_2 - t_1}$$

and

$$a \text{ (observed by B)} = \frac{(v'_2 - v'_1)}{(t_2 - t_1)} = \frac{(v_2 + k) - (v_1 + k)}{t_2 - t_1}$$

$$= \frac{v_2 - v_1}{t_2 - t_1}$$

Since such observers obtain the same accelerations they will also assign the same implied force as the requirement for the measured rate of change of momentum. From this we conclude that Newton's second law of motion applies to phenomena noted by all observers moving with constant velocity with respect to each other. Since in any such system of reference a body apparently offers the same inertial resistance to a change in its state of rest or motion such systems are often called **inertial systems.** In all such systems moving with constant velocity with respect to one another the simple laws of Newtonian mechanics apply, and we may say that in such inertial systems descriptions of phenomena according to Newtonian mechanics are equivalent.

On the other hand, a third observer not moving with uniform velocity with respect to either of the first two, but moving with an acceleration, would see things differently. His observations would not lead to the same implied forces but to entirely different forces depending upon the acceleration of his own frame of reference with respect to the frames of reference of the other observers. Consequently descriptions of phenomena in terms of Newtonian mechanics by observers in differently accelerated systems would not agree. Such accelerated systems are not inertial systems, and they do not belong to the group of equivalent inertial systems. To avoid embarrassing questions as to what the "actual" velocity or acceleration of a system was, Newton felt forced to assume the existence of an absolute and universal frame of reference to which all other measurements could in theory be referred. Thus an object could be in a state of absolute rest or motion with respect to such a system, but with the coming of the Einstein theory such a privileged frame of reference became obsolete, and it was now seen that there could be no state of absolute rest or motion. But first let us consider the type of relativity of motion as recognized by Galileo and Newton.

This Galilean-Newtonian type of relativity applies to strictly mechanical phenomena. This is the relation involved when we say that, if one automobile traveling 40 miles per hour is passed by an automobile traveling in the opposite direction 60 miles per hour, the relative velocity of one car with respect to the other is 100 miles per hour. In obtaining this result we have shifted the frame of reference from an observer by the roadside to an observer in one of the cars. The only difference noted by observers in each car is the difference in direction. This is the common type of relativity, more or less clearly recognized by everyone as a matter of highway safety if nothing more. It is not the type of relativity developed by Einstein although it is included in it as a special case.

7-3. Origin of the Einstein Theory

Einstein developed his theory of relativity in response to a definite and urgent need. The need arose from two sources, one experimental and the other theoretical. Although Galilean-Newtonian relativity seemed to be all that was required to describe ordinary mechanical phenomena it did not work in certain extreme cases, and it did not work when applied to optical or other electromagnetic phenomena. The simple relativity of motion commonly observed with moving objects was not found at all in the motion of light waves. Here, indeed, there seemed to be no relativity at all. The measured velocity of light waves was found to be apparently independent of the motion of the observer. Such a contradiction of the common-sense application of Galilean-Newtonian relativity could not be tolerated. If light waves moved as real objects move, then the measured velocity should depend on the motion of the observer. However, no such dependence could be found, although many experiments were tried.

Suspicion had also arisen from theoretical considerations that all was not well in the over-all viewpoint of Galilean-Newtonian relativity.

7-4. The Theoretical Dilemma

It was gradually becoming apparent that the equations of transformation from one reference system to another system moving with a constant velocity with reference to it were in general unsatisfactory. For one thing, they did not take into consideration the fact that intervals of time measured in the two systems might not be the same. Worse yet, although the fundamental relations of mechanics were invariant in form for the Galilean-Newtonian transformation, Maxwell's well-known equations of the electromagnetic field were completely changed by the transformation, and consequently different observers would be led to different and conflicting results. In other words, the forms of the laws of electromagnetic theory were not invariant for the Galilean-Newtonian transformation.

Now it is common knowledge that a game of billiards or other mechanical processes could be carried out in the parlor car of a smoothly riding train moving at constant velocity just as well as if the train were at rest. Why should not electromagnetic phenomena in such a moving laboratory likewise conform to the usual relations, and why should this not appear in the invariance of the appropriate equations expressing fundamental laws? Here was a dilemma indeed.

7-5. The Experimental Dilemma

A number of experiments have been performed in an attempt to detect any Galilean-Newtonian relativity in the motion of light waves. Of these the most famous was that of Michelson and Morley, begun in 1883. The Michelson and Morley experiment was an attempt to test the hypothesis that all space is filled with some mysterious medium, called the **ether,** which has the property of transmitting visible light and other electromagnetic waves. Ever since light had been recognized as a form of wave motion it had been thought to be a wave motion of *something.* It had been considered unthinkable for a wave to exist without existing in something. In the days when light was considered to be a mechanical wave, the ether, presumed to fill space, was thought of as a mechanical medium. Since other types of transverse waves were known to be transmitted only through the body of a solid substance, that is, a substance capable of sustaining a shearing stress, the conclusion seemed inescapable that the ether of space had to be a solid though at the same time it was too tenuous to be directly detected. All in all, such an explanation of the propagation of light was highly objectionable because of several irrational properties which had to be assigned to this apparently solid but indetectable medium.

Upon the development of the electromagnetic theory of light in the latter half of the last century it became necessary to replace the assumed *mechanical ether* by an assumed *electromagnetic ether.* However, it was difficult also not to carry over into the new theory some irrational requirements of the old.

Furthermore, if light waves in the electromagnetic ether behaved like all other known forms of wave motion their speed with respect to a given frame of reference should be a function of the medium, and any measured speed should depend upon the state of rest or motion of the observer and his frame of reference, as in Galilean-Newtonian relativity. It was this dependence on the state of rest or motion of the observer that Michelson and Morley set out to test, for according to the ether hypothesis the motion of the earth through space should affect the measurements of the speed of light. They made use of Michelson's newly invented **interferometer,** which was the most precise scientific instrument devised for this kind of work up to that time and one with which it should have been quite possible to detect the predicted changes in the measured speed of light.

Michelson who originated the experiment reasoned that, if the electromagnetic ether exists and penetrates all objects, the earth in its motion must pass through this ether, producing the effect of an "ether wind" blowing past the earth in the opposite direction. Light waves traveling in a direction opposite to this ether wind would be slowed down. Light waves traveling in the same direction as the ether wind would be speeded up. Light waves traveling in paths that cross the ether wind would be affected, though to a somewhat lesser degree than waves traveling directly with or against it.

The essence of the Michelson-Morley experiment was the comparison of the times of travel of two trains of light waves, one traveling down and back along the ether wind, the other traveling across and back. Since the train of light waves traveling along the ether wind would lose more on the slow part of the journey than it would gain on the fast part of the journey, it would have a net loss of time because of the ether wind. The wave train moving the same distance across the ether wind and back would also lose a little time but not so much. If the wave trains had started exactly in phase they would be out of phase on their return.

The experimental arrangement is shown in Fig. 7-1. Monochromatic light from a source S is split into two beams by partial reflection at mirror M_1. The reflected beam goes to mirror M_2 where it is reflected, and some of the light passes through M_1 to the eye at E. The beam transmitted by M_1 goes to mirror M_3 and is reflected to M_1 where some

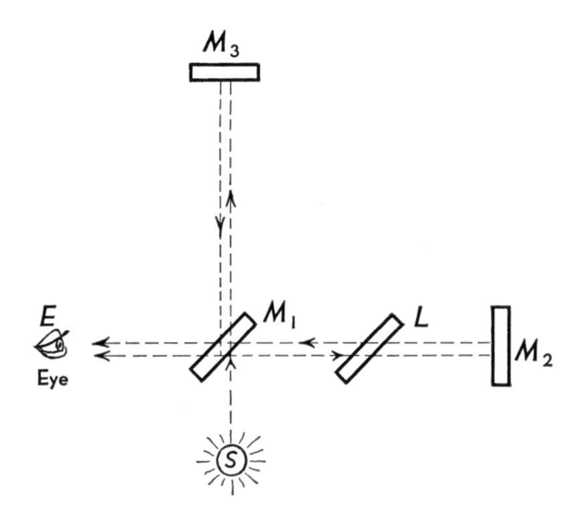

Fig. 7-1. Michelson-Morley experiment. Light from source *S* is split into two beams by partial reflection at half-silvered mirror face M_1. Beams reunite in eye to give interference or reinforcement depending on relative phase. *L* is an equalizer plate to make both beams travel same distance in glass.

of the beam is reflected to the eye at E. If the two beams reach the eye in phase they will reinforce, and a bright field is observed. If they reach the eye in opposite phase they interfere, and a dark field is observed. Any change in velocity of one beam more than of the other would shift the field of view from light to dark, or vice versa. If the experiment is arranged with one of the mirrors M_2 or M_3 slightly tipped so as to produce light and dark bands (fringes) in the field of view owing to reinforcement and interference, the effect of the ether stream would be to shift these bands or fringes a measurable amount.

To make a long story short, the expected difference in travel time of the two beams was not found, and thus the idea of an ether filling all space and a consequent ether wind had to be abandoned. (For a more complete description of this experiment with the accompanying mathematics the student is referred to more advanced books.) It should be noted that the difference of time for the light following the two paths of equal length s at right angles to each other would be sv^2/c^3 where v, the velocity of the ether stream, is assumed to be small compared to c, the velocity of light.

Seldom has an experiment in which the observers failed to find what they were looking for had such an effect on later scientific development. Other experimenters working with even greater precision have since obtained similar null results, and still others have tried entirely different experimental arrangements, but all have failed to demonstrate the existence of an ether stream. One of the more famous of the latter experiments was performed in 1902 by Trouton and Noble. Instead of an optical method they devised a sensitive electromagnetic experiment with capacitor plates. Electromagnetic theory showed that a torque should be exerted on these plates if the ether-wind theory were correct, but no such effect was found.

7-6. Possible Solutions of the Problem

The problem that we have just outlined was not new with Einstein. Scientists had been wrestling with it for some time, and several possible solutions had been suggested. For one thing, the assumed existence of an ether wind might be a mistake. The ether might be dragged along with the earth, and there would be no relative motion to detect. This would explain the null result of the Michelson-Morley experiment. However, it would be presumed that all stars and planets would also drag ether with them, thus producing slippage or distortion of the ether some place in the space between. Not only would this be difficult to imagine, but also it would have detectable effects on the passage of light through space. Consequently that explanation was unsatisfactory.

Fitzgerald and later Lorentz proposed a clever but questionable solution, known as the **Lorentz-Fitzgerald contraction** hypothesis. If the measuring apparatus is assumed to contract in the direction of motion by an amount proportional to $\sqrt{1-(v^2/c^2)}$ the contraction would exactly cancel the expected variation in measured velocity of light waves so that no effect would be observed. It is like Lewis Carroll's old man who was always thinking of a plan for dyeing his whiskers green and using a fan so large they could not be seen. Since this explanation seemed to be too "made to order," it was not generally accepted. The more satisfactory answer came from Einstein's interpretation of a set of equations that Lorentz had derived for the transformation from one system to another, moving with constant relative velocity. Out of these equations came the same shrinkage factor $\sqrt{1-(v^2/c^2)}$, but now the interpretation was quite different. These equations were not at all like those of the Galilean-Newtonian transformation, and they embodied the new idea that time intervals measured in the two systems are not the same. In what follows we shall attempt a simplified derivation of the equations of the *Lorentz transformation.*

7-7. The Lorentz Equations of Transformation

Let us first consider the equations of the Galilean-Newtonian transformation. The equations of transformation from a system of reference in uniform motion with respect to the observer, to the system in which the observer is at rest, are easily derived for Galilean-Newtonian relativity. Let us take x',y',z' as the coordinates of a point in the moving system and x,y,z as the coordinates in the "rest system." Now assume that

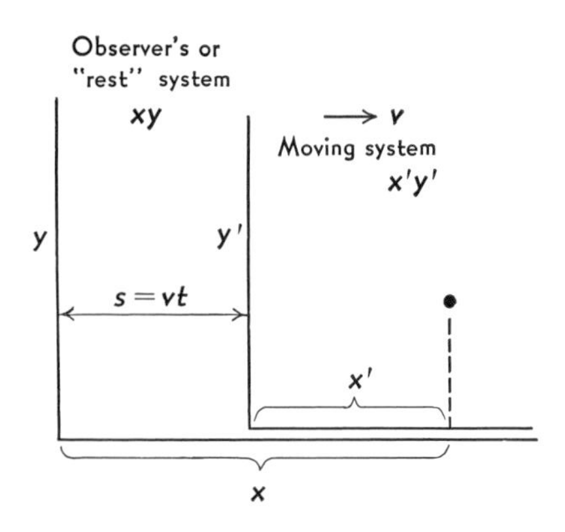

Fig. 7-2. Relation between the x coordinates of a point in the observer's or "rest" system (x,y,z) and in a system (x',y',z') moving to the right, with respect to the observer, with velocity v. For simplicity z coordinates are omitted.

the velocity of the moving system with respect to the observer's system is v, taken along the x axis for simplicity (Fig. 7-2). A distance x' to a point in the moving system of coordinates must be added to the space $s = vt$ passed over by the moving system since the two systems were in coincidence, in order to obtain the distance x to the same point measured in the observer's rest system. Then

$$x = x' + vt$$

where t is the elapsed time since the zeros of the two systems coincided. Similarly the distance x in the observer's stationary or rest system of coordinates must have the distance vt subtracted from it to give the distance to the same point in the stationary system.

$$x' = x - vt$$

Since motion along the x direction does not affect the y and z coordinates,

$$y = y' \qquad \text{and} \qquad z = z'$$

In Galilean-Newtonian relativity it is assumed that time intervals measured in both systems are the same; consequently,

$$t = t'$$

Thus, for the equations of the Galilean-Newtonian transformations we have

$$\begin{aligned} x &= x' + vt' & \qquad \text{and} \qquad & x' = x - vt \\ y &= y' & & y' = y \\ z &= z' & & z' = z \\ t &= t' & & t' = t \end{aligned} \qquad [7\text{-}1]$$

Yet, how are these equations to be modified if we are to solve the dilemma with which Lorentz was faced? Perhaps time intervals need not be the same in the two systems, but the speed of light must be the same to accord with the results of the Michelson and Morley experiment. If we modify the equations of transformation so as to preserve invariant the laws of electromagnetic theory, we may do violence to the laws of mechanics, but if we try to preserve Newtonian mechanics we may do violence to electromagnetic theory. Can the equations be so modified as to satisfy both requirements?

Einstein, applying the Lorentz transformation, emphasized the universal constancy of the velocity of light by making it a starting point rather than an objective to be attained. Let us write the following equations for the distance that light waves travel along the x axis in each system in a given time interval.

$$x = ct \qquad \text{and} \qquad x' = ct' \tag{7-2}$$

These equations imply the constancy of the speed of light in the two systems. Let us now make a provisional assumption as to what transformation equations might be used that would be of a more general nature than those of the Galilean-Newtonian transformation. It seems reasonable to try the assumption that measured quantities in one system are proportional to measured quantities in the other; therefore, let us write

$$x = k(x' + vt') \tag{7-3}$$

$$x' = k(x - vt) \tag{7-4}$$

where k is a constant of proportionality to be evaluated, x and t belong to the system in which the observer is at rest, and x' and t' belong to the system that is moving with respect to the observer. As before, v is the velocity of the moving system, which for simplicity is presumed to move in the x direction. Substituting Eq. 7-4 in Eq. 7-3, we obtain

$$x = k^2(x - vt) + kvt' \tag{7-5}$$

and solving this for t' we have

$$t' = kt + \left(\frac{1 - k^2}{kv}\right) x \tag{7-6}$$

Putting the values of x' (Eq. 7-4) and t' (Eq. 7-6) into the second part of Eq. 7-2 we have

$$k\,(x - vt) = c\left[kt + \frac{x}{kv}\,(1 - k^2)\right] \tag{7-7}$$

Since all terms are now in the unprimed system, in order that the constancy of the velocity of light be preserved, an x in this equation should have the value $x = ct$. Setting the x on the right equal to ct, the other on the left becomes equal to ct if k has the value

$$k = \frac{1}{\sqrt{1 - \frac{v^2}{c^2}}} \qquad [7\text{-}8]$$

Making use of this value of k, we can reduce Eq. 7-6 to

$$t' = k\left(t - \frac{vx}{c^2}\right) \qquad [7\text{-}9]$$

and we have equations for x' (Eq. 7-4) and t' (Eq. 7-9) in terms of x and t.

We may now write the equations of the Lorentz transformation, and since these are symmetrical with respect to observers in both systems we may write a similar set for quantities in the system at rest with respect to the observer, only making a change in signs representing the change in direction of motion. We then have for the equations of the Lorentz transformation:

$$\begin{aligned}
x &= (x' + vt')\frac{1}{\sqrt{1 - \frac{v^2}{c^2}}} & x' &= (x - vt)\frac{1}{\sqrt{1 - \frac{v^2}{c^2}}} \\
y &= y' & y' &= y \\
z &= z' & z' &= z \\
t &= \left(t' + \frac{vx'}{c^2}\right)\frac{1}{\sqrt{1 - \frac{v^2}{c^2}}} & t' &= \left(t - \frac{vx}{c^2}\right)\frac{1}{\sqrt{1 - \frac{v^2}{c^2}}}
\end{aligned} \qquad [7\text{-}10]$$

7-8. Einstein's Restricted Theory of Relativity

The equations of the Lorentz transformation led Einstein to his restricted or special theory of relativity, published in 1905. This theory is based on two postulates:

1. The speed of light is a universal constant independent of the motion of the observer.
2. Those mathematical relationships which we speak of as the laws of physics should have the same form for all systems moving with a constant velocity with respect to one another, or, in other words, they should be invariant for all inertial systems.

Some implications of this theory, as obtained from a further analysis and application of the equations of the Lorentz transformation, seem at first revolutionary and surprising. For instance, the length of a rigid body measured in the direction of motion of the body depends upon its speed relative to the observer.

The observer moving with reference to the object with speed v measures its length l_v to be the difference between two readings x'_2 and x'_1 on his scale. An observer at rest with respect to the object measures on his scale a length equal to the difference between the points x_2 and x_1 on his scale. The two lengths are related by the equation

$$l_v = x'_2 - x'_1 = (x_2 - x_1)\sqrt{1 - \frac{v^2}{c^2}} \qquad [7\text{-}11]$$

or the length at any speed v when l is measured in the direction of v is

$$l_v = l_0\sqrt{1 - \frac{v^2}{c^2}} \qquad [7\text{-}12]$$

where $l_0 = x_2 - x_1$ is called the rest length or length measured by an observer at rest with respect to the object. This relation, which comes directly from the first equation of the Lorentz transformation, indicates that as the speed of the body approaches that of light the measured length approaches zero. For instance, the length of a meter stick moving at a speed of 259,000 km/sec (161,000 mi/sec) would be measured as 50 cm, but, measured by an observer moving with it, it would have its normal rest length of 100 cm (Fig. 7-3).

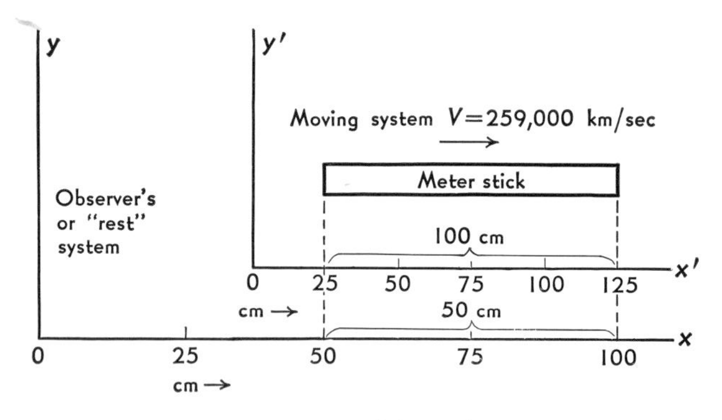

Fig. 7-3. Measurements on a meter stick moving with a speed of 259,000 km/sec (161,000 mi/sec) with respect to the observer would show it to be 50 cm long.

It is further deduced from the Lorentz transformation that the mass of a body in motion with respect to an observer will increase with increasing speed according to the equation

$$m_v = \frac{m_0}{\sqrt{1 - \frac{v^2}{c^2}}} \qquad [7\text{-}13]$$

where m_v is the mass at velocity v and m_0 is the so-called rest mass or mass measured by an observer moving with the object. It is seen that, as the relative speed of the body approaches the speed of light, the observed mass of the body approaches infinity.

From this it is seen that, if Newton's second law is taken to define force F as ordinary mass times acceleration or as ordinary rate of change of momentum, it is no longer universally valid. The force can no longer be measured by the acceleration that it produces in a given mass since the mass changes in the process. The law does, however, become valid when force is defined as rate of change of momentum provided that momentum is now defined relativistically as

$$\frac{m_0 v}{\sqrt{1 - \frac{v^2}{c^2}}}$$

where m_0 is the rest mass.

Time intervals show a dilation similar to that of mass. Moving clocks will apparently slow down according to the relation

$$t_v = \frac{t_0}{\sqrt{1 - \frac{v^2}{c^2}}} \qquad [7\text{-}14]$$

Thus quantities of mechanics which had been thought of as invariant are found according to the relativity theory to depend upon the relative motion of the frame of reference in which they are measured. It is to be noted, however, that the relativistic variations in length, mass, and time are extremely small except when relative speeds are extremely large. For the ordinary speeds of everyday life these variations are entirely negligible, and the more general relativistic formulas reduce to those of ordinary mechanics for the special case of moderate speeds.

If the Lorentz transformation is applied to Maxwell's equations for the electromagnetic field the form of the equations is not altered, and hence they are invariant for this transformation just as the velocity of light is invariant. Thus the Gordian knot was cut by sacrificing the invariance of mass, length, and time of classical mechanics and gaining much in electromagnetism. As it turns out, the sacrifice in classical mechanics is only apparent since no appreciable violence is done to the Newtonian mechanics of everyday life and the changes are only appreciable in the region where classical mechanics had not previously been applied. It is a mistake to say that the Einsteinian revolution has overthrown the Newtonian system. More properly it has supplemented and extended the range of application of that system by refining it and correcting it for high speeds, and Newtonian mechanics is seen to be a special case of the more general relativistic mechanics when the speeds are low.

Newton had believed, provisionally at least, that time is something absolute like a mighty river flowing on and on, and he also believed in an absolute space in which bodies may either be at rest or in motion. Lorentz held in part to this Newtonian idea of time, and thought of the time measurements in the reference system at rest as the true or proper time intervals whereas he referred to those in the moving system as apparent. Thus he spoke of proper time and apparent time. Einstein showed that there was no logical basis for assuming a preferred reference system for either spatial or temporal measurements since an observer in either system could think of his own as the proper system and the other as the apparent one. Consequently the distinction vanishes and there can be no state of absolute rest or motion. As an example involving only ordinary mechanics, consider an observer in a smoothly flying airplane, moving with constant velocity. If he looks out of the window and sees nothing but another passing airplane, there is no way in which he can tell whether or not his own plane is moving. Only the relative velocity of the two planes can be observed. The absolute velocity of either one could not be observed directly or detected in any way; in fact, the idea would have no meaning since velocities must always be measured with respect to something.

It is apparent from the Lorentz equations that space and time measurements are no longer independent, as in the Newtonian world picture. The three dimensions of space and the one dimension of time can be thought of as forming a four-dimensional continuum of **space-time.** Any point in the space-time continuum locates what is called an *event,* and an event is defined by any particular set of values of x, y, z, and t. For instance, a particle in passing through space-time occupies a sequence of points representing a sequence of events. These points define a line called the **world line.** Although the use of time as a fourth dimension is common in daily life, as, for instance, in a railroad timetable, in the ramifications of the Einstein theory it may involve the use of four-dimensional geometry. For instance, in three-dimensional Euclidean space a line interval ds is given in terms of the component intervals along the x,y,z axes, as follows:

$$(ds)^2 = (dx)^2 + (dy)^2 + (dz)^2$$

In four-dimensional space with coordinate axes x,y,z,w the interval would be given by

$$(ds)^2 = (dx)^2 + (dy)^2 + (dz)^2 + (dw)^2$$

When time is used as the fourth dimension in the relativity theory the demands of the Lorentz transformation make it necessary to substitute for $(dw)^2$ not simply $(dt)^2$ but $-(cdt)^2$. The interval ds is then the segment of a world line between two "events," and since it is invariant under the Lorentz transformation it has the same value for all observers moving with constant velocity with respect to one another.

7-9. Validity of the Restricted Theory

The question now arises as to possible proofs of the Einstein theory in the circumstances in which it seems to do violence to the ordinary concepts of mechanics. One of the first pieces of evidence was obtained in the study of the motion of electrons. Although ordinary objects cannot be studied at extremely high speeds, electrons can be studied at speeds approaching that of light. A decrease in the value of e/m for electrons with increased speeds had been observed before the development of Einstein's theory and had been attributed to an increase in effective mass. Further tests were now made, and in 1908 Kaufmann and Bucherer, using high-speed electrons (beta rays) from a radioactive substance, confirmed that the mass increases with increasing speed, in agreement with Eq. 7-13 of the relativity theory (§ 1-11) (Fig. 1-7).

One of the most striking verifications of the restricted theory of relativity came from confirmation of Einstein's deduction of the energy-mass relation, in which he predicted the equivalence of energy and mass (§ 7-10). This relation, first verified on a small scale, was amply and violently confirmed before the whole world with the explosion of the first atom bombs.

7-10. Equivalence of Energy and Mass

Let us take Eq. 7-13

$$m_v = \frac{m_0}{\sqrt{1 - \frac{v^2}{c^2}}}$$

for the relativistic mass at a given velocity v in terms of m_0, the rest mass. The right-hand side of this equation may be expanded by means of the binomial theorem to give a rapidly converging infinite series

$$m_v = m_0 + \frac{1/2\, m_0 v^2}{c^2} + \frac{3/8\, m_0 v^4}{c^4} + \cdots \qquad [7\text{-}15]$$

Considering only the first two terms, since the third is usually very small, we have

$$m_v = m_0 + \frac{1/2\, m_0 v^2}{c^2} = m_0 + \Delta m \qquad [7\text{-}16]$$

where Δm is the increase in mass due to the increase in velocity. From this

$$\Delta m = \frac{1/2\, m_0 v^2}{c^2} = \frac{\text{kinetic energy}}{c^2} \qquad [7\text{-}16a]$$

Since $\frac{1}{2} m_0 v^2$ is the kinetic energy of the particle it is seen that the mass to which this energy is equivalent is obtained by dividing by c^2 (the square of the velocity of light), and conversely the energy to which a given mass is equivalent is obtained by multiplying by c^2. Multiplying both sides of Eq. 7-16 by c^2 it becomes evident that $m_0 c^2$ gives the equivalent energy of the rest mass of a particle or of any object of mass m_0.

The energy equivalent E of mass m is then in general

$$E = mc^2 \qquad [7\text{-}17]$$

This is the famous Einstein energy-mass relation.

$$E(\text{joules}) = m(\text{kg})c^2(\text{m/sec})^2$$

$$E(\text{ergs}) = m(\text{gm})c^2(\text{cm/sec})^2$$

From this relation 1 gram of matter of any kind has an energy equivalent of 9×10^{13} joules or 9×10^{20} ergs. If liberated in one second this would be 9×10^{13} watts or 0.12 million million horsepower. Thus it is evident that a very small amount of mass is equivalent to an extremely large amount of energy. This accounts for the fact that in the atom bomb, even though only a fraction of the mass of the atoms that are split is transformed directly into energy, an extraordinary amount of energy is released (Chap. 19).

Hence we see that it is necessary to modify previous ideas of the laws of conservation of energy and conservation of mass. No longer can we consider mass and energy to be distinct entities. We must now formulate a new law of **conservation of energy-mass** which states that total energy, whether in the form of matter or in the form of energy, is conserved. In other words, when energy is transferred from one body to another the mass of the first decreases and the mass of the second increases.

7-11. Electron-Pair Production and Annihilation

Confirmation of the energy-mass relationship is obtained from studies in nuclear physics, where it is found that under certain conditions a gamma ray representing radiant energy may be transformed into an electron pair consisting of a positive electron and a negative electron. To create such a pair without giving these particles any kinetic energy at all would require a gamma ray of minimum energy

$$E = 2m_ec^2 \qquad [7\text{-}18]$$

where m_e is the mass of each electron. This turns out to be 2(0.51) Mev or 1.02 Mev. In agreement with this, gamma rays of lower energy than 1.02 Mev have not been observed to form electron pairs. Gamma rays of higher energy form electron pairs, with the excess energy divided between the electrons in the form of kinetic energy of motion.

The reverse process of electron-pair annihilation has also been observed. Here a positive and a negative electron unite to "annihilate" each other as particles, but, by the law of conservation of energy-mass, the energy equivalent now goes to form two or more gamma rays. These processes of pair production and annihilation will be discussed again in the chapter on nuclear physics (§ 15-10), but they are among the most impressive bits of evidence in confirmation of the Einstein energy-mass relation.

7-12. The Addition Theorem for Velocities

Since the mass of a moving body increases in such a way as to approach infinity as the speed or velocity approaches that of light, it becomes evident that the velocity of light is thus an upper limit which may be approached but not surpassed by any material object. If this is true, very high velocities or speeds may no longer be added directly, as in the Newtonian transformation.

Consider a particle moving with a large velocity v with respect to the observer, the velocity v being to the left. If a second particle moves to the right with a large velocity v_2, and if the observer now moves toward the left along with the first particle and with the same velocity v, the velocity of the second particle as measured by the observer moving with the first particle can no longer be given as $v + v_2$, for this might easily in the case of electrons amount to more than the velocity of light. Let us see then how such velocities must be added.

Consider the observer moving with speed v to the left with the first particle. He sees his original frame of reference now moving with a speed v to the right, and in this system the second particle is moving to the right with a velocity v_2 relative to that system of reference. It is now desired to add the velocities v and v_2, by means of the Lorentz transformation. The two equations required are

$$x_1 = k(x_2 + vt_2) \qquad [7\text{-}19]$$

and

$$t_1 = k\left(t_2 + \frac{vx_2}{c^2}\right) \qquad [7\text{-}20]$$

where

$$k = \frac{1}{\sqrt{1 - \frac{v^2}{c^2}}}$$

Differentiating each of these with respect to t_2 we have

$$\frac{dx_1}{dt_2} = k\left(\frac{dx_2}{dt_2} + v\right) = k(v_2 + v)$$

$$\frac{dt_1}{dt_2} = k\left(1 + \frac{v}{c^2}\frac{dx_2}{dt_2}\right) = k\left(1 + \frac{vv_2}{c^2}\right)$$

Then dividing the first by the second

$$v_1 = \frac{dx_1}{dt_1} = \frac{v_2 + v}{1 + \dfrac{vv_2}{c^2}} \qquad [7\text{-}21]$$

From this v_1 is the relativistic sum of v and v_2. It is the velocity of the second particle as measured by an observer moving with the first particle. If we try this addition theorem, we find that even when v and v_2 each are equal to the velocity of light their sum is also equal to the velocity of light.

Equation 7-21 may be arrived at without the necessity of using calculus, by dividing Eq. 7-19 by Eq. 7-20, then interpreting x_1/t_1 as v_1, and x_2/t_2 as v_2, where x_1 is the space passed over in time t_1 and x_2 is the space passed over in time t_2.

Example Consider a frame of reference in which an observer detects two electrons with velocities $-0.7c$ and $+0.8c$ moving in opposite directions along the x axis, c being the velocity of light. In a Galilean system their velocity relative to one another would be $1.5c$, which is impossible according to the basic postulate of restricted relativity. According to the Einstein law of addition, the relative velocity is

$$v = \frac{0.8c + 0.7c}{1 + \dfrac{0.8(0.7)c^2}{c^2}} = \frac{1.50}{1.56}c = 0.96c$$

7-13. Concept of Simultaneity; Operational Viewpoint*

Einstein found that not only do our common ideas of mass, length, and time have to be revised but that other concepts hitherto unquestioned require rigorous definition and must be submitted to searching analysis. Chief of these is the concept of simultaneity. Before Einstein pointed the finger of suspicion at this concept it had been taken for granted by most people that they knew intuitively what was meant by two events being simultaneous or not being simultaneous. According to older standards there seemed to be a definite meaning to the statement that two events are simultaneous.

Yet, if we observe two events occurring at the same moment we may forget that the light signal coming to us from one event may have come further than from the other. Since it takes finite time for light to travel, two events which appear to be simultaneous may not be simultaneous.

* Optional.

So, also, of two events which we define as simultaneous, either may appear earlier than the other depending on conditions of observation. Einstein has pointed out the effect on the observer when the observer is moving. Assume that lightning strikes simultaneously at points A and B (Fig. 7-4). If the observer is at point C, halfway between A and B, and if the velocity of light is finite and is assumed to take the same time in going from A to C as in going from B to C, the observer will see both flashes of light at the same moment, and the events will appear simultaneous (Fig. 7-4*a*). However, if the observer at C is moving in the direction of A (Fig. 7-4*b*) he will move enough to receive the flash from A sooner, and he will think the lightning stroke at A occurred before that at B. If moving toward B (Fig. 7-4*c*) he will think the stroke at B occurred before that at A. Yet the assumption that the events are simultaneous when the observer is at the midpoint C

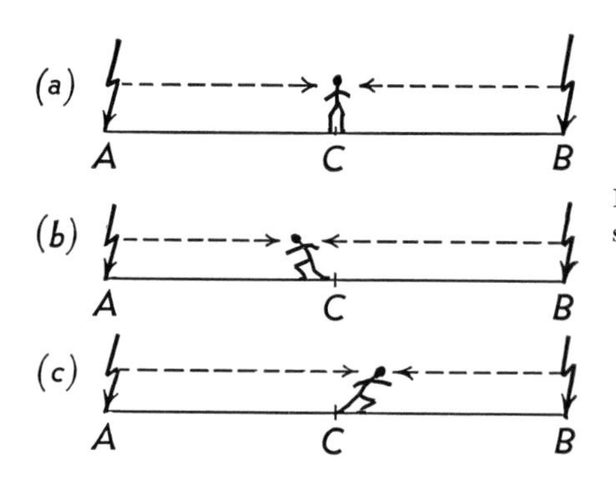

Fig. 7-4. Effect of motion of observer on apparent simultaneity of two events.

and receives the light flashes at the same time may be false, for the whole ABC system may be moving to the right or the left. If moving to the left the light from A again does not have so far to go, and the light from B has further to go. Events that seemed to be simultaneous to the observer at C may not be so. Consequently simultaneity is not something absolute but something to be carefully defined.

Two observers some distance apart may conclude that events are simultaneous if they refer to their clocks, but only if their clocks are running in synchronism. It is then necessary to define what is meant by synchronism. How can we define two clocks as being in synchronism? Einstein has given us a definition of simultaneity and a method of setting two clocks in synchronism according to the definition. Consider two clocks at positions A and B. If an observer at A sends a light signal to an observer at B, B may reflect it back to A. The clocks may be defined to be in synchronism when A and B are at rest with respect to one another, if B starts his clock on receiving the light signal and if A adjusts his clock so that it would have read zero at the middle of the time interval beween sending and receiving the light signal. Yet, although A and B are at rest with respect to one another both may move along the line AB. In that event one observer may be moving toward the signal and will receive it sooner, and the other may move away from the reflected signal and will receive it later. Consequently there can be no concept of absolute simultaneity. Events can only be simultaneous or not, depending on how simultaneity is defined. In defining simultaneity for observers moving with constant velocity with respect to one another the aid of the Lorentz transformation must be sought.

The fundamental need for having a workable definition of simultaneity is evident if we consider how we might measure the length of an object if the object is moving past the observer. The length of the object can be measured by two observers noting the coincidence of the two ends of the object with points on a scale as the object moves past them. Still, this only gives the length correctly if both readings are taken at the same moment, that is, if they are made simultaneously. Einstein has shown that measurements made simultaneously by an observer at rest with respect to the moving object would not necessarily be simultaneous for observers moving with the object. Thus the two sets of observers would get different results for the length of the body. The difference in results is the same as that given by the Lorentz transformation, and the amount of the "shrinkage" of a body moving with respect to an observer is given by Eq. 7-12.

The definition of simultaneity as given by Einstein thus becomes a part of the restricted theory of relativity. It also is one of the great examples of Einstein's demonstration that definitions are only valid and precise in terms of the operations required to be performed. This is known as the operational method or the operational viewpoint. For instance, we may ask, what is the real length of the object as it passes us? Is it the length which we obtain if we have been moving with the object? The answer is that from the viewpoint of relativity either answer is equally valid though the two may differ. There is no such thing as a *real* or *absolute* length of an object, just as there is no *real* or *absolute* time or mass. These things depend on the state of rest or motion of the observer with respect to the object, and they have meaning only in terms of the operations which have to be performed to obtain them.

7-14. Is There an Ether?

In the Einstein theory the idea of an ether filling all space is apparently relegated to the ash heap of worn-out concepts. Einstein was able to develop his theory without the aid of an artificial ether, but this hardly means that the existence of every kind of ether is disproved, and a serious problem remains. He himself spoke of "empty space," and we must then say that empty space has the property of transmitting light. Apparently we do not completely know what we mean when we say *empty space.* If we can for all purposes interpret the properties of space geometrically the need of a medium filling space vanishes, but the question is not yet finally solved, and the ether concept has shown signs of being revived in a more sophisticated form.

7-15. The General Theory of Relativity*

Einstein developed his special or restricted theory of relativity on the assumption that physical laws should be invariant in form for all systems of reference moving with constant velocity with respect to one another (inertial systems). The question arose in Einstein's mind as to whether or not this might be extended to include systems of reference which were accelerated with respect to one another. This attractive idea would involve a much more generalized theory and would mean that laws of physics were invariant in form for all systems of reference regardless of their relative motion. The development of this theory presented great mathematical difficulties, and to follow it far involves the use of the calculus of tensors. However, some aspects of the general theory are of particular interest.

Einstein was able to incorporate in his more general theory a consideration of the mysterious force of gravitation. In this he was led to his principle of equivalence, which states that it is impossible to distinguish between the effects of a gravitational field of force acting in one direction and the acceleration of a frame of reference in the op-

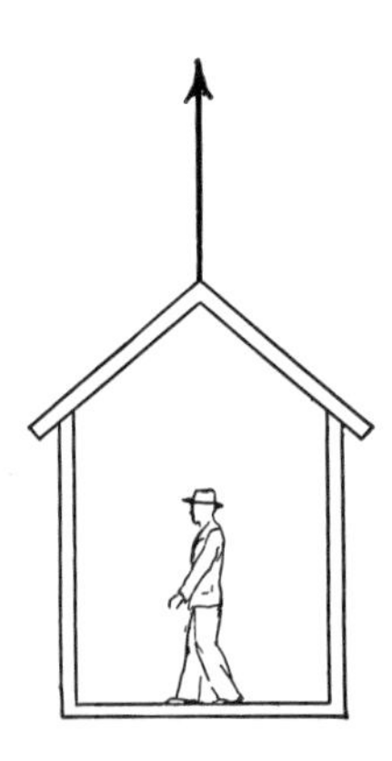

Fig. 7-5. Principle of equivalence. Man in elevator cannot distinguish between gravitation force pulling downward and an acceleration of car upward.

* Optional.

posite direction. If a system of reference is accelerated, objects in this system would seem to have forces acting on them in the direction opposite to the direction of acceleration of the system of reference. For instance, if a man were in an elevator car in a region of space far removed from appreciable gravitational force and if the car were suddenly accelerated in the direction of the arrow (Fig. 7-5), the man could equally well make two assumptions: (*a*) that a mysterious force had pulled him downward, or (*b*) that the car had suddenly been accelerated upward. Between these assumptions he could not possibly make a choice by means of any experiments carried on inside the car.

Einstein was finally led to the possibility of a new interpretation of gravitation. Instead of thinking of gravitation as a force, perhaps it could be treated as a property of space. A further development of the theory indicated that it was possible to consider three-dimensional space about a gravitational body as being warped or distorted in a fourth dimension of space. Since there is no way in which man, who is strictly a three-dimensional creature, can directly detect a fourth spatial dimension if it exists, there can be no direct test of this idea. However, the theory led to certain conclusions that could be tested, and confirmation of the theory does entitle us to believe that we live in a multidimensional world, having as many dimensions as are required to explain observed phenomena.

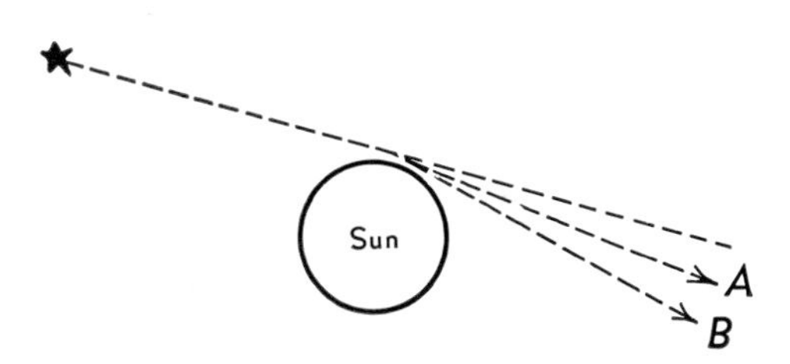

Fig. 7-6. According to relativity theory, light passing through the intense gravitational field near the sun should be bent so as to follow path *B*, whereas classical theory would predict a smaller bending along *A*.

Since the difference between the results predicted by ordinary Newtonian theory and those by general relativity is so small for most of the situations that can be readily investigated, a complete proof of the general theory is difficult. However, tests of the following predictions from the theory have been made: (*a*) that light passing near a star in an intense gravitational field would be bent more than it should be according to Newtonian theory (Fig. 7-6); (*b*) that light radiated from a star would be affected by the gravitational field of the star in such a way as to have its frequency lowered; (*c*) that certain discrepancies in the periods of rotation of the planets (advances of perihelia) could be explained.

As nearly as can be determined at the present time the tests appear to confirm the general theory, but the mathematical intricacies of the theory make it possible that the confirmation is not final.

On the other hand, the special theory of relativity not only has been generally accepted, but its application has led to new and startling developments of great importance that were unforeseen at the time of the development of the theory.

7-16. The Expanding Universe*

Ramifications of the general theory of relativity, together with the possibility of different mathematical solutions for the defining equations, have led to some results which, though highly speculative, are of great interest regarding the structure of the universe as a whole. One view, reached by Einstein himself, was that the universe instead of being infinite is actually finite, that it curves about on itself in a fourth dimension to form a closed region, much as the two-dimensional surface of a sphere curves about itself in a third dimension to form a closed region which is limitless though finite. For instance, as long as one confines himself to the surface of a sphere one does not reach a boundary, so that although finite it is limitless in two dimensions; Einstein has proposed that our universe may likewise be finite in four dimensions though limitless in three dimensions.

In a somewhat different development, Lemaître and others arrived at the conclusion that the universe is not in a stable state but that it may be expanding like a giant bubble. This astonishing suggestion seems to be confirmed by a study of the light coming to us from distant stellar galaxies. In every instance a shift of known spectral lines toward the red end of the spectrum is found. This, according to the Doppler principle, indicates that these galaxies all are moving away from the earth, and the more remote they are the faster they are moving. Until a more satisfactory interpretation of the red shift is reached we are forced provisionally at least to accept the concept of an expanding universe. Such cosmological speculation, however, must be left for the student to follow in more specialized books.

* Optional.

PROBLEMS

1. A man in a rowboat on a river rows downstream 2 miles and back to the starting point. If he can row at a rate of 3/4 mi/hr and if the current in the water is 1/4 mi/hr, how long does it take him to go down and back? In how much faster or slower time could he make the round trip in still water?

Ans. 6 hr; 0.67 hr better time.

2. At what speed in m/sec and mi/hr will an electron have an effective mass 3 times its rest mass?

Ans. 2.83×10^8 m/sec or 175,000 mi/sec.

3. Compute the velocity for which an object would apparently shrink to three-fourths its length in the direction of motion.

Ans. 1.98×10^8 m/sec.

4. Find (in per cent) the relativistic increase in mass of a proton and an electron each of which has been accelerated by a difference of potential of 10 million volts.

Ans. 1.07%; 1957%.

5. An ocean liner weighs 25,000 tons and travels 30 mi/hr. What is its relativistic increase in mass?

Ans. 1.59×10^{-6} oz.

6. Show that the energy equivalent of an electron pair at rest is 1.02 Mev.

7. Compute the energy equivalent of an ice cube weighing 15 gm. If this energy were released gradually during a period of 10 years, compute the average horsepower.

Ans. 5.8×10^3 hp.

8. Two observers *A* and *B* set their clocks in synchronism as they pass one another. *B* is traveling 161,000 mi/sec with respect to *A*. At the end of 10 minutes by *A*'s clock, *A* looks at *B*'s clock through a telescope. The elapsed time indicated by it is what? If at the end of 10 minutes by *B*'s clock *B* looks at A's clock, what time does he read?

Ans. 2.74 min;
2.74 min.

9. Two observers *A* and *B* set their clocks in synchronism as they pass one another. Each is traveling 104,000 mi/sec with respect to the other. After 10 minutes by *B*'s clock *A* holds up a clock and signals with a flashlight for *B* to look at it through a telescope. What is the time by *A*'s clock as *B* sees it, and at what time by *B*'s clock does *B* view the signal?

Ans. 8.3 min; 22.7 min.

SUGGESTED READING

F. K. Richtmyer, E. H. Kennard, and T. Lauritsen, *Introduction to Modern Physics*, 5th ed. (New York, McGraw-Hill, 1955).

A. d'Abro, *The Evolution of Scientific Thought* (New York, Dover Publications, 1950).

A. Einstein, *The Meaning of Relativity*, 2nd ed. (Princeton, Princeton Univ. Press, 1950).

H. Dingle, *The Special Theory of Relativity* (New York, Chemical Publ. Co., 1941).

A. Einstein and L. Infeld, *The Evolution of Physics* (New York, Simon & Schuster, 1938).

A. S. Eddington, *Space, Time and Gravitation* (London, Cambridge Univ. Press, 1923).

CHAPTER 8

THE HYDROGEN ATOM AND SPECTRA

8-1. Historical

Newton conceived of matter as being composed of atoms which were tiny spheres, hard, massive, and indestructible. These ideas were more or less generally accepted for nearly two centuries. Such atoms were fairly satisfactory building blocks of solid matter, and they lent themselves to the explanation of chemical combination to form molecules, but the properties of the Newtonian atom could not explain the forces which bind atom to atom. When assumed to be perfectly elastic such atoms furnished a basis for the kinetic theory of gases, but they could not explain the emission of light, and with the discovery of radioactivity and the electron the Newtonian atom was found to be not only inadequate but in direct conflict with observed facts as well.

With the coming of Maxwell's electromagnetic theory and the recognition that light is an electromagnetic wave motion it became evident that something of an electromagnetic character must exist in the atom to act as a vibrator or source of these waves, but not until 1896 was direct evidence obtained. In that year Zeeman found that, when atoms are excited sufficiently to give off light, they may be affected by a magnetic field. Going back as far as Faraday, previous attempts to detect such an effect had failed for want of optical instruments with sufficient resolving power. For the simplest cases Zeeman found that a single spectral line of an element could be split into two or three lines when the atoms were subjected to a strong magnetic field.

This splitting of spectral lines in a magnetic field is called the **Zeeman effect** (§ 9-3) and was the first experiment to give direct indication that moving electric charges in an atom produce the light emitted. With the discovery of radioactivity, and of the electron the year following, the evidence for electric charges within the atom became more definite.

The discovery of spectral lines, as distinguished from the continuous spectrum of the rainbow or of an incandescent solid, dates from the time of Kirchhoff and Bunsen in Germany, together with Dr. D. Alter in this country, near the middle of the nineteenth century. The existence of sharply defined lines in the spectra of the elements indicates that only the specific frequencies represented by these lines are emitted by the atom. As we now see it, these spectral lines pose several problems that are closely related. What is the relationship between the lines given off by any one type of atom? How can different types of atoms emit such different and characteristic spectra? What can these lines tell us of the nature of the atom that emits them?

8-2. Balmer and the Hydrogen Spectrum

In 1888 Balmer who had been studying the visible lines of the hydrogen spectrum proposed a formula to account for the four lines that he was able to see and measure. These are known as the H_α, H_β, H_γ, and H_δ lines, the positions of which in the visible spectrum are represented in

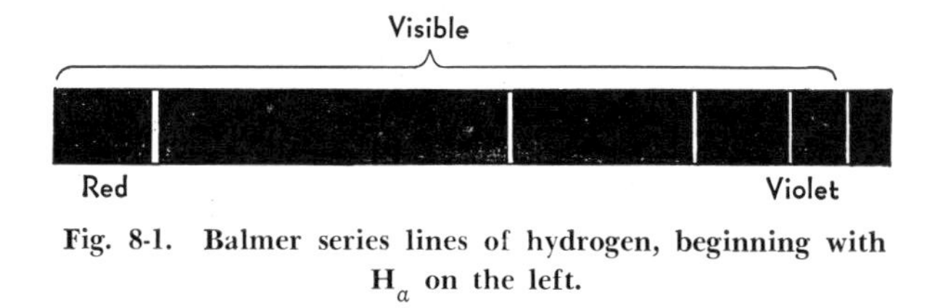

Fig. 8-1. Balmer series lines of hydrogen, beginning with H_α on the left.

Fig. 8-1. Balmer showed that these lines are closely related when he obtained a single formula by means of which the wavelengths of the lines could be computed. Balmer's formula in angstrom units is

$$\lambda = 3645.6\left(\frac{n^2}{n^2 - 4}\right) \qquad n = 3, 4, 5, \cdots \qquad [8\text{-}1]$$

where n takes successive integral values, each value of n giving the wavelength of a different line in the series. This formula is what is known as an empirical formula. It was not based upon theoretical considerations, and it was not aimed at explaining anything. It was merely a formula deduced from observations in order to bring all four observed hydrogen lines into some mathematical relationship. This it did very well for values of n up to $n = 6$, as can be seen from Table 8-1.

TABLE 8-1. WAVELENGTHS OF BALMER LINES IN HYDROGEN
(angstrom units)

Line	n	Observed by Balmer	Computed
H_α	3	6562.10	6562.08
H_β	4	4860.70	4860.80
H_γ	5	4340.10	4340.10
H_δ	6	4101.30	4101.20

Balmer's formula also predicted the possible existence of other lines of hydrogen belonging to the same series. The wavelengths of these should be given by letting n have integral values greater than 6. This prediction was later verified, and many more lines have been observed in the ultraviolet, especially in stellar spectra. The frequency difference between the lines as n increases becomes less and less, approaching zero at a frequency known as the limit of the series. The observed lines become fainter and closer together as they approach this limit, and these lines form what is called the **Balmer series** in hydrogen.

Balmer's formula may be rearranged and written in terms of the frequency. Frequencies, it will be remembered, are given by the common formula for wave motion

$$f = \frac{c}{\lambda} = \frac{3 \times 10^{10}\ \text{cm/sec}}{\lambda(\text{cm})} \qquad [8\text{-}2]$$

Since for visible light these frequencies are extremely high, running to hundreds of millions of millions per second, it is common for spectroscopists to use instead of the frequency, or number of waves per second, the number of waves in one centimeter. This is called the **wave number** and is the frequency divided by the velocity of light or the reciprocal of wavelength in cm. If we define ν as the wave number, ν is $1/\lambda$ (cm), and Balmer's formula becomes

$$\nu = 4k\left(\frac{n^2 - 4}{4n^2}\right) \qquad [8\text{-}3]$$

where k is a constant and $4k = 109{,}678$. Consequently

$$\nu = 109{,}678\left(\frac{1}{2^2} - \frac{1}{n^2}\right) \tag{8-4}$$

and this can be written

$$\nu = R\left(\frac{1}{2^2} - \frac{1}{n^2}\right) \tag{8-4a}$$

where the first term in the parenthesis has a constant value for the Balmer series and n in the second term takes successive integral values, as in Eq. 8-1. This is the form of the equation used by Rydberg in extensive experiments following those of Balmer. The number represented by R is now called the **Rydberg constant.**

Not only did the Balmer formula predict more lines in the series than Balmer himself observed, but the possibility of varying the constant term in Eq. 8-1 or the first term in Eq. 8-4 would seem also to suggest other series. These are now well known; chief among them are the **Lyman series** in which the $1/(2^2)$ of Eq. 8-4 is replaced by $1/(1^2)$, and the **Paschen series** in which the $1/(2^2)$ is replaced by $1/(3^2)$. The complete formulas are as follows:

Lyman series

$$\nu = R\left(\frac{1}{1^2} - \frac{1}{n^2}\right) \qquad n = 2, 3, 4, \cdots \tag{8-4b}$$

Paschen series

$$\nu = R\left(\frac{1}{3^2} - \frac{1}{n^2}\right) \qquad n = 4, 5, 6, \cdots \tag{8-4c}$$

A few lines in other series also emitted by hydrogen have been found

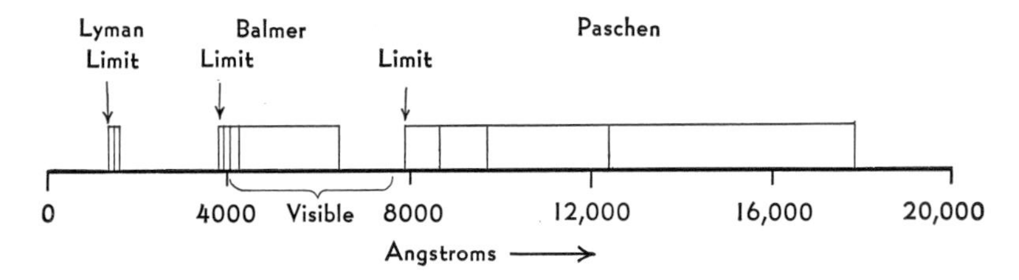

Fig. 8-2. Location of principal series of spectral lines of hydrogen in terms of wavelengths.

by substituting for the constant term $1/(4^2)$ and $1/(5^2)$. These series are called, respectively, the fundamental or **Brackett series,** and the **Pfund series.** The Lyman series is in the ultraviolet region of the spectrum, the Balmer series is in the visible and infrared, and the Paschen series is in the infrared (Fig. 8-2). The remaining series are still further in the infrared region. In each of these series the most striking feature is the orderly relation of the lines, which stimulated a search for the reasons.

8-3. Early Atom Models and Rutherford's Scattering Experiment

As soon as it became recognized that an atom must be some kind of electric structure, attempts were made to formulate a model atom that would serve to explain observed phenomena. J. J. Thomson suggested an atom consisting of a volume of positive electricity of atomic proportions in which electrons were embedded. Vibrations of the electrons would then be assumed to produce light waves. This model of the atom has been lightly called the "pumpkin-seed atom," and was referred to by Thomson himself as the "plum-pudding atom." However, attempts by means of this model to account for spectral frequencies gave results far out of agreement with experiment.

Others suggested that the positive electricity might be at the center of the atom instead of distributed through it. Rutherford in 1911 conceived of the critical experiment which decided the question, and he published a brilliant analysis. This was the famous Rutherford scattering experiment, based on preliminary experiments of Geiger. Under Rutherford's influence these experiments were carried further by Geiger and Marsden and were later repeated with even more precision by Chadwick in 1920. The experiment took the form of shooting high-speed, positively charged particles at atoms and studying the angles of scattering of the particles. Alpha particles from a radioactive substance were used, and the angles of scattering were measured when these particles passed through very thin metal foils. On the assumption that the nucleus of the atom is very small, that it possesses Z charges, and that the inverse square law of force is obeyed, it can be shown that the fraction f of alpha particles scattered through an angle greater than θ (Fig. 8-3) is given by the formula

$$f = \frac{4\pi N Z^2 e^4}{\epsilon_0^2 M^2 v^4} \cot^2 \frac{\theta}{2} \qquad [8\text{-}5]$$

where N is the number of atoms per cm² of the foil, M is the mass of the alpha particle, and v is its velocity. Also it can be shown that the nearest distance d that the alpha particle can approach the nucleus when moving directly toward it is

$$d = \frac{4Ze^2}{\epsilon_0 M v^2} \tag{8-6}$$

Rutherford showed that the angles of scattering agreed with the theory and thus substantiated the hypothesis that the nucleus was very small in comparison with the size of the atom. From Eq. 8-6 it was deduced that for the maximum observed angles of scattering the alpha particles approached to within 3.2×10^{-12} cm of the nucleus for gold atoms and consequently that the radius of the nucleus must be less

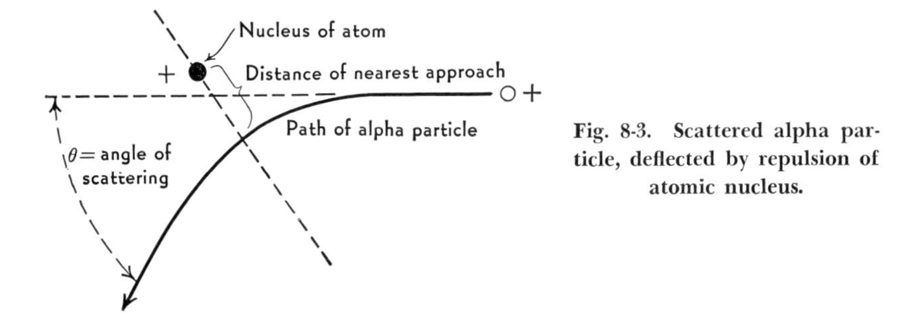

Fig. 8-3. Scattered alpha particle, deflected by repulsion of atomic nucleus.

than this. For silver atoms the distance of nearest approach was 2×10^{-12} cm. These experiments were accepted as conclusive proof that the atom has a tiny, positively charged nucleus, exceedingly small in comparison with the atom itself and that any electrons belonging to the atom must be found in the relatively large region outside this nucleus. In Chadwick's repetition of these experiments the precision was sufficient to enable the charge on the nucleus of the scattering atom to be determined, and this was direct evidence that nuclear charge increases with increasing atomic weight.

To explain why electrons in this outer region of the atom are not attracted to the nucleus, so that they would fall into it and suffer annihilation, there seemed to be two chief possibilities. If the electrons were not moving about the nucleus, a force of repulsion could be assumed to exist and only be effective at the small distances involved in the interior of the atom. Such a quasi-elastically held electron would vibrate very much like a weight on the end of a spring and could not give the proper frequencies to explain observed spectral lines. It would be more likely to give harmonic frequencies such as are encountered in the subject of sound, but it has been thoroughly proved that spectral lines do not represent harmonic frequencies.

The alternative was to copy the motion of the planets around the sun. The reason planets do not fall into the sun is that they have reached stable orbits in which the centripetal force required to constrain them in their orbits is exactly the force of gravitation pulling them in. In other words, their velocities are such that gravitation can only constrain them to move in their particular orbits. Similarly in the atom, a revolving electron if moving fast enough would not fall into the positively charged nucleus; the attraction between them would merely constrain the electron to move about the nucleus in an elliptical orbit, or in a circular orbit as a special case.

Here again, however, a difficulty arose in trying to explain how such revolving electrons could emit the characteristic frequencies observed in the spectra of the atoms. Not only was it impossible for such an atom, according to classical electromagnetic theory, to emit just the correct frequencies and no more; there was an even greater difficulty. According to classical theory any accelerated electric charge should radiate energy in the form of wave motion. This energy could only come from the energy already possessed by the electric charge producing it. An electron revolving about a central nucleus would be continually accelerated toward the center of path and consequently should emit radiation continuously. Yet, under this loss of energy the electron would be unable to sustain itself in its orbit. As the electron lost energy by radiation it would presumably spiral into the nucleus and be lost, and the atom would collapse in something like a hundred-billionth of a second.

8-4. The Bohr Theory of the Hydrogen Atom

It was to solve the apparently insuperable difficulties of previous atom models that in 1913 the brilliant young Danish physicist Niels Bohr proposed his revolutionary model of the atom. Just as Einstein had seized upon Max Planck's quantum hypothesis to explain the photoelectric effect, so Bohr seized upon the quantum hypothesis to help explain the nature of the atom. Bohr based his new and revolutionary theory on certain assumptions involving both classical theory and quantum theory. These he combined with Rutherford's new concept of the nuclear atom in what is often called the Rutherford-Bohr atom model. In the deduction of a theory from such postulates or assumptions as Bohr introduced, the validity of the assumptions is determined by the correctness of the deductions which can be made from the theory. The extraordinary successes of the Bohr theory showed that a new age of physical science was being opened up, in which the scientific problems presented must be conquered by entirely new methods and ideas.

Since the hydrogen atom is the simplest one of all, Bohr assumed it to consist of a single proton as the nucleus and of a single external electron. He then applied himself to an explanation of the various lines of the hydrogen spectrum. In the development of his theory he accepted the classical idea of attraction between the central, positively charged nucleus of an atom and the electron revolving about it. However, to get around the difficulty that a revolving electron manifestly cannot continuously radiate energy he introduced the radical assumption of nonradiating orbits. This assumption, contrary to classical electrodynamics, is that the atom possesses certain possible orbits in which the electron can revolve without radiating and that an electron can never revolve in an intermediate orbit.

To explain radiation and absorption of energy Bohr further assumed that radiation only happens when an electron transition or "jump" occurs, in which the electron passes from an orbit of higher energy to another orbit of lesser energy, or, as we now say, since orbits are no longer sharply defined, from a higher energy level or energy state to another, lower energy level or state. Absorption of energy would then occur when the transition is in the opposite direction. That an electron possesses more energy in an orbit of larger radius is fairly evident, since work would have to be done against the attraction of the nucleus just as work is done in raising an object above the surface of the earth. A large-scale example is that of an earth satellite. Such a satellite requires a large amount of energy to raise it above the earth's surface and give it enough speed so that it will stay there in an orbit.

Bohr next introduced the Planck quantum hypothesis and assumed that in a transition between two energy levels a single quantum of energy hf is emitted or absorbed in the form of radiation of frequency f, where the quantum of energy is equal to the difference between the energies in the initial and final states:

$$hf = E_2 - E_1 \qquad [8\text{-}7]$$

The frequency is now sharply defined in terms of the energy difference between orbits or energy levels, and it only remains to satisfactorily define the energy levels, or in other words to locate the required nonradiating orbits. Bohr accomplished this by making a new application of the idea of quantization, not involved in the original Planck quantum hypothesis. Reasoning in part by analogy, Bohr decided to extend the idea of quantization and to quantize the angular momentum possessed by the rotating electron. By such quantization Bohr arrived at just the right sequence of possible orbits by means of which he could describe the observed frequencies of the hydrogen spectra.

8-5. The Derivation of the Bohr Equation for Hydrogen

According to the classical inverse square law of Coulomb, the force of attraction between the central positive nucleus of charge $+e$ and the revolving electron of charge $-e$ at a distance r is $F = -(e^2/\epsilon_0 r^2)$ where the negative sign indicates attraction toward the nucleus. In mks units ϵ_0 is the permittivity of free space and has the value $1/(9 \times 10^9)$ whereas in cgs units its value is unity. This attraction furnishes the centripetal force mv^2/r required according to Newtonian mechanics to constrain the electron of mass m and charge e to move in a circular orbit of radius r where v is the orbital velocity of the electron. Consequently, equating magnitudes we may write

$$\frac{e^2}{\epsilon_0 r^2} = \frac{mv^2}{r} \qquad [8\text{-}8]$$

Bohr next made the revolutionary assumption of nonradiating orbits and the further assumption that the energy E_q of an emitted quantum of light is equal to the energy difference between the energy E_2 of the electron in an outer orbit and the lesser energy E_1 in an inner orbit. According to the Planck hypothesis the energy of this quantum is hf; consequently

$$E_q = E_2 - E_1 = hf \qquad [8\text{-}9]$$

To determine the radii of the nonradiating orbits it became necessary to quantize the angular momentum, and the required unit of angular momentum was found to be $h/2\pi$ where h is the Planck constant. It is then assumed that the angular momentum mvr of the electrons revolving about the nucleus can only have values that are integral multiples of the fundamental unit. We may then write as the fundamental quantum condition for angular momentum

$$mvr = \frac{nh}{2\pi} \qquad n = 1, 2, 3, \cdots \qquad [8\text{-}10]$$

where n is called the **principal quantum number.** This number determines the orbit. When n is 1 the electron is in the innermost orbit, and when n is 2 the electron is in the next outer orbit, and so on.

It is next required to find how much energy an electron may have in any orbit. The total energy of an electron in a given orbit is partly potential owing to the central attracting force and partly kinetic $\frac{1}{2}mv^2$ owing to the motion of the electron with velocity v in the orbit. Since the force between electron and nucleus is $-(e^2/\epsilon_0 r^2)$, the potential energy at distance r is $-(e^2/\epsilon_0 r)$. If the kinetic energy of the electron were greater than this potential or binding energy the electron would escape from the nucleus. It does not escape because the binding energy is greater. The net available escape energy of the electron is therefore negative, or, in other words, there is a deficit, and the amount of available energy E is the sum of the available kinetic energy $\frac{1}{2}mv^2$ and the negative potential energy $-(e^2/\epsilon_0 r)$.

$$E = \frac{1}{2}mv^2 - \frac{e^2}{\epsilon_0 r} \qquad [8\text{-}11]$$

The four equations 8-8, 8-9, 8-10, and 8-11 represent the basic assumptions of the Bohr theory, and they are the four relations required in the derivation of the Bohr formula for hydrogen. Multiplying both sides of Eq. 8-8 by $r/2$ we find that

$$\frac{1}{2}mv^2 = \frac{e^2}{2\epsilon_0 r}$$

Putting this into Eq. 8-11 we have for the net energy E of the electron in an orbit of radius r

$$E = \frac{e^2}{2\epsilon_0 r} - \frac{e^2}{\epsilon_0 r} = -\frac{e^2}{2\epsilon_0 r} \qquad [8\text{-}12]$$

The negative sign means that this is the amount of energy that would have to be supplied to remove the electron completely from the nucleus. For particular orbits having values of r such as r_1 and r_2 we may write the equations for the energy in each of those orbits as

$$E_1 = -\frac{e^2}{2\epsilon_0 r_1} \qquad \text{and} \qquad E_2 = -\frac{e^2}{2\epsilon_0 r_2} \qquad [8\text{-}13]$$

We are now in a position to find the radius of any Bohr orbit. Equation 8-10 is solved for v and then squared, and the value of v^2 thus obtained is put into Eq. 8-8. The resulting equation solved for r gives the radius of any orbit of quantum number n.

$$r_n = \frac{\epsilon_0 n^2 h^2}{4\pi^2 m e^2} \qquad [8\text{-}14]$$

Putting this value of r in Eq. 8-13, for E_1 and E_2 representing the energies of the electron in each of these two orbits:

$$E_1 = -\frac{2\pi^2 m e^4}{\epsilon_0^2 h^2 n_1^2} \qquad \text{and} \qquad E_2 = -\frac{2\pi^2 m e^4}{\epsilon_0^2 h^2 n_2^2} \qquad [8\text{-}15]$$

where n_1 is the value of n for one orbit and n_2 is the value for the other orbit. Putting these values of E_1 and E_2 into Eq. 8-9 we have

$$hf = E_2 - E_1 = \frac{2\pi^2 m e^4}{\epsilon_0^2 h^2 n_1^2} - \frac{2\pi^2 m e^4}{\epsilon_0^2 h^2 n_2^2} \qquad [8\text{-}16]$$

If Eq. 8-16 is solved for the frequency, we have

$$f = \frac{2\pi^2 m e^4}{\epsilon_0^2 h^3}\left(\frac{1}{n_1^2} - \frac{1}{n_2^2}\right) \qquad [8\text{-}17]$$

This is the Bohr equation, but it is more often written in terms of the wave number, as follows:

$$\nu = \frac{1}{\lambda} = \frac{f}{c} = \frac{2\pi^2 m e^4}{c\epsilon_0^2 h^3}\left(\frac{1}{n_1^2} - \frac{1}{n_2^2}\right) \qquad [8\text{-}18]$$

$$= R\left(\frac{1}{n_1^2} - \frac{1}{n_2^2}\right) \qquad [8\text{-}18a]$$

where in cgs units $\epsilon_0 = 1$, and R is the Rydberg constant.

8-6. Spectral Series of Hydrogen

The Bohr equation was an immediate success despite limitations to be uncovered later. It was recognized at once as the Rydberg form of Balmer's equation, this time not obtained empirically but derived from radical modifications of fundamental theory. It gave the correct frequencies not only for the lines of the Balmer series but for the other known series, and a physical interpretation of the formula could be given in terms of the Bohr picture of the revolving electron and its possible orbits. If n_1 is set equal to 2 and n_2 is permitted successive integral values the frequencies of the Balmer series are obtained. The first line is represented by the transition from orbit 3 to orbit 2. The second line is given by the transition from orbit 4 to orbit 2, and so on (Fig. 8-4).

With $n_1 = 1$ and transitions from outer orbits to the innermost orbit, the frequencies of the Lyman series observed by Lyman in 1906 are emitted, and similarly transitions from outer orbits to the third orbit give the frequencies of the lines of the Paschen series observed by Paschen in 1908.

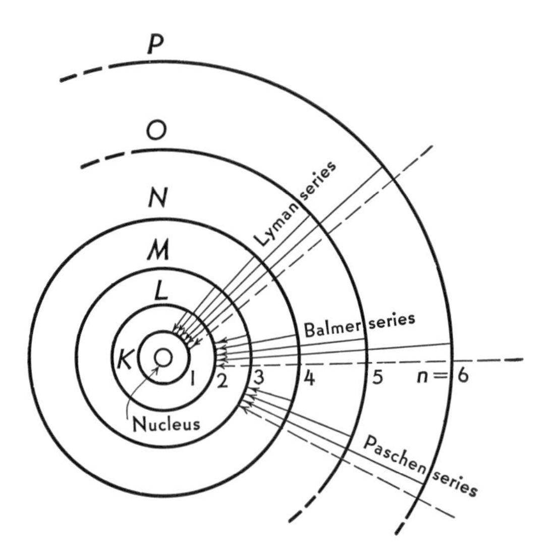

Fig. 8-4. How electron transitions in a hydrogen atom produce various characteristic series of spectral lines, according to the original Bohr theory.

As it later turned out transitions ending on the third, fourth, and fifth orbits become less probable; therefore the intensities of the lines become less, and these fainter lines are more difficult to detect. The spacing between the lines of any series decreases as n_2 increases, and a limiting frequency is reached for $n_2 = \infty$. This is called the series limit and represents the frequency of radiation emitted when an electron which has been completely removed from the influence of the nucleus returns to the lowest energy level for the given series.

The Bohr theory explains another phenomenon which puzzled earlier investigators. The question was, how can any one atom emit so many frequencies representing different spectral lines at the same time? Actually no atom radiates more than one frequency at a time, but different atoms may be undergoing different electron transitions, and consequently from a large number of atoms various frequencies are simultaneously emitted.

8-7. Further Successes of the Bohr Theory

The radius of the hydrogen atom The Bohr equation did more than just account for the spectral frequencies of hydrogen and explain the origin of the various series. Equation 8-12 gives the radius of the Bohr orbit for any orbit of number n. If n is put equal to 1, it then gives the radius for the innermost orbit, which is the normal orbit for the unexcited atom. This radius can be readily computed, and in terms of the known values of the quantities involved it turns out to be 0.529×10^{-8} cm or 0.529 angstrom unit. This is in good agreement with the best values for the radius of the hydrogen atom obtained by experimental methods, such as those involving the kinetic theory of gases (§ 11-1).

Hydrogenic atoms The Bohr theory applies particularly to an atom composed of a positively charged nucleus with one external electron. The helium atom has two external electrons, and if they are assumed to rotate about the positively charged nucleus the mathematical problem they present has never been completely solved. In astronomy such a problem is known as the three-body problem. However, if we consider a helium atom which has been singly ionized, it now has only one electron and it is said to be hydrogen-like or hydrogenic, the difference being only in the charge on the nucleus. Similarly, lithium which has three planetary electrons per atom would be hydrogenic if it were doubly ionized. The Bohr formula gives the correct frequencies for the lines observed from these hydrogenic atoms, but since the charge on the nucleus is $2e$ for helium, $3e$ for lithium, and so on for heavier atoms the Bohr equation must be derived for these charges and becomes

$$\nu = \frac{2\pi^2 m Z^2 e^4}{\epsilon_0^2 c h^3}\left(\frac{1}{n_1^2} - \frac{1}{n_2^2}\right) \qquad [8\text{-}19]$$

where Z is the number of positive electronic charges on the nucleus. For corresponding orbital transitions the formula now predicts higher frequencies. This has been confirmed by experiment, and two well-known series of lines, called the Fowler and Pickering series whose origins had been unknown, were found to be produced by ionized helium.

The Rydberg constant The theory also provided the basis for a satisfactory explanation of the constant involved in Balmer's equation and, in particular, the form in which Rydberg applied it (Eq. 8-4*a*). Balmer arbitrarily chose a numerical constant that would fit into the formula and give as nearly as possible the measured wavelengths. In Rydberg's form of the equation this constant became known as the Rydberg constant R, and from Eq. 8-17 it is seen that

$$R = \frac{2\pi^2 e^4 m}{\epsilon_0{}^2 c h^3} \qquad [8\text{-}20]$$

Instead of being simply an empirical number Bohr thus was able to derive the Rydberg constant from basic physical quantities.

However, the agreement of the Bohr equation with the frequencies of observed spectral lines has been found to be not quite accurate if the same value is used for the Rydberg constant for different atoms. Bohr originally treated the electron as if it rotated about a fixed point or, what is the same thing, about a nucleus of infinite mass. The nucleus of an atom is so much more massive than an electron that it behaves almost, but not quite, as if it were fixed in position. The nucleus tends slightly to revolve about the electron. Actually the two form a kind of one-sided dumb-bell arrangement in which each revolves about the center of mass of the two. This means that the effective mass of an electron is slightly less than the actual mass, and it was found necessary to make a small correction in the electron mass in the Bohr formula to take care of it. The correction can be made by replacing the mass of the electron with what is called the **reduced mass** μ where

$$\mu = \frac{Mm}{M + m} \qquad [8\text{-}21]$$

M being the mass of the nucleus and m the mass of the electron. Since the reduced mass of the electron depends upon the mass of the nucleus the Rydberg constant varies slightly for different atoms and should be written with μ instead of m.

$$R = \frac{2\pi^2 \mu Z^2 e^4}{c \epsilon_0{}^2 h^3} \qquad [8\text{-}22]$$

Values of the Rydberg constant determined from spectroscopic data for different atoms of the hydrogenic type are given in Table 8-2. Without the correction the value of R is called R_∞, meaning the value that it would have if the mass of the proton were infinite.

TABLE 8-2. RYDBERG CONSTANT FOR DIFFERENT ATOMS

Atom	Rydberg Constant (cm^{-1})
Hydrogen ($_1H^1$)	109677.58
Deuterium ($_1H^2$)	109707.42
Helium ($_2He^4$)	109722.27
Lithium ($_3Li^7$)	109728.72
Oxygen ($_8O^{16}$)	109733.54
Infinite mass	109737.31

8-8. Ionization and Resonance Potentials

The Bohr theory was also successful in that it enabled theoretical calculations to be made of the ionization potential and also excitation potentials for the hydrogen atom. The ionization potential of hydrogen represents the energy required to remove the electron completely from its nucleus. In terms of the Bohr orbital picture this is equivalent to raising the electron up to that orbit for which n equals infinity. Putting n equal to infinity in Eq. 8-16, we have for the energy difference

$$E_\infty - E_1 = hf = \frac{2\pi^2 me^4}{\epsilon_0{}^2 h^2}\left(\frac{1}{n_1{}^2} - \frac{1}{\infty}\right) \qquad [8\text{-}23]$$

or

$$hf = \frac{2\pi^2 me^4}{\epsilon_0{}^2 h^2}\left(\frac{1}{n_1{}^2}\right) = \frac{2\pi^2 me^4}{\epsilon_0{}^2 h^2} \qquad [8\text{-}24]$$

since $n_1 = 1$. This may be reduced to electron volts by dividing by 1.6×10^{-12} erg/ev when the energy is computed in ergs. Putting in the appropriate values for the different quantities and making the computation, we find

$$\text{Ionizing potential} = 13.56 \text{ ev}$$

This is in quite good agreement with the ionization potential of atomic hydrogen obtained by electrical means when molecular hydrogen is dissociated.

Excitation potentials may be similarly computed. For instance, the energy in electron volts required to raise the electron from its normal orbit to the second orbit, which represents the first excited state, is the first excitation potential. This is found to have a computed value of 10.2 ev for hydrogen (see Table 4-1, p. 64).

8-9. Isotope Shift and Deuterium

The fact that the reduced electron mass in the corrected Bohr formula depends upon the mass of the nucleus to an appreciable degree means that a sufficient variation of the mass of the nucleus of an atom would appear as a small frequency shift and a slight displacement of the spectral lines. If the isotopes of an element differ sufficiently in mass this shift, called the isotope shift, should be detectable. The largest shift would of course be between isotopes having the largest relative difference in nuclear mass. Even after isotopes were discovered the possibility that hydrogen itself might have isotopes was not at first considered, but when slight unaccounted variations of chemical atomic weights suggested it, Urey, Brickwedde, and Murphy, in 1932, by sensitive spectroscopic means found a faint trace of a spectral line of hydrogen displaced slightly from the normal. Succeeding experiments confirmed their hypothesis that this was due to the heavy hydrogen atom H^2, and so it was the isotope shift that led to the discovery of heavy hydrogen or deuterium.

8-10. Determination of e/m by Spectroscopic Methods

It is always desirable to obtain confirmation of measurements of fundamental quantities by different methods, thus establishing the validity of the measurements. One such quantity which can be confirmed by spectroscopic means is e/m for the electron. Because of the interest in confirming this ratio by methods far removed from direct deflection methods, one of the spectroscopic methods will be given here.

It is possible by measurements of spectroscopic lines to obtain experimental values of the Rydberg constant for different hydrogen-like atoms. If this is done for hydrogen and for ionized helium, since the value of the constant depends upon the reduced mass of the electron in each instance, it can be shown that

$$\frac{R_{\mathrm{He}}}{R_{\mathrm{H}}} = \frac{\mu_{\mathrm{He}}}{\mu_{\mathrm{H}}} = \frac{\left(\dfrac{3.97mM}{3.97M + m}\right)}{\left(\dfrac{mM}{M + m}\right)} = \frac{1 + \dfrac{m}{M}}{1 + \dfrac{1}{3.97}\dfrac{m}{M}} \qquad [8\text{-}25]$$

From this M/m, the ratio of the mass of a proton to the mass of an electron, can be obtained. If both numerator and denominator of the ratio M/m are multiplied by e the fraction may be written $\dfrac{e/m}{e/M}$. However, e/M is the same as the ratio of the charge to mass for a hydrogen ion. This is known accurately from electrolysis, and consequently e/m for the electron can be computed. The agreement with other experimental values is very close. Still another check on the value of e/m is obtained from measurements of the Zeeman effect.

8-11. Successes and Limitations of the Bohr Theory

By way of summary let us first restate some of the chief successes of the Bohr theory:

1. It accounted for the Balmer and other hydrogen series.
2. It derived the Rydberg constant from known physical quantities.
3. It gave a satisfactory value for the radius of the hydrogen atom.
4. It accounted quantitatively for ionization and resonance potentials.

It had several other successes, such as the explanation of the normal Zeeman effect (§ 9-3) and the explanation of the spectra of hydrogen-like atoms.

Despite these successes the Bohr theory had definite limitations:

1. It failed to account for the spectra of complex atoms.
2. It could not deal with atoms as simple as neutral helium having more than one electron.
3. It did not permit the calculation of the intensities of lines.
4. It failed to give correct results in the more complicated conditions of splitting of lines by a magnetic field, known as the anomalous Zeeman effect (§ 9-3).
5. It did not account for the fine structure observed in the hydrogen lines, and it did not account for such simple matters as the doublet structure of the alkali metal spectra.

8-12. Sommerfeld's Modification of the Bohr Theory

The need for modification of the simple Bohr theory as applied to hydrogen became apparent when observations were made by means of spectroscopic apparatus of very high resolving power. Some of the principal hydrogen lines were then found not to be single lines, as they at first seemed to be, but were actually composed of finer lines extremely close together. This is what is known as the **fine structure** of hydrogen lines.

The starting point of Sommerfeld's extension of the Bohr theory was the recognition that circular orbits are not the most general type of orbit when one body revolves about another body. For instance, in planetary motion the planets revolve in elliptical orbits about the sun, and the ellipse is the most general form of such an orbit. It was evident that electrons might revolve in elliptical as well as circular orbits about the atomic nucleus. From such a viewpoint the circular orbit is merely the special case of an elliptical orbit where the major and minor axes are equal.

However, in order to follow the idea of Bohr and quantize angular momentum, it became necessary for Sommerfeld to choose only certain permissible elliptical orbits in addition to the usual circular orbits. Evidently only such elliptical orbits could be possible for which the electron would be left with an integral number of units of angular momentum. The energy of an electron in a circular orbit is due entirely to its angular motion in its circular path. Nevertheless, consideration of an elliptical orbit shows that the electron not only moves around the focal point toward which a central attracting force acts, but it also moves in and out along the radius. Some energy of the electron is represented by this radial motion. The greater the ellipticity of the orbit, the greater would be the radial motion, and for a fixed amount of energy in an orbit the less would be the angular momentum.

For instance, the third orbit is designated by the Bohr quantum number 3, and in a circular orbit the angular momentum would be three times what it is in the first orbit. We now have two possible quantized elliptical orbits at this level, in addition to the circular orbit. In one ellipse the angular momentum is only two times that in the first orbit, or $2h/2\pi$. This orbit is then designated as having a total quantum number 3, but an angular momentum quantum number 2. The latter may be represented by k and is sometimes called the *azimuthal quantum number.* There is one further possibility for a third orbit at this level. It still must have a total quantum number 3, but the orbit may be even more elliptical, so that only one unit of angular momentum is left for the electron. We may abbreviate the description of these three possible orbits by designating them in terms of the total quantum number and the angular quantum number as follows, $n = 3$, $k = 3$; $n = 3$, $k = 2$; and $n = 3$, $k = 1$. The first one represents a simple circular orbit with zero ellipticity; the second represents the next possible orbit with the minimum ellipticity greater than zero; and the last represents the next and final possibility with maximum ellipticity at this level. From this it is seen that there would be two possible orbits for total quantum number 2, one only for total quantum number 1, and so on.

Now, if the different orbits for a given total quantum number were found to have slightly different energies the fine structure of the hydrogen lines might be explained, but alas! mathematical analysis, as Bohr himself knew, showed that all orbits belonging to any one group represented exactly the same energy.

Sommerfeld's next step was to introduce relativistic mechanics into the analysis of the motion of the electron. Since an electron moving in an elliptical orbit is continually moving nearer to and further from the center of attraction it is continually gaining velocity and losing it at each revolution. This variation in velocity of the electron in its orbit leads to a relativistic variation of the mass and of the energy of the electron. The result is that, after all, the different orbits in a group are found to represent slightly different energy levels. It is also worth noticing that the relativistic correction implies that the electron will no longer move in a closed elliptical orbit but that the orbit forms a rosette (Fig. 8-5), giving the effect of a precession of the orbit.

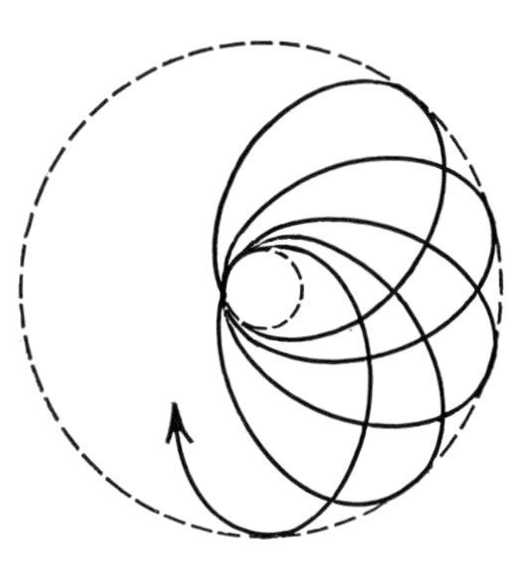

Fig. 8-5. Elliptical orbit of electron in Sommerfeld's modified Bohr theory precesses due to relativistic change of mass thereby becoming, in effect, an open spiral.

This extension of the simple Bohr theory showed that what had been thought of as single energy levels could actually be groups of slightly different energy levels. This is called the splitting of energy levels, resulting from the relativistic corrections. Electron transitions between slightly different energy levels would naturally lead to the emission of slightly different spectral frequencies by the atom, and it was evident that this might explain the observed fine structure of the hydrogen lines.

8-13. Fine Structure, Quantum Numbers, and Selection Rules

The confirmation of Sommerfeld's explanation of fine structure was sought by a number of experimenters, and it was found that the so-called splitting of the energy levels led to an explanation of the fine structure of hydrogen that seemed to agree with observations, except that for the larger orbits there were entirely too many levels leading to too many possible transitions and predicting more fine structure than was observed. It then became necessary to artificially restrict the possible transitions by introducing what are called **selection rules** to indicate which transitions may be expected or permitted, and which ones may not be permitted. The selection rule adopted is that in any electron transition the azimuthal quantum number k can change by only plus or minus 1, or in symbols

$$\Delta k = \pm 1$$

This means that in any electron transition the angular momentum can change by plus or minus one unit, and transitions with larger changes or zero change are said to be "forbidden." Application of this rule indicated that Balmer lines may consist of three components, and this led to more satisfactory agreement with experiment.

At the present time the analysis of hydrogen fine structure is based on more advanced quantum-relativistic considerations and is now made from a different viewpoint, involving the spin of the electron (§ 9-2). However, substantially the same conclusions have been reached as with the simpler theory, and despite the great experimental difficulties involved there is close agreement between theory and experiment.

For present purposes, it is important to note that the description of an energy level now involves two quantum numbers n and k and that these, together with a selection rule, specify allowed transitions. To describe energy levels of the more complex atoms more quantum numbers and other selection rules are required, and these will be introduced as needed.

PROBLEMS

1. Compute the radius of the normal hydrogen atom (first Bohr orbit).

Ans. 0.529 A.

2. Compute the Rydberg constant for a nucleus of infinite mass by the Bohr formula.

Ans. 109,740.

3. Show that the electron rotating about the proton in a hydrogen atom actually rotates about the center of gravity of the two with an effective or reduced mass $\mu = \frac{Mm}{M + m}$, where m is the mass of the electron and M is the mass of the proton.

4. Show that for the electron in a deuterium atom the reduced mass of problem 3 is approximately $\mu = \frac{2Mm}{2M + m}$, where the symbols have the same meaning as in problem 3.

5. What would be the linear velocity of an electron in the first Bohr orbit of hydrogen?

Ans. 2.2×10^8 cm/sec.

6. Compute the first and second excitation potentials of hydrogen.

Ans. 10.15 ev; 12.05 ev.

7. What is the gravitational attraction between the electron and proton in a hydrogen atom if the distance between the two is 0.5 A? How does this compare with the electric force of attraction?

Ans. *a.* Grav. force, 4.05×10^{-42} dyne;
b. Elec. force, 9.22×10^{-3} dyne;
$a/b = 4.4 \times 10^{-40}$.

8. Will the H_a line for deuterium be higher or lower in frequency than H_a for hydrogen? Why?

9. Find the angular momentum in gm cm²/sec or in kg m²/sec of the electron in the third Bohr orbit of hydrogen.

Ans. 3.18×10^{-27} gm cm^2/sec;
3.18×10^{-34} kg m^2/sec.

10. Compute the wave numbers of the first three lines of the Lyman and Paschen series by the simple Bohr formula in cm^{-1}.

Ans. Lyman series: 82,303 cm^{-1}; 97,544 cm^{-1}; 102,879 cm^{-1}.
Paschen series: 5,335 cm^{-1}; 7,804 cm^{-1}; 9,145 cm^{-1}.

11. Compute, by means of the simple Bohr formula, the wave numbers and the wavelengths in angstrom units of the limits of the Lyman and Paschen series of hydrogen.

Ans. Lyman series: 109,678 cm^{-1}; 912 A.
Paschen series: 12,186 cm^{-1}; 8,205 A.

12. Compute the limit of the Balmer series in wave numbers, in angstrom units, and in electron volts.

Ans. 27,420 cm^{-1}; 3,645 A; 3.4 ev.

SUGGESTED READING

M. Born, *Atomic Physics,* 5th ed. (New York, Steckert-Haffner, 1951).
F. K. Richtmyer, E. H. Kennard, and T. Lauritsen, *Introduction to Modern Physics,* 5th ed. (New York, McGraw-Hill, 1955).
O. H. Blackwood, T. H. Osgood, and A. E. Ruark, *An Outline of Atomic Physics,* 3rd ed. (New York, Wiley, 1955).
G. Herzberg, *Atomic Spectra and Atomic Structure,* 2nd ed. (New York, Dover Publications, 1944).

CHAPTER 9

ATOMIC SPECTRA AND X-RAY SPECTRA

9-1. Spectra of the Alkali Metals

The spectra formed by the atoms of the alkali metals are more complex than the spectrum of hydrogen but less complex than most spectra formed by atoms having more than one electron. Although the atoms of each of the alkali metals possess more than one electron the spectrum of each is formed by transitions involving only one electron. The other electrons of each atom group themselves in what we shall soon find (§ 9-6) are filled or closed orbits, to which is given the somewhat better name of filled or closed shells (§ 9-7). The spectra of the alkali metals are thus spoken of as one-electron spectra. Spectra of atoms involving two or more electrons, on the other hand, are more complex. The spectra of the various alkali metals are closely related because of their one-electron origin and because in the different metals these electrons undergo similar transitions. The single electron outside a closed shell not only accounts for the optical similarity of the atoms of the alkali metals but also accounts for the chemical similarity, since these elements all have a chemical combining power (valence) of one. This electron is variously spoken of as the optical electron or the valence electron.

The work of Rydberg and others before the development of the theory of the electronic structure of the atom showed that empirical formulas could be set up to describe the spectra of the alkali metals, just as Balmer had set up an empirical formula to describe lines in the visible spectrum of hydrogen. These formulas can now be interpreted in terms of the electronic structure of the alkali metals and in terms of energy states involving this structure.

Upon first examining the spectrum of lithium (Fig. 9-1), or sodium, or any other alkali metal, it appears difficult to see any order or relationship between the lines. More careful examination, however, leads to the discovery that there are certain differences and that the lines may be sorted into groups. The brightest lines were named **principal lines;** those which appeared most clearly and sharply defined were called **sharp lines;** and another group of lines from their appearance were called **diffuse lines.** When the lines of each group are examined they show clearly that they form a series in which with increasing

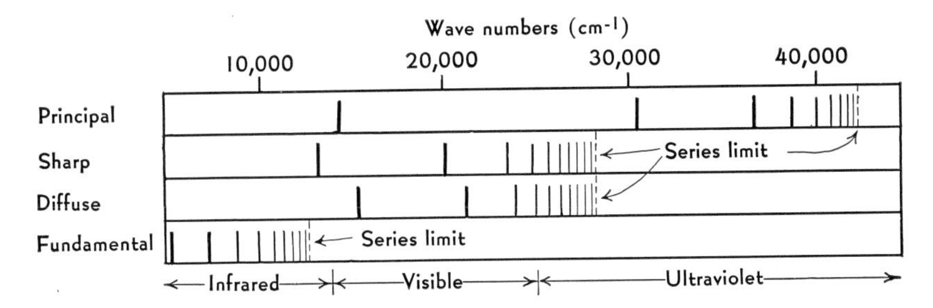

Fig. 9-1. Spectrum of lithium. The lines of the lithium spectrum may be sorted into the overlapping series shown.

frequency the lines come closer and closer together, approaching a limit, just as was true of the various hydrogen series. These series were then called the principal, sharp, and diffuse series, respectively. A fourth series, called the fundamental series, was badly misnamed since it was no more fundamental than any of the others. In designating the energy levels of the atom that give rise to these series the initials *S, P, D, F* are commonly assigned.

Rydberg showed, in 1889, that the frequencies of the lines in a series, or rather their wave numbers, could be represented empirically by an equation similar to that for hydrogen. For instance, the formula for the wave numbers of principal series lines can be written

$$\nu = R\left[\left(\frac{1}{n_1^2 + a^2}\right) - \left(\frac{1}{n_2^2 + b^2}\right)\right] \qquad [9\text{-}1]$$

Comparing this with the Bohr or Rydberg equations for hydrogen, it is apparent that here again the frequency (or wave number) may be interpreted in terms of a difference between energy levels. However, a correction a^2 or b^2 was arbitrarily added in the denominator of each term to permit agreement with experimental observations. These quantities a and b are now called quantum defects. The formula for the principal series of sodium may be abbreviated and represented symbolically as

$$\nu = 3S - nP \qquad n = 3, 4, 5, \cdots \tag{9-2}$$

where nP is the variable term representing a series of different energy levels. The wave numbers of the sharp series may be represented as

$$\nu = 3P - nS \qquad n = 4, 5, 6, \cdots \tag{9-3}$$

The diffuse series may be represented as

$$\nu = 3P - nD \qquad n = 3, 4, 5, \cdots \tag{9-4}$$

and the fundamental series is

$$\nu = 3D - nF \qquad n = 4, 5, 6, \cdots \tag{9-5}$$

Similar representations may be made for the various series of any of the alkali metals.

Evidently four sets of energy levels, S, P, D, F, are required to represent the transitions indicated by these equations and to give proper values for the observed spectral lines. The lithium atom has 3 electrons surrounding its nucleus. Since the spectral lines appear to be formed by transitions of 1 electron, the other 2 electrons may be assumed to form a closed inner ring or shell. This assumption will be found later to be broadly justified. Similarly, in the sodium atom with 11 electrons, 2 may be assumed to form a first closed shell, and 8 may be assumed to form a second closed shell, again leaving 1 electron to account for the spectral lines of sodium by its transitions.

Energy levels for the four series of sodium are shown in Fig. 9-2. The innermost orbit in which the outer electron can exist is number 3, as indicated on the diagram by the lowest available S level. Transitions to this orbit may be made from higher P levels, as indicated by Eq. 9-2. Notice that transitions may not be made from levels belonging to the same group and transitions must be made from an adjacent group. This rule will soon be given an important physical interpretation.

Equation 9-3 indicates that sharp series lines are described as transitions from any higher S level to the lowest vacant *P* level, known as 3*P*. Diffuse series lines result from transitions from any higher *D* level to the lowest available *P* level. Such an empirical scheme explains the origin of the various series in the sodium spectrum so long as one does not examine the lines too closely and observe their fine structure.

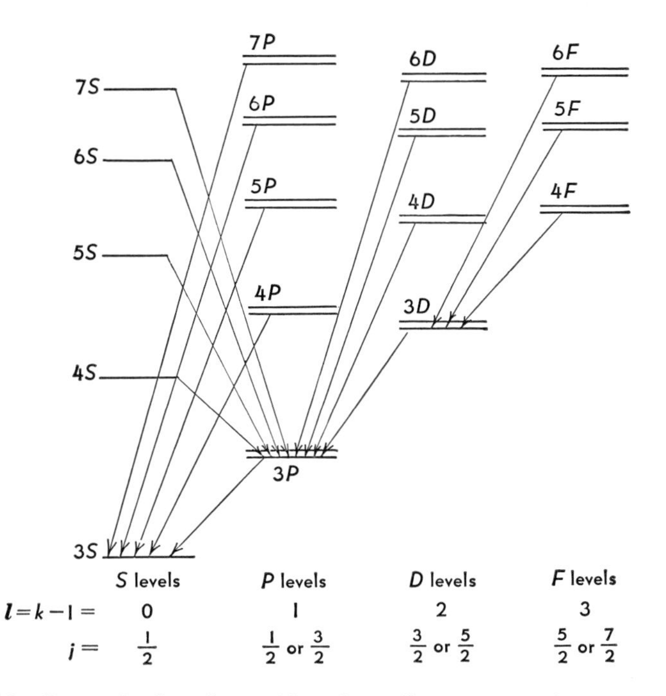

Fig. 9-2. Energy levels and transitions for sodium. *P*, *D*, and *F* levels are double because of electron spin. *S* levels are single (see text), and are lowest because the electron paths are most elliptical and penetrate closer to the nucleus.

Sommerfeld gave a physical explanation, on the basis of the modified Bohr theory, that S, *P*, *D*, and *F* levels are due to the existence of orbits of different degrees of ellipticity. There is a similarity here between these orbits and those of different degrees of ellipticity in hydrogen, but here the energy differences are greater, and what had accounted for fine structure in hydrogen was assumed by Sommerfeld to account for the overlapping of the series of lines in the spectra of the alkali metals. Sommerfeld assigned to all S levels an orbital angular momentum quantum number $k = 1$, to all *P*, *D*, and *F* levels orbital angular momentum quantum numbers 2, 3, and 4, respectively. The required transitions between levels may now be described as transitions in which the orbital angular momentum quantum number, as in the case of hydrogen, can only change by plus or minus 1 but not by 0. In symbols the change in k is Δk (§ 9-2), and the rule is

$$\Delta k = \pm 1 \qquad \Delta k \neq 0$$

This **selection rule** "forbids" transitions between levels having the same angular momentum quantum number and permits transitions only between adjacent sets of levels. This simple theory, however, failed to account for all aspects of the spectra of the alkali metals, and revisions and extension of the theory were required.

9-2. Electron Spin and Alkali Metal Doublet Spectra

Close examination of the spectrum of sodium with a spectroscope of even moderate resolving power shows that lines which appear single are actually composed of at least two components close together. This well-known fine structure of the alkali metal spectra is known as doublet structure. For instance, the common yellow line of sodium is easily observed to be a doublet. One component has a wavelength of 5890 A, and the other has a wavelength of 5896 A. Thus the difference between the two lines of the doublet is 6 A. The lighter the atom is, the less is the doublet separation; for lithium the doublet separation is so small as to be difficult to observe experimentally, but for the heaviest of the alkali metals, cesium, the separation is more than 400 A. Sommerfeld's extension of the Bohr theory made it possible to describe the various series and to give a physical interpretation to the description, but the theory was helpless to explain the relatively large energy difference representing the observed doublet structure of most of these lines.

This impasse lasted until 1925 when the extremely fruitful proposal of **electron spin** was made by Goudsmidt and Uhlenbeck, following a suggestion by Pauli. It had been evident that another property of orbital electrons must be recognized for which another quantum number must be added to the two already accepted, the total quantum number and the orbital angular momentum quantum number. Goudsmidt and Uhlenbeck suggested this new property of the electron: that it spins on its own axis at the same time that it revolves in its orbit about the nucleus. Here was a further application of ideas from planetary motion, since the earth spins on its axis at the same time that it revolves about the sun. Since any spinning body possesses angular momentum because of its spinning motion the total angular momentum of an electron would now be thought of as the vector sum of the angular momentum due to spin and that due to orbital motion. The vector sum is required since the electron in its orbital motion may spin in either one of two directions, parallel or antiparallel with respect to the axis of the orbital motion. The effect of this spin may add to or subtract from the orbital rotation.

Evidently the energy of the electron, referred to the atom as a whole, would be slightly different for the two different directions of spin. The suggestion of electron spin appeared to be just what the theorists needed to advance the theory another step and to account for the doublet structure of the alkali metal spectra. It also appeared to be just what the spectroscopists needed to account for certain discrepancies which they had met in trying to fit quantum numbers to energy levels. It had happened that the most convenient mathematical scheme for the spectroscopists to describe levels assigned to observed lines involved half integers instead of integers. Since the Bohr-Sommerfeld atomic theory had been based on integers for all forms of quantization it now became evident that this difficulty could be cleared up if there were assigned to the quantum number a half-integral value representing the amount of angular momentum of the electron due to spin alone. There remained the question of the energies involved.

Since the unit of angular momentum, according to the Bohr theory, was $h/2\pi$ the spinning electron was accepted as having an angular momentum of $+\frac{1}{2}(h/2\pi)$ or $-\frac{1}{2}(h/2\pi)$, depending on the direction of spin with respect to the orbital motion. These spin quantum numbers are designated by the letter s, where $s = \pm \frac{1}{2}$, and this property of spin is an intrinsic property of all electrons along with charge and mass.

It now becomes clear that, if electron energies are slightly different depending on the direction of electron spin, energy levels will also be slightly different, that is, the levels represented in Fig. 9-2 will be split into double levels or doublets. For *P*, *D*, and *F* levels this was in satisfactory agreement with spectroscopic data, but there was evidence that S levels were single despite electron spin.

It was here that further progress in atomic theory occurred as a result of the development of the new methods of analyzing atomic phenomena based on the new wave mechanics or quantum mechanics of Heisenberg and Schrödinger (Chap. 10). By these theoretical methods physicists arrived at the need for two sets of quantum numbers comparable to the n and k of the Bohr-Sommerfeld theory, except that instead of k with integral values starting at unity the theory indicated integral values starting at zero. To designate this new set of numbers the letter l was adopted. It is sometimes called the reduced orbital angular momentum quantum number, and it may be substituted for k in the scheme of energy levels for the alkali metal spectra if l is set equal to $k - 1$, as indicated in Fig. 9-2. The selection rule now becomes

$$\Delta l = \pm 1 \qquad \Delta l \neq 0$$

If l is also taken as representing angular momentum, as k was, the zero value poses a difficulty. It was originally thought that the angular momentum quantum number k could not be zero because this would represent motion with zero angular momentum or, in other words, motion in a straight line, and the electron would apparently have to do the impossible of passing back and forth through the nucleus. With $l = 0$ the same difficulty arises. Since the electron can hardly pass back and forth through the nucleus some other explanation seems necessary, and one possibility is to assume a more complicated motion for which there is no net circulation of mass. It now becomes evident that with the S levels, where the orbital angular momentum is taken to be zero, the direction of spin cannot affect the total energy of the electron and S levels consequently remain single. However, the principal, diffuse, and fundamental energy levels become doublet levels. Since the transitions from S levels to P levels may take place with either of the members of the doublet P levels the sharp series lines possess doublet structure.

When transitions are from one doublet level to another doublet level it would seem that four different transitions are possible and four slightly different frequencies should result. It is found, however, that all such transitions "obey" a new selection rule in terms of a new quantum number j. This new quantum number, sometimes called the inner quantum number, is not new in the sense of being independent as n, l, s are, but it is the sum of l and s for any one set of levels.

Let us now see what the j values are for S, P, D, and F levels. For S levels $j = 0 \pm \frac{1}{2} = 1/2$ since here the sign does not matter. For P levels $j = 1 \pm \frac{1}{2} = 1/2$ or $3/2$, and for D and F levels $j = 3/2$ or $5/2$ and $j = 5/2$ or $7/2$, respectively. Since the energies of the levels involve the j values, the P, D, and F levels under the influence of electron spin become doublet levels. The selection rule governing j value transitions is that j can change by only $\pm$ 1 or 0, but the probability of zero change is small. In symbols the change in j is Δj, and the rule is

$$\Delta j = \pm 1 \text{ or } 0$$

It will be found that this forbids one of the four possible transitions mentioned as involving a larger change of angular momentum ($\Delta j = 2$) than the electron can ordinarily make at one jump. Consequently we can now see that sharp and principal series lines are composed of actual doublets. Diffuse and fundamental series may have a third and often fainter line, called a satellite, along with each doublet, but the series is still called a doublet series.

9-3. Space Quantization and the Zeeman Effect

As previously mentioned (§ 8-1), Zeeman in 1896 found that a magnetic field will affect the frequencies of light given off by atoms in the field. In the so-called normal Zeeman effect a spectral line is split into three components (Fig. 9-3*a*) when observed at right angles to the field. The middle line has the frequency of the original line. The other two have frequencies larger and smaller. Usually a more complicated pattern is observed (Fig. 9-3*b*), called the anomalous Zeeman

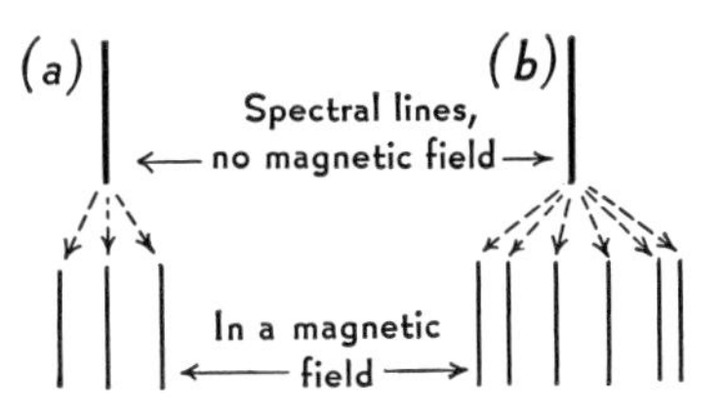

Fig. 9-3. Zeeman effect: *a*, Normal effect, a singlet line split into 3 components when observed at right angles to the magnetic field; *b*, anomalous effect, a triplet line split into several components.

effect, although in the light of modern quantum theory there is nothing really anomalous about it. The so-called normal effect is one in which electron spin does not enter. It occurs in atoms for which electrons occur in pairs with opposite spins and the effects of spin cancel. In the anomalous Zeeman effect electron spin enters in, and there is more splitting of energy levels; consequently there are more possibilities for transitions between levels, and more observed splitting of lines.

The normal Zeeman effect is the result of the effects of the magnetic field on the orbital motion of the radiating electrons, and it may be given a very simple explanation on the basis of classical electrical theory. However, classical theory is helpless to explain the more complicated patterns of the anomalous Zeeman effect, and quantum methods are necessary. Indeed, this more complex Zeeman effect is now considered to give some of the strongest evidence in support of quantum ideas and in particular of the idea of quantization of position, or what is often called **space quantization.**

An ordinary magnet may be held in a magnetic field with its axis at any desired angle to the field. It could not remain at such an angle without being held, unless it were endowed with the properties of a spinning top. Yet, if it were so endowed it could remain inclined at any angle to the field because it would precess about the direction of the field at that angle. Now, an electron revolving in its orbit about the nucleus of an atom is like a spinning top in that it has angular momentum. Like a magnet it also possesses magnetic moment resulting from rotation or spin of electric charge. Unlike the spinning magnet of the foregoing example, however, if placed in a magnetic field it can only sustain itself with its axis at certain preferred angles to the direction of the field. To fully describe the state of the system it becomes necessary to add a fourth quantum number m to the quantum numbers n, l, s previously required. This is called the *magnetic quantum number.* It represents a kind of spatial quantization but only with respect to an impressed magnetic field.

Quantum theory leads to the rule that the only permissible angles of such space quantization are those for which the projection of the angular momentum quantum number l on the direction of the field has integral values represented by m. Consequently m may take any in-

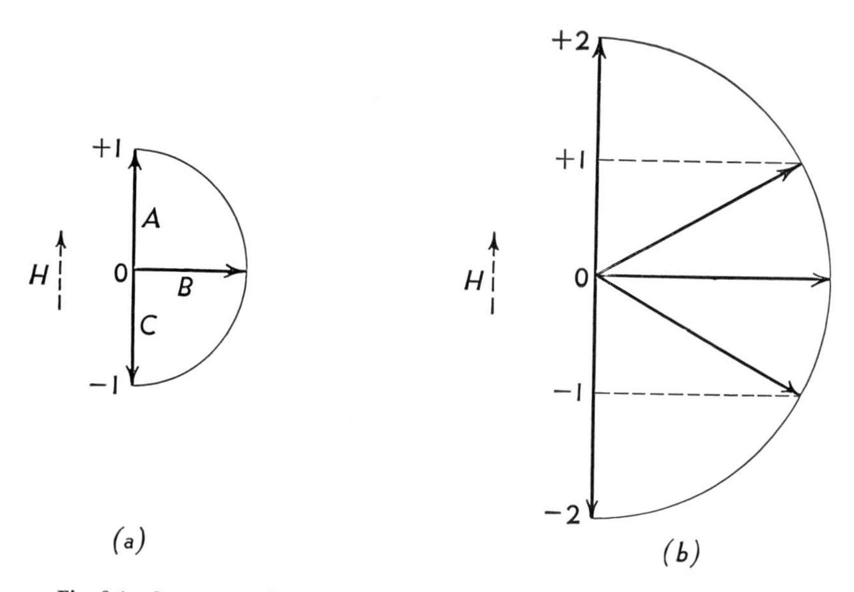

Fig. 9-4. Space quantization in magnetic field according to vector model of atom. Vector representing magnetic moment can only take positions for which the projection on a line in the direction of the field H is integral or zero.

tegral value from $-l$ to $+l$, including zero. This is indicated in Fig. 9-4, where H represents the direction of the field. At a, it is seen that if $l = 1$ there are three possible directions A, B, and C, the projections of which are $+1$, 0, and -1. At b, where $l = 2$ it is seen that there are five possible directions for which the projections may take the values $m = -2, -1, 0, +1$, or $+2$. These new ideas now afford the basis for an explanation of the Zeeman effect even in its more complex aspects. Of the nine possible transitions between the two sets of levels just mentioned, the allowed transitions being given by the selection rule $\Delta m = \pm 1$ or 0, there are only three separate groups representing slightly different energy differences. These account for the normal Zeeman effect in which the original line is split into three components. In more complicated Zeeman patterns the spin of the electron must be considered, and the space quantization represented by m is determined by $j = l \pm \frac{1}{2}$ instead of just l. The introduction of the idea of spin leads to further multiplicity of levels and more possible electron transitions in which theory is remarkably confirmed by experiment.

The Zeeman effect is not easy to observe and requires optical equipment of high resolving power; however, it has been intensively studied because of the information that it gives about the atom. It has been frequently used to help sort out the lines belonging to one series of an element. In complex spectra the overlapping of different series often obscures the fact that there are definite series or groups, but all such closely related lines always show the same characteristic Zeeman pattern.

9-4. The Bohr Magneton

An electron revolving in the innermost orbit of hydrogen has a magnetic moment which is often taken as a unit of measurement and is called the Bohr magneton. The numerical value is frequently given in cgs units by the following equation

$$M_B = \frac{eh}{4\pi mc} = 9.25 \times 10^{-21} \text{ emu} \qquad [9\text{-}6]$$

To derive this equation we recall that by electrical theory the magnetic moment M (emu) of a current loop is equal to the product of the current strength i (emu) by the area A, but for a stream of electrons i (emu) is equal to nev/c where n is the number of electrons per unit length of path moving with velocity v and nev is the amount of charge (esu) passing a point per second. For a single electron revolving in a circular orbit the number of times per second it passes a point is $v/2\pi r$ and the current (emu) is equal to $ev/2\pi rc$. Then $M = iA$ for a circular path is

$$M = \frac{ev}{2\pi rc} \times (\pi r^2) = \frac{evr}{2c} = \frac{e\omega r^2}{2c} = \frac{e\,(m\omega r^2)}{2mc} \qquad [9\text{-}7]$$

where $\omega =$ angular velocity ($v = r\omega$), and both numerator and denominator have been multiplied by m, the mass of the electron. It is now seen that $m\omega r^2$ is the angular momentum of the electron, but it will be recalled that according to the Bohr quantum restrictions on angular momentum only integral values of the fundamental unit $h/2\pi$ are permissible. Substituting this unit for $m\omega r^2$ in Eq. 9-7 we obtain for the Bohr magneton, the unit of magnetic moment M_B,

$$M_B = \frac{e}{2mc}\left(\frac{h}{2\pi}\right) = \frac{eh}{4\pi mc} \qquad [9\text{-}8]$$

This is the minimum magnetic moment that an electron would possess according to the Bohr theory as a result of orbital motion, and wave-mechanical theory gives a similar result. Although in practice measured values of magnetic moments may not come out as integral multiples of this unit, it is nevertheless a useful unit and it has been found that the electron spinning on its axis actually possesses a magnetic moment of one Bohr magneton. This has been confirmed by the experiment to be described in the next section.

9-5. The Stern-Gerlach Experiment

The idea of space quantization in a magnetic field can be very directly tested by experiment. In the Stern and Gerlach experiment, one of great historical importance, a beam of silver atoms was passed through a nonuniform magnetic field. The beam was observed to be split into two parts, one deflected in the direction of the field, the other deflected in the opposite direction. Now, a silver atom has one electron outside a filled shell neither accompanied by nor paired with others. Since all other electrons are paired their effects cancel, and what effect there is is due to the remaining electron. Consequently the silver atom is normally in an S state, and the magnetic moment and angular momentum that it has are due entirely to the spin of this electron and not to orbital motion. According to the idea of space quantization in a magnetic field there should be only two possible positions for the direction of the axis of spin of this electron. It should point in the direction of the magnetic field or in the opposite direction. If the atoms are in a nonuniform magnetic field they should then be pulled in one direction or the other. The experiment of Stern and Gerlach showed that the beam divided into two parts and that actually only two positions were taken by the silver atoms in the field. This is direct confirmation of space quantization since by classical theory the silver atoms, no matter what their original position, would all turn similarly to "line up" with the field, or at least to precess about it.

A magnet in a uniform magnetic field has no resultant force acting on it, since in a field of strength H the force Hm on one pole of strength m is exactly balanced by the force $-Hm$ on the opposite pole. However, in a nonuniform field changing in the x direction at a rate $\partial H/\partial x$ the increased force on one pole is

$$m \frac{\partial H}{\partial x} \Delta x$$

where Δx is the separation of the poles and $m \Delta x$ is the magnetic moment M of the magnet. The force on the magnet is then

$$\begin{aligned} F &= \left(mH + m \frac{\partial H}{\partial x} \Delta x\right) - mH = m \frac{\partial H}{\partial x} \Delta x \\ &= \frac{\partial H}{\partial x} M \end{aligned} \qquad [9\text{-}9]$$

From this it is seen that only in a nonuniform field where $(\partial H/\partial x) \neq 0$ is there any force, and to get maximum force the field must diverge as much as possible.

In the Stern and Gerlach experiment a strongly nonuniform field was obtained by means of a magnet with one pole in the form of a sharp edge facing an opposite pole with a broad face (Fig. 9-5). Silver atoms were evaporated from a tiny furnace and allowed to pass between the poles of this magnet. The vapor was detected by condensing it on a glass plate placed in the path of the beam (Fig. 9-6). From the amount of separation of the two parts of the beam when the field was on, together with the field intensity, the magnetic moment of the silver atom could be computed. This turned out to be one Bohr magneton, and therefore represents the magnetic moment of one spinning electron.

In hydrogen the situation is similar. Since the electron in hydrogen is in an S state there can be no orbital motion and, as with silver, no

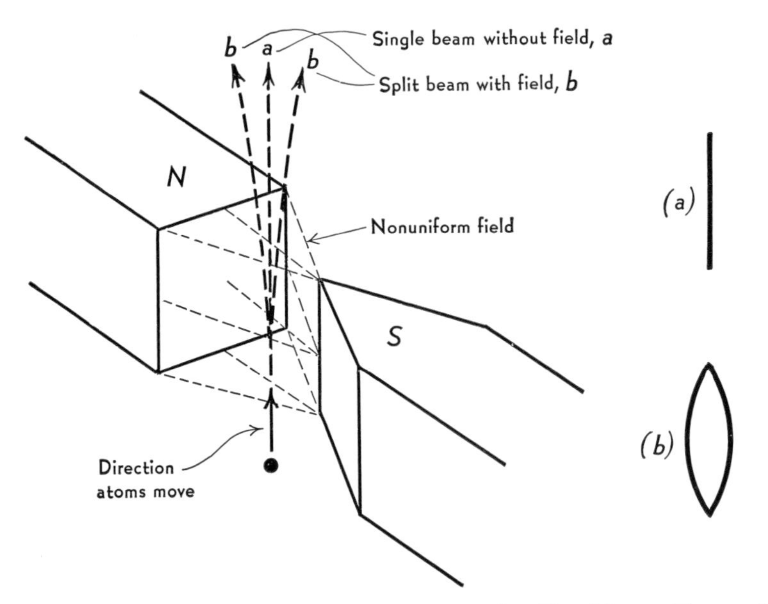

Fig. 9-5. Stern-Gerlach experiment. Shape of magnet poles to give nonuniform field in experiment. Beam of silver atoms passing through field is split into two parts. One part is deflected toward the South Pole, the other toward the North Pole.

Fig. 9-6. *a*, Trace of silver atoms where beam strikes detecting plate (no field); *b*, with field, trace shows splitting of beam.

Zeeman effect. If there is no orbital motion there can be no orbital magnetic moment, and any magnetic moment in hydrogen must therefore also be the result of spin of the electron about its own axis.

9-6. The Pauli Principle

By what now seem to be awkward and difficult methods Bohr and others had arrived at the conclusion that a given orbit in an atom can contain only a certain number of electrons before it becomes filled. All atoms with a large number of electrons would have several filled orbits, any remaining electrons being in the next outer orbit. There was evidence that in the first orbit there could be only 2 electrons, that in the second orbit there could be only 8 electrons, or, in other words, that 2 electrons filled the first orbit and 8 electrons filled the second orbit. The evidence for the number of electrons in succeeding orbits was not entirely clear, but the attempt was made to assign electrons to successive orbits for heavier and heavier atoms in such a way as to fulfill the periodicity of chemical and physical properties represented in the periodic table of the elements.

In 1925 W. Pauli suggested a new rule, known as the **Pauli exclusion principle,** for determining the numbers of electrons in filled orbits based on quantum theory. This rule was later confirmed by theory, and it is now recognized that deductions from wave-mechanical theory only have physical significance when interpreted in accordance with this rule. Thus it has become one of the most important principles of atomic

TABLE 9-1. NUMBERS OF ELECTRONS IN GROUPS OR SHELLS ACCORDING TO PAULI'S PRINCIPLE

Orbital Group or Shell	n	l	m	s	No. of Electrons in Subgroup or Subshell	No. of Electrons in Completed Group or Shell
1	1	0	0	$+\frac{1}{2}$	2 s	2
	1	0	0	$-\frac{1}{2}$		
2	2	0	0	$+\frac{1}{2}$	2 s	8
	2	0	0	$-\frac{1}{2}$		
	2	1	−1	$+\frac{1}{2}$	6 p	
	2	1	−1	$-\frac{1}{2}$		
	2	1	0	$+\frac{1}{2}$		
	2	1	0	$-\frac{1}{2}$		
	2	1	1	$+\frac{1}{2}$		
	2	1	1	$-\frac{1}{2}$		
3	3	0	0	$+\frac{1}{2}$	2 s	18
	3	0	0	$-\frac{1}{2}$		
	3	1	−1	$+\frac{1}{2}$	6 p	
	3	1	−1	$-\frac{1}{2}$		
	3	1	0	$+\frac{1}{2}$		
	3	1	0	$-\frac{1}{2}$		
	3	1	1	$+\frac{1}{2}$		
	3	1	1	$-\frac{1}{2}$		
	3	2	−2	$+\frac{1}{2}$	10 d	
	3	2	−2	$-\frac{1}{2}$		
	3	2	−1	$+\frac{1}{2}$		
	3	2	−1	$-\frac{1}{2}$		
	3	2	0	$+\frac{1}{2}$		
	3	2	0	$-\frac{1}{2}$		
	3	2	1	$+\frac{1}{2}$		
	3	2	1	$-\frac{1}{2}$		
	3	2	2	$+\frac{1}{2}$		
	3	2	2	$-\frac{1}{2}$		

structure. The Pauli exclusion principle states: *In any atom no two electrons may have the same set of quantum numbers n, l, m, s.* This is equivalent to saying that electrons and atoms preserve a kind of individuality which may not be infringed upon by other electrons. To see how the rule operates, consider the number of electrons permitted in the first orbital group (shell), for which $n = 1$. It must be remembered that l may have all integral values from 0 to $n - 1$, and m may have all integral values from $-l$ to $+l$. For the first orbital group, since $n = 1$, $l = 0$ and $m = 0$, but s may be plus or minus ½. This means that in this first group there may be two electrons identical except that their spins are in opposite directions.

Now for the second orbital group ($n = 2$) l may have the values 0 or 1. If $l = 0$, $m = 0$, and two electrons are permitted with these quantum numbers if they have spins $+½$ and $-½$, respectively. The remaining electrons for which $l = 1$ may have values of $m = -1$, 0, or $+1$, and for any of these the spins may be $-½$ or $+½$. This permits six electrons with $l = 1$. These together with the two for $l = 0$ make eight electrons permitted in orbital group number two. Similarly, for group three, 18 electrons will be permitted, for group four 32, and for group five 50. The distribution of quantum numbers for groups one, two, and three are shown in Table 9-1.

Electrons in the first group, since they have values of $l = 0$, are known as *s*-electrons. In the second group there are two subgroups. Two electrons are *s*-electrons, and the remaining six are known as *p*-electrons since $l = 1$. In the third group there would be 2 *s*-, 6 *p*-, and 10 *d*-electrons if the orbit were filled.

9-7. Shell Structure of the Atom

In place of the terminology of the orbital model of the atom it is now customary to speak of shells instead of orbits. This is more in agreement with newer ideas concerning atomic structure, and also places greater emphasis on the three-dimensional nature of the atom.

The innermost orbital grouping of electrons is now referred to as the *K* shell; the second orbital grouping, the *L* shell; the third, the *M* shell; and so on. Because in the *L* and outer shells there are electrons with different values of l known as *s*-, *p*-, or *d*-electrons, it is customary to speak of the *s*-, *p*-, and *d*-subshells. The *L* shell, for instance, has two subshells, *s* and *p*, the *M* shell has three subshells, *s*, *p*, and *d*. The *N* shell has four subshells, *s*, *p*, *d*, and *f*. For the heaviest atoms the outermost shell is the *Q* shell; there are only a few electrons in this shell.

For any completely filled shell the total angular momentum is zero, since for every electron there is one other electron with oppositely directed angular momentum and they cancel by pairs.

9-8. Periodic Table of the Elements

The Pauli exclusion principle gives us the key to building up the atoms of the elements and to their relations as represented by the periodic table (Appendix 3). By adding successive positive charges to the nucleus, together with an equal number of electrons surrounding the nucleus, we can account for the periodic relationship between the atoms. Only two different atoms representing two elements exist in the first period of the periodic table, since only two electrons are permitted in the first or K shell. Eight atoms representing eight elements occur in the next period of the periodic table, since eight electrons are permitted in the second or L shell. The third period of the periodic table also has eight atoms representing eight more elements formed by adding the 2 s-electrons and the 6 p-electrons of the third shell. Here, however, the first of several deviations from the regular order begins. Starting with potassium, instead of adding the d-electrons belonging to the third shell, the s-electrons of the next or fourth shell are added first, and other irregularities follow in such a manner as to explain how the next three periods are double ones involving eighteen elements each.

The electronic structure of the atoms and the way in which the periodic table is built up on this basis are shown better in Table 9-2, and the order of filling the shells is indicated. In the long period from potassium K to krypton Kr it is indicated how $3d$ electrons are filled in underneath $4s$ electrons. It is likewise seen that the group of similar elements from $Z = 57$ to $Z = 72$, known as the rare-earth elements which could not be easily crowded into the older form of the periodic table, now represent the filling in of the $4f$ electrons beneath outer $6s$ electrons. A similar filling in of the $5f$ electrons beneath $7s$ electrons also accounts for the new man-made elements from neptunium Np ($Z = 93$) upward.

The structure of the periodic table thus can be shown to be in agreement with the ideas of filled shells and subshells as predicted by the Pauli principle. In addition, we now have the satisfaction of having a principle based on quantization which gives results entirely in agreement with observations. We also now have an explanation of the so-called "noble" elements, which do not interact chemically because of

TABLE 9–2. PERIODIC SYSTEM OF THE ELEMENTS*

(The boxed-in elements are man-made.)

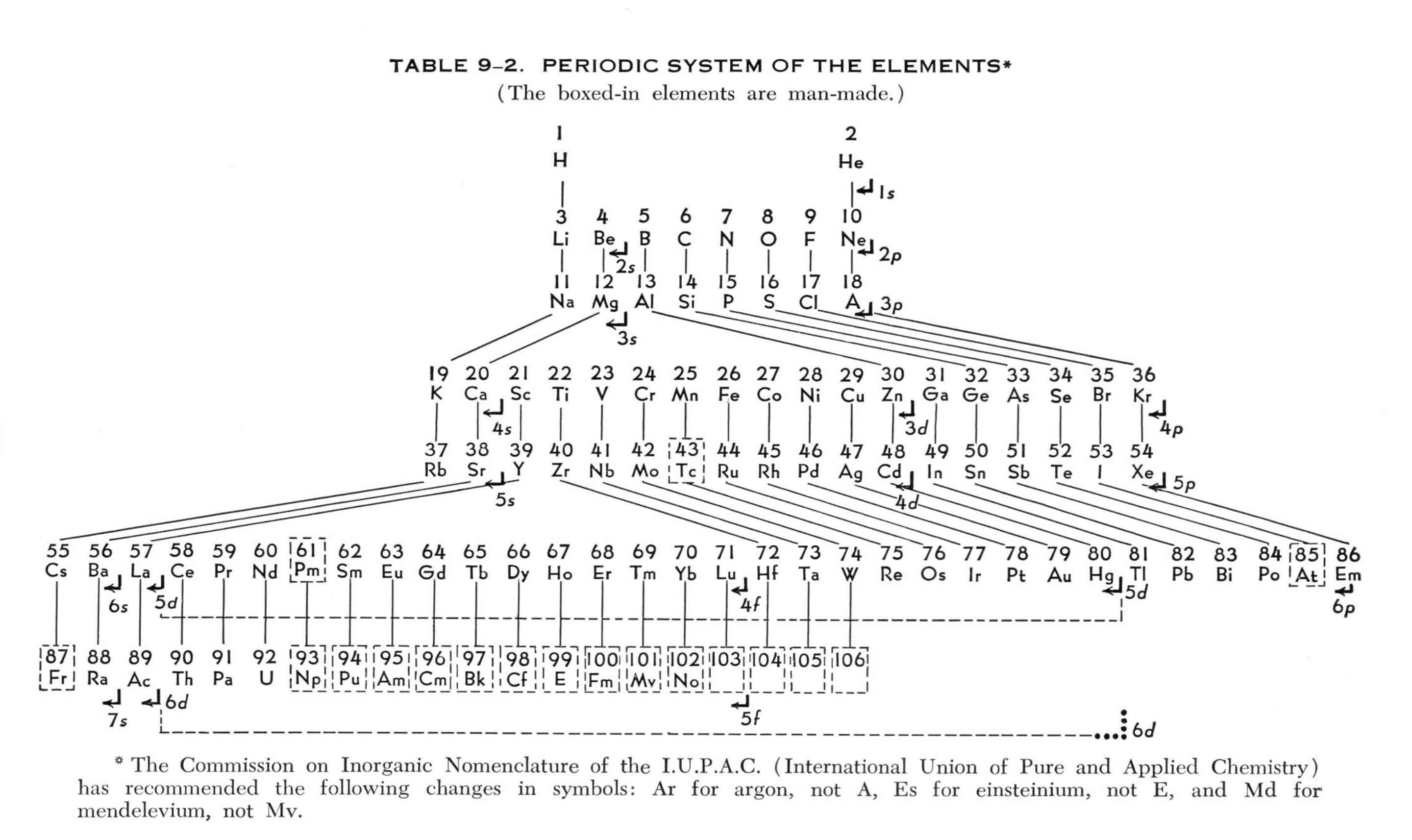

* The Commission on Inorganic Nomenclature of the I.U.P.A.C. (International Union of Pure and Applied Chemistry) has recommended the following changes in symbols: Ar for argon, not A, Es for einsteinium, not E, and Md for mendelevium, not Mv.

filled shells. These elements, beginning with helium with 2 electrons, neon with 10, and so on, represent atoms with completely filled outer shells and subshells, and they have no valence electrons.

The electronic structure of an atom may be represented in terms of filled or partly filled shells; for instance, an aluminum atom would have the following electronic structure, $1s^2$, $2s^2$, $2p^6$, $3s^2$, $3p$, and the normal state of the atom is said to be the P state. The symbol $1s^2$ indicates that in the first shell there are 2 s-electrons. In the second shell $2s^2$ and $2p^6$ indicate that there are 2 s-electrons and 6 p-electrons, in the third shell 2 s-electrons and 1 p-electron. The lowest or normal state of an atom is the state of the last valence electron. It is frequently designated by the j value as a subscript after the letter, and a superscript before the letter indicates whether the state is a singlet, doublet, triplet, etc., as follows: oxygen ($^3P_2$), sodium ($^2S_{1/2}$). For the aluminum atom just discussed, the symbol for the lowest state is $^2P_{1/2}$. Although S levels behave as single levels they are designated as double since it is only for the special case of $l = 0$ that both levels have the same value and cannot be distinguished. When such levels cannot thus be distinguished they are said to be *degenerate*. The electronic structure of some of the elements is given in Table 9-3.

TABLE 9-3. SYMBOLIC REPRESENTATION OF ELECTRON STRUCTURE OF SELECTED ATOMS

Element	Electron Structure					Normal State
	K shell	*L* shell	*M* shell	*N* shell	*O* shell	
1 H	$1s$					$^2S_{1/2}$
2 He	$1s^2$					$^1S_0$
6 C	$1s^2$	$2s^2$ $2p^2$				$^3P_0$
10 Ne	$1s^2$	$2s^2$ $2p^6$				$^1S_0$
11 Na	$1s^2$	$2s^2$ $2p^6$	$3s$			$^2S_{1/2}$
13 Al	$1s^2$	$2s^2$ $2p^6$	$3s^2$ $3p$			$^2P_{1/2}$
29 Cu	$1s^2$	$2s^2$ $2p^6$	$3s^2$ $3p^6$ $3d^{10}$	$4s$		$^2S_{1/2}$
47 Ag	$1s^2$	$2s^2$ $2p^6$	$3s^2$ $3p^6$ $3d^{10}$	$4s^2$ $4p^6$ $4d^{10}$	$5s$	$^2S_{1/2}$

9-9. Nuclear Spin

Another type of fine structure observed in the spectra of some elements cannot be ascribed to any of the physical characteristics so far mentioned. This is called **hyperfine structure** and can be explained if the assumption is made that the nucleus of the atom also spins. If the formula for the Bohr magneton is applied to the spinning nucleus it is possible to put into the denominator of the formula not the mass of an electron but the very much larger mass of the nucleus. This leads to a value for the magnetic moment of the nucleus which is very much smaller than for the magnetic moment of the electron. By using this value to compute a further splitting of energy levels it is possible to explain hyperfine structure.

It is not the purpose here to go into the subject of hyperfine structure, but the concept of nuclear spin is of great importance in the field of nuclear physics, and in Chap. 17 more direct methods of measuring nuclear spin will be given. Spin is a natural property of the protons and neutrons making up a nucleus, but for some nuclei the resultant spin (vector sum) is zero. Other subatomic particles, particularly among the mesons (Chap. 20), may also have zero spin.

9-10. Complex Spectra

Atomic spectra range from the simplest such as that of hydrogen to spectra such as that of iron, so complex that there may be several thousand lines in the visible region and as many more in the ultraviolet and infrared. Spectra of heavier atoms and those with more outer electrons become increasingly complex. In general it is convenient to classify spectra as **one-electron spectra,** with 1 electron outside a closed shell as in the alkali metals; **two-electron spectra,** with 2 electrons outside a closed shell as in helium, mercury, and calcium; **three-electron spectra,** with 3 such electrons as in aluminum, boron, etc. One-electron spectra are doublet spectra, two-electron spectra may be singlet or triplet spectra, three-electron spectra may be doublet or quadruplet spectra, and so on. These relationships which rise and fall as one passes from column to column across the periodic table are known as the *multiplicity of spectra.*

It is of interest to examine the energy-level scheme for a two-electron spectrum. Mercury is a good example (Fig. 9-7). Other elements such as zinc and cadmium in the second column of the periodic table have similar spectra. These elements show spectra, some of the lines of which arise from transitions between singlet levels and others from triplet levels. These lines all arise from the transitions of one of the two "optical" electrons. Some important lines occasionally arise from transitions of one electron between singlet and triplet levels. This means that the electron reverses its axis of spin in the transition. Certain important complex groups of lines arise from transitions involving both electrons at once. The lines so formed are called **multiplets,** and

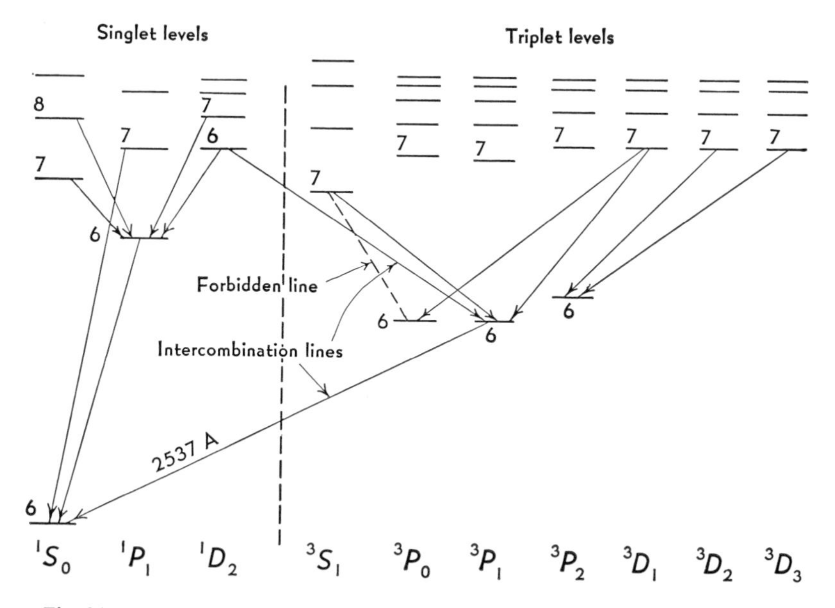

Fig. 9-7. Energy levels for a two-electron spectrum, mercury, involving singlet and triplet levels. For singlet levels the two outer electron spins are opposed, and the vector sum is zero. For triplet levels the spins are parallel, and the vector sum is 1. When the spin and orbital angular momentum vectors are combined for the triplet state there are three different values for each level shown, but in the interest of simplicity the triplet levels are here represented by single lines.

some of these groups appear as *triads of complex triplets.* They involve complications and cannot be discussed here.

In two-electron spectra, singlet levels arise from those atoms in which the spins of the two outer electrons are in opposite directions (antiparallel). The effects of spin cancel, leaving only orbital angular momentum. There will then be no splitting of levels due to spin and consequently no fine structure. In what is called the vector model of the atom the angular momentum is represented by an arrow along the axis of revolution or of spin as in ordinary mechanics. The vectors representing the orbital angular momenta l_1 and l_2 of the two electrons combine to form a resultant L (Fig. 9-8). However, according to quantum rules they only combine in such a manner that the resultant L is always an integral multiple of $h/2\pi$. Here it should be mentioned that it is common custom to use small letter s, l, and j to represent quantum numbers applying to a single electron. When the vector sum of the s values or the l or j values for two or more electrons is taken, the custom is to use capital letters S, L, or J for these sums. The capital letters may then be thought of as applying to the atom as a whole, whereas the small letters apply to individual electrons.

In triplet levels, the electron spins of the two outer electrons are in the same direction (parallel), and the resultant spin designated by S is $\frac{1}{2} + \frac{1}{2} = 1$. By the quantum rule the vectors L and S now form a resultant J which can only take integral values from $L + S$ to $L - S$.

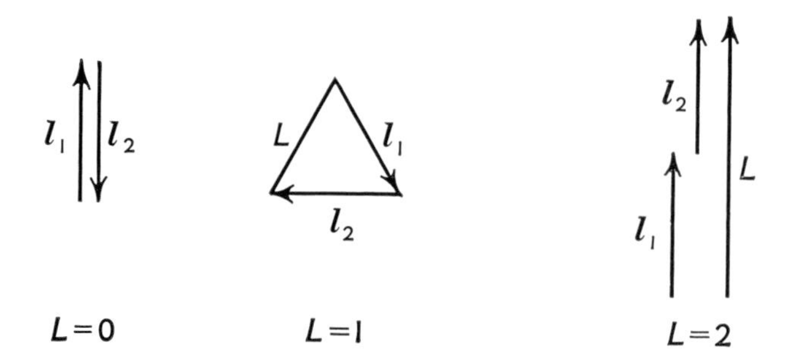

Fig. 9-8. Vector model of atom. Total orbital angular momentum L is vector sum of separate values l_1 and l_2 for each electron. If $l_1 = 1$ and $l_2 = 1$, three values of L are obtained. In the triplet state $s_1 + s_2 = S = 1$, and S combines with L to give integral values of J from $L - S$ to $L + S$. For $L = 2$ and $S = 1$, J has values 1, 2, 3, and the energy levels are designated $^3D_1$, $^3D_2$, $^3D_3$.

As with the alkali metals, the selections rule for J is that it may change by ± 1 or zero, excluding zero-zero transitions. By these concepts the spectra of two-electron atoms may be quite accurately described. The process may be extended to the three-electron atoms of the third column of the periodic table, and so on.

Metastable states When the selection rule just mentioned is applied to these atoms certain apparently plausible transitions are forbidden. For instance, the transition from the level 7^3S_1 to the level 6^3P_0 is forbidden. By this rule an electron raised to the 7^3S_1 level cannot ordinarily return to the normal state by radiation. It is then in what is called a metastable state, in which it will stay until released by some special process, such as perhaps being raised to another level from which it can return by radiation, or it may give up energy at the moment of collision with another atom. Such a collision is called a *collision of the second kind.*

9-11. Characteristic X-ray Spectra

Characteristic x-rays are particular x-ray frequencies produced by excitation of atoms in the target (§ 5-13), and they depend on and are characteristic of the material of the target. In Fig. 9-9 the curve is shown representing the combined continuous spectrum and characteristic spectrum of x-rays produced when electrons strike a target with sufficient speed. The two peaks on the curve represent the characteristic frequencies resulting from excitation of the atoms of the target.

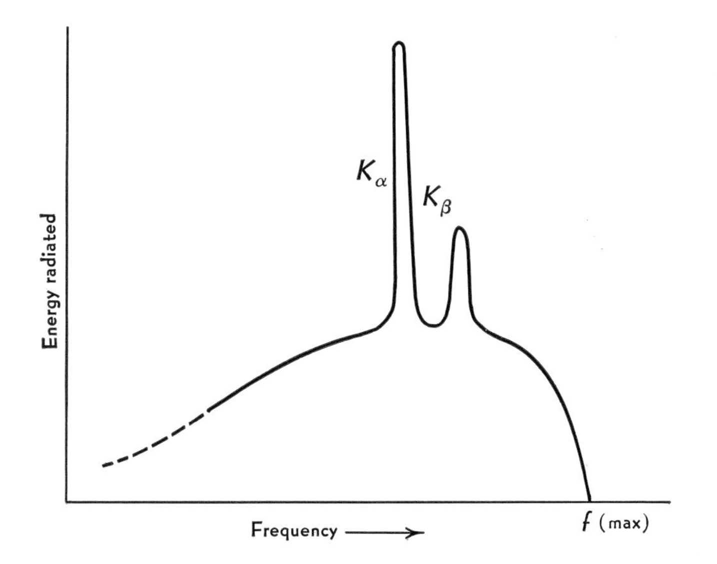

Fig. 9-9. Characteristic x-ray lines of the target (sharp peaks) superposed on the continuous background of general x-rays.

Although Barkla and Sadler discovered characteristic x-rays in 1908 and distinguished between what they called *K* and *L* rays, it was a number of years before the origin of these rays was understood and before the names *K* and *L* were given to the electron shells of the atom. Visible spectra are produced by excitation of an atom so that one or more outer electrons are raised to higher energy states. Characteristic x-ray excitation, on the other hand, involves the displacement of an inner electron as, for instance, one in what we now call the *K* or *L* shells. Since there are usually no nearby vacant energy levels to which these electrons may be raised, such excitation involves removing them altogether from the atom (ionization). This permits transitions of nearby electrons to the vacancy thus created in an inner shell.

The transitions most likely to occur are those in which the vacancy is filled by a nearby electron from a higher energy state. In the transition a characteristic x-ray photon is radiated. The vacancy left by this electron is in turn filled by the transition of another electron from a still higher energy state with radiation of a photon of somewhat lower frequency. Thus the displacement of one inner electron may permit a series of transitions, with each of which emission of radiation occurs.

Since the electrons in the innermost or K shell of an atom are those most tightly bound to the nucleus they require bombardment by higher energy electrons to displace them than do electrons in L or outer shells. In Table 9-4 ionization energies are given for K and L electrons of some atoms. If displacement of a K electron is followed by transition of an electron from an L to a K shell, an x-ray quantum is emitted representing the first line of the K series of characteristic x-rays. This is called the K_α line. If the transition is from the M to the K shell, the emitted quantum represents the second or K_β line of the K series. Since the energy difference between levels is greater for the latter than for the former transition the second line of the series will have a higher frequency, and the K series will be composed of lines of increasing frequency approaching a high-frequency limit. As the probability of transition decreases rapidly for the higher-frequency members of the series only a few lines of the K and L series can be readily detected except in the elements of high atomic weight.

TABLE 9-4. SOME IONIZATION ENERGIES IN EV FOR K AND L ELECTRONS

	K	L
Hydrogen	13.6	——
Carbon	282	——
Aluminum	1487	——
Nickel	7477	849
Copper	8047	928
Silver	22162	2984
Tungsten	59310	8396
Gold	69794	9711
Uranium	98428	13613

In the L, M, and higher shells there are electrons with different j values representing slight differences in energy. Consequently the characteristic lines may be expected to have a fine structure, and in accordance with the selection rule for Δj the K_α line is actually composed of two lines close together, $K_{\alpha 1}$ and $K_{\alpha 2}$. Lines in the L spectra of an element may be represented as L_α, L_β, and so on, and each of these may show a similar fine structure for the same reason.

9-12. Moseley's Rule and Atomic Numbers

In 1913, Moseley used the Bragg-type crystal spectrograph to make an extensive study of the similarities and relations between the characteristic x-ray spectra of a considerable number of the heavy elements. In passing from one element to another of higher atomic weight no simple relation is to be observed for the ordinary visible spectra. However, Moseley found a very simple relationship between the characteristic x-ray spectra of the elements. These spectra all appear very similar, and, with few exceptions, with increasing atomic weight the lines of a given element are merely shifted in the direction of higher frequencies or shorter wavelengths (Fig. 9-10). When the few ex-

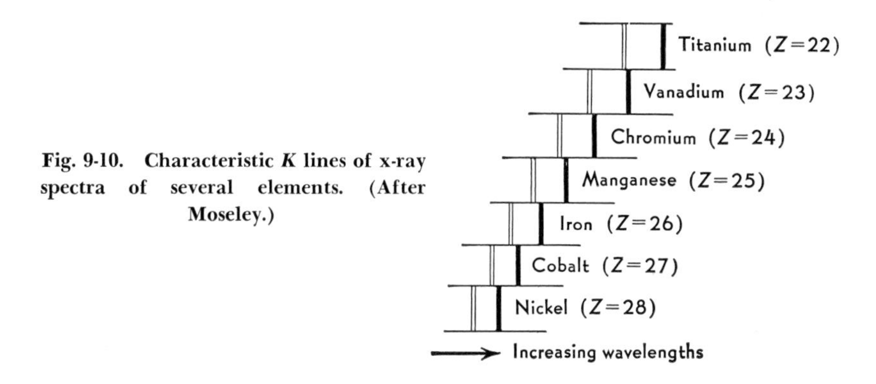

Fig. 9-10. Characteristic *K* lines of x-ray spectra of several elements. (After Moseley.)

ceptions were straightened out by changing the order of certain elements, the numbers given to the elements were called by Moseley atomic numbers.

Moseley plotted a diagram of the K series, as in Fig. 9-11, in which the square root of the wave number is closely proportional to these atomic numbers. This surprisingly simple but regular relationship of the characteristic x-ray spectra made possible the location of missing elements at once in the periodic table. Furthermore it contributed to our knowledge of the atoms themselves.

After the success of the Bohr theory of the atom in explaining hydrogen spectra, it became evident that the simple theory might help to explain characteristic x-ray spectra if the atomic number was identified as Z, the number of charges on the nucleus. For instance, if one

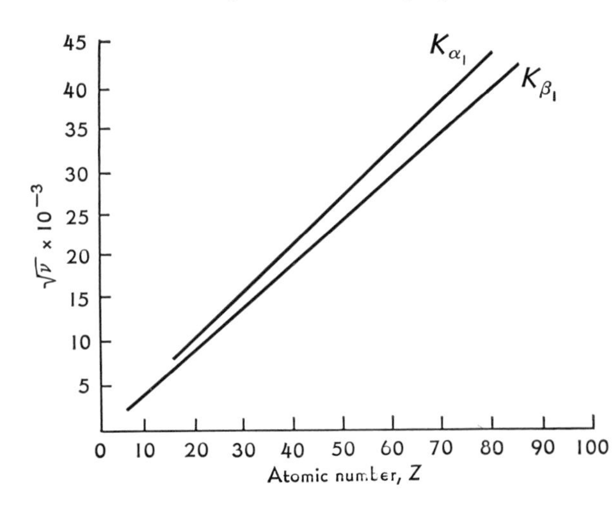

Fig. 9-11. Moseley diagram, showing uniform relation between square root of wave number and atomic number Z.

of the *K* electrons of an atom were removed, an *L* electron would be attracted toward the nucleus in very much the same way as the single electron of a hydrogen atom is attracted toward its nucleus, with two important differences. The attractive force is much greater for the *L* electron of a heavy element because of the large number of charges on the nucleus. Then the effect of the remaining *K* electron must be taken into consideration.

Since the remaining *K* electron is much nearer the nucleus than the *L* electron, in part it exerts a screening effect reducing the attraction of the nucleus for the *L* electron. This screening effect may be described in terms of reduction of the effective nuclear charge, and if the number of nuclear charges of the atom is *Ze* the effective charge on the nucleus, as far as the *L* electron is concerned, then becomes approximately $(Z - 1)e$. Putting this into the Bohr equation (Eq. 8-18*a*), and remembering that when an *L* electron falls into a *K* orbit the quantum number *n* changes from 2 to 1, we find that the wave number of a K_α line of an element of atomic number Z should be

$$\nu = R(Z - 1)^2 \left(\frac{1}{1^2} - \frac{1}{2^2}\right) \qquad [9\text{-}10]$$

This can be rewritten, if the constants are replaced by their numerical value, as

$$\nu = 8.23 \times 10^4 \, (Z - 1)^2 \qquad [9\text{-}11]$$

From this it is seen that the Bohr theory predicts that the square roots of the frequencies or wave numbers are proportional to $(Z - 1)$. Moseley's graph (Fig. 9-11) demonstrated this relationship, and the agreement between theory and observed values is surprisingly good. For other lines in the K series and for the lines of other series the simple Bohr theory does not so directly apply, but a simple relationship between spectra remains.

The most important conclusion emerging from this and related work is that the atoms of successive elements of the periodic table belong to a series representing integral increases in the positive electronic charge on the nucleus. This, of course, also means increasing numbers of electrons surrounding the nucleus for all neutral atoms. The study which Rutherford made of the scattering of alpha particles (§ 8-3) led to the idea that the charge on each nucleus was at least of the order of magnitude of its number in the series of atoms, starting with hydrogen as 1, and further confirmation was obtained by Chadwick (1920). With Moseley's work the growing weight of evidence indicated that the simplest and lightest atom, that of hydrogen, must have 1 positive electronic charge on its nucleus, and that all the elements could be arranged in the regular order of increasing number of charges on the nucleus from hydrogen 1, helium 2, lithium 3, up to the heaviest known natural atom, uranium, having 92.

Thus developed what is known as the **atomic number series** of the elements. The series has now been extended by the "man-made" elements to over 100 (Appendix 4). This arrangement of the elements in the atomic number series cleared up several contradictions which appeared when the atoms were put in the order of their atomic weights in the periodic table of the elements, and it became apparent that atomic number was something more fundamental than mass or weight.

9-13. X-ray Absorption Spectra

X-ray spectra, like optical spectra, may be studied either by examining emission lines or by examining the lines absorbed from a continuous background. It has been previously indicated that x-ray absorption in any material follows a logarithmic decay curve, the intensity of the beam decreasing logarithmically as the thickness of the absorber increases. It is now possible to say more about just what causes absorption. Generally, any process by which energy is removed from an x-ray beam causes what we think of as absorption. Energy may be removed from a beam by the general process of scattering of radiation; it may be removed by x-ray photons losing energy in collision with electrons

(Compton effect); or an x-ray photon may be absorbed by an atom producing a photoelectric ejection of an electron from the atom. It is the latter process which we now wish to consider.

When the absorption of any element is measured at different frequencies of the incident x-ray beam, sudden increases of absorption are noted as the frequency of the incident x-ray is increased. The sudden increase in absorption is the result of photoelectric dislodgment of L or K or other electrons from the atom, and it is represented by sudden increases in the absorption coefficient, as shown on the curve of Fig. 9-12. These points of sharp increase in absorption are called **absorption edges.** The experiment may be done by measuring with an ionization chamber or other detecting device the intensity of the x-rays that pass through a layer of absorber at different frequencies. By means of a crystal spectrograph of the Bragg type any particular frequency may be selected from the continuous spectrum produced by an x-ray tube, and if necessary the spectrum may be pushed to higher limits by an increase in the voltage applied to the x-ray tube.

It will be noticed, for instance, that in the curve representing the absorption by platinum, as the wavelength is decreased (or as the frequency is increased) three absorption edges represented at L_3, L_2, L_1 appear. Then as the frequency is further increased the rays become more penetrating, and the absorption drops to a low level until another sudden increase occurs representing the ejection of K electrons.

The three peaks marked L_1, L_2, L_3 represent successive ejections of

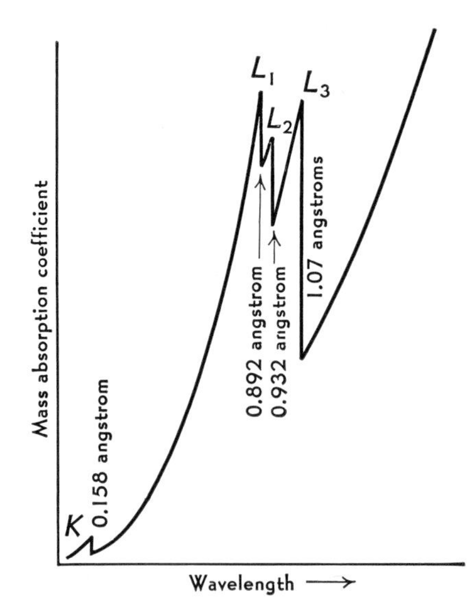

Fig. 9-12. X-ray absorption curve for platinum, showing "edges" where marked absorption begins.

L electrons of slightly different energies, and the fact that there are three absorption edges for L electrons, whereas there is only one for K electrons, indicates that in the K shell there is one energy level whereas in the L shell there are three energy levels. Experimental studies show that for M electrons similarly there are five absorption edges and consequently five energy levels.

At first it might seem that in the L shell there are only two kinds of electrons, s-electrons and p-electrons; however, of the eight electrons in an L shell there are four different possible combinations of quantum numbers l and s to give three different j values.

$$\left.\begin{array}{ll} l = 0 & s = -\frac{1}{2} \\ l = 0 & s = +\frac{1}{2} \end{array}\right\} \quad L_1 \text{ level}$$

$$l = 1 \quad s = -\tfrac{1}{2}\} \quad L_2 \text{ level}$$

$$l = 1 \quad s = +\tfrac{1}{2}\} \quad L_3 \text{ level}$$

However, according to the concept that, when $l = 0$, there is no net orbital angular momentum, the two different values of s associated with $l = 0$ do not represent two different energy levels but only one. Consequently this one level with the two different levels when $l = 1$ gives three energy levels L_1, L_2, and L_3, thus explaining the three absorption edges in the L shell. The five edges for the M shell may be similarly explained.

In the region of the x-ray spectrum between the groups of levels represented by the absorption edges it will be noticed from Fig. 9-12 that, with increasing frequency (to the left in the figure), the absorption coefficient decreases rapidly, approximately as the inverse cube of the frequency. Penetration, in other words, increases as the cube of the frequency over a considerable range.

PROBLEMS

1. Which two series of the alkali metals approach the same series limit? Why?

2. Which electrons s, p, d, or f would have the more elliptic orbits and might be expected to penetrate other shells? Which of these would be more uniformly screened from the nucleus by the inner electrons? For which would the quantum defect be larger?

3. Draw energy levels for the Zeeman effect and show the transitions that are possible for the levels and splitting described in the text.

4. How may the simple Zeeman effect be explained by classical electrical theory? (Refer to other books to check your hypothesis.)

5. Compute the wavelength of the K_a line of carbon with the aid of Table 9-4.

6. Compute the wavelength of the K_a line of gold with the aid of Table 9-4.

SUGGESTED READING

M. Born, *Atomic Physics,* 5th ed. (New York, Steckert-Haffner, 1951).
H. Semat, *Introduction to Atomic and Nuclear Physics,* 3rd ed. (New York, Rinehart, 1954).
F. K. Richtmyer, E. H. Kennard, and T. Lauritsen, *Introduction to Modern Physics,* 5th ed. (New York, McGraw-Hill, 1955).
G. Herzberg, *Atomic Spectra and Atomic Structure,* 2nd ed. (New York, Dover Publications, 1944).
H. E. White, *Introduction to Atomic Spectra* (New York, McGraw-Hill, 1935).

CHAPTER 10

WAVE MECHANICS

10-1. Introduction

In the realm of common phenomena the behavior of a particle can be adequately described in terms of Newtonian mechanics, but in the atomic realm where particles are found to have a wave-like character as well this description is inadequate. The problem of how to describe the behavior of a particle in terms of its wave-like character was greatly clarified by Erwin Schrödinger, when he proposed his now famous wave-mechanical differential equation in 1926. This equation was based on de Broglie's work on the wavelength of a moving particle. The previous year Heisenberg had developed a method involving matrix algebra. Later the two mathematical methods of approach were proved to be equivalent. Additions to the theory by Born, Jordan, and Dirac brought it to a high degree of development, and it has proved more successful than any other theory in dealing with atomic and subatomic phenomena.

10-2. De Broglie Waves and the Bohr Atom

When Bohr derived his successful equation for the hydrogen atom, the possible stable or nonradiating orbits for the electron were obtained by quantizing the angular momentum and assigning to each orbit an integral number of the fundamental unit $h/2\pi$. Bohr, of course, knew nothing at that time of the wave character of the electron, which was to be discovered more than a decade later, and de Broglie was the first to recognize a possible connection between the wave character (§ 6-3) of the electron and the quantization of the Bohr orbits.

According to the wave picture it should be possible to describe the orbit of an electron, moving around the nucleus of a hydrogen atom, in terms of its associated wavelength. De Broglie approached the matter from the viewpoint of selecting orbits that would be stable on the basis of the wave picture. Instead of the number n specifying, as in Bohr's work, the number of units of angular momentum in an orbit of quan-

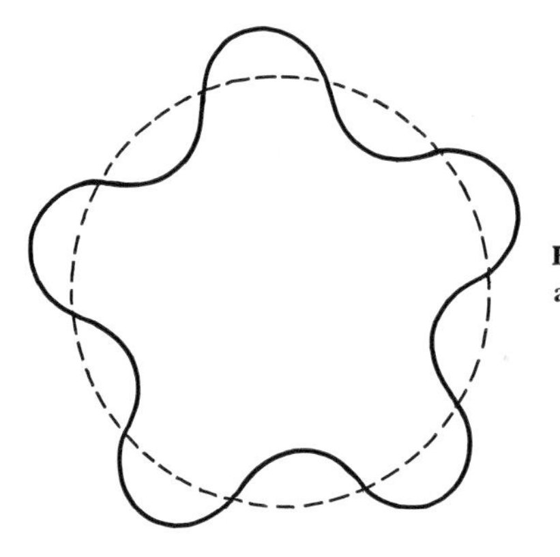

Fig. 10-1. The orbit for $n = 5$ in hydrogen, according to the de Broglie wave concept.

tum number n, de Broglie found that n could be used to specify the number of whole wavelengths of the electron in a complete circumference of the orbit (Fig. 10-1). From this viewpoint it would appear that a stable orbit is formed only if it contains an integral number of wavelengths or, in other words, if a kind of repeatable wave pattern is formed.

If n is the number of whole wavelengths λ in the circumference of an electron orbit, the circumference is

$$2\pi r = n\lambda \qquad [10\text{-}1]$$

From de Broglie's equation for the wavelength λ of an electron of momentum mv (Eq. 6-12)

$$\lambda = \frac{h}{mv}$$

Consequently

$$2\pi r = \frac{nh}{mv} \qquad [10\text{-}2]$$

Rearranging this explicitly for the angular momentum mvr

$$mvr = n\frac{h}{2\pi} \qquad [10\text{-}3]$$

But this is exactly the condition imposed by Bohr for the quantization of the angular momentum of the electron where the angular momentum mvr in an orbit of radius r must be an integral number n times the fundamental unit $h/2\pi$. The two methods of Bohr and de Broglie are thus seen to be equivalent.

Since, in Fig. 10-1, there are five whole wavelengths represented this would be the orbit of total quantum number 5. Following through on this, the first orbit should have only one wavelength, but that is more difficult to picture. Nevertheless, de Broglie was able, by means of the wave concept of the electron, to arrive at exactly the same sequence of orbits as had been arrived at by Bohr on the basis of the particle picture of the electron.

10-3. The Schrödinger Wave Equation*

The Schrödinger equation is the fundamental equation in the historical development of wave mechanics. It in turn goes back to the familiar equation of wave motion of classical physics.

$$\frac{\partial^2 A}{\partial x^2} + \frac{\partial^2 A}{\partial y^2} + \frac{\partial^2 A}{\partial z^2} = \frac{1}{u^2}\frac{\partial^2 A}{\partial t^2} \qquad [10\text{-}4]$$

This is often written in operator form as

$$\nabla^2 A = \frac{1}{u^2}\frac{\partial^2 A}{\partial t^2} \qquad [10\text{-}5]$$

where ∇^2 represents the operator

$$\nabla^2 = \frac{\partial^2}{\partial x^2} + \frac{\partial^2}{\partial y^2} + \frac{\partial^2}{\partial z^2}$$

* Optional.

In this equation A is the displacement of the wave and is a function of x, y, z, and t, and u is the velocity of the wave. The equation could represent a mechanical wave, or it could represent the electric or magnetic components of an electromagnetic wave. In the case of a wave in a string, moving only in the x direction, the equation reduces to

$$\frac{\partial^2 A}{\partial x^2} = \frac{1}{u^2}\frac{\partial^2 A}{\partial t^2} \qquad [10\text{-}5a]$$

where the displacement A is a function of x and t.

The Schrödinger equation is closely related to the classical wave equation but goes much further. It includes not only the ideas of the classical wave equation but also the de Broglie wavelength of a particle $\lambda = h/mv$, which itself includes the fundamental constant h of the quantum theory. Consequently the appropriateness of the name *wave mechanics* is evident. For simplicity in deriving the Schrödinger equation, we shall start with the well-known wave equation of classical physics, but we shall write the quantity ψ for the displacement, in view of its common usage. We then have

$$\frac{\partial^2 \psi}{\partial x^2} + \frac{\partial^2 \psi}{\partial y^2} + \frac{\partial^2 \psi}{\partial z^2} = \frac{1}{u^2}\frac{\partial^2 \psi}{\partial t^2} \qquad [10\text{-}6]$$

A simple solution of this equation is well known to be

$$\psi = a \sin \omega t \qquad [10\text{-}7]$$

where a is the amplitude of a sine wave. Then the second derivative of ψ with respect to t is

$$\frac{\partial^2 \psi}{\partial t^2} = -\omega^2 a \sin \omega t = -\omega^2 \psi \qquad [10\text{-}8]$$

Putting this into Eq. 10-6 and dropping terms in y and z, since it is simpler to consider a wave moving in the x direction only, we have

$$\frac{d^2 \psi}{dx^2} + \frac{\omega^2 \psi}{u^2} = 0 \qquad [10\text{-}9]$$

In this equation ω is the usual symbol for angular velocity, and

$$\omega = 2\pi f = 2\pi \frac{u}{\lambda}$$

Substituting this value of ω in Eq. 10-9

$$\frac{d^2\psi}{dx^2} + \frac{4\pi^2\psi}{\lambda^2} = 0 \qquad [10\text{-}10]$$

If we now interpret λ not as the wavelength of a classical wave but as the de Broglie wavelength of a particle of mass m, moving with velocity v, we have $\lambda = h/mv$. By classical mechanics the momentum mv of a particle moving with velocity v may be written

$$mv = \sqrt{2m\,(E - V)} \qquad [10\text{-}11]$$

where E is the total energy, kinetic plus potential, and V is the potential energy. Substituting these values in Eq. 10-10 we arrive at the Schrödinger wave equation for wave velocity in the x direction only:

$$\frac{d^2\psi}{dx^2} + \frac{8\pi^2 m}{h^2}\,(E - V)\psi = 0 \qquad [10\text{-}12]$$

For a wave front in three dimensions it would be

$$\left(\frac{\partial^2\psi}{\partial x^2} + \frac{\partial^2\psi}{\partial y^2} + \frac{\partial^2\psi}{\partial z^2}\right) + \frac{8\pi^2 m}{h^2}\,(E - V)\psi = 0 \qquad [10\text{-}13]$$

10-4. Born's Interpretation of ψ

The quantity ψ had at first little physical significance except that it was spoken of as the wave displacement. Since the electron was chiefly described by the wavelength, the wave displacement seemed a more or less indefinite if not superfluous quantity. However, a brilliant suggestion was made by Born in 1926 by which the quantity ψ^2, the square of the wave displacement, was given a most important physical interpretation.

Born suggested that the wave equation applies not so much to a single particle such as an electron as it does to a very large number. He then took the value of ψ^2 to represent the probability of finding electrons in a given region, that is, as representing the electron density. This is in direct analogy with an electromagnetic wave in which the square of E, the electric field strength in the wave (or of H, the magnetic field strength), determines the energy density of the wave. For these reasons ψ^2 has been called the **probability density,** and ψ has been called the **probability amplitude.**

The use of the wave function to obtain a probability distribution has its direct counterpart in physical optics. Photons are the quantized units of radiant energy, and quantum descriptions should apply equally to them. That they do is evident if one considers a diffraction pattern formed by light. According to classical wave theory, a smooth distribution curve representing bright and dark regions is obtained. However, according to quantum theory, this curve may equally well be interpreted as representing the density distribution of photons making up the light beam.

Instead of ψ^2 the probability density is often written $\psi\psi^*$ in more advanced work, since ψ itself may be a complex quantity and ψ^* is its complex conjugate, but for our purposes ψ^2 may be taken to be equivalent to $\psi\psi^*$.

There are two ways of using the quantity ψ. If ψ is taken to refer to a single electron instead of a large number, ψ^2 is no longer the electron density but is interpreted as representing the probability of finding that electron in a given region. Numerical values must then be adjusted so that, by integrating the probability of finding any one electron throughout all available space, the answer is unity. The adjustment of the numerical values so that the integral is unity is called **normalization.** It imposes upon the electron the condition that it cannot be in more than one place at any instant and that it must be somewhere since a probability of 1 represents certainty.

As we shall see later in this chapter, the Born interpretation of ψ^2 leads to a new wave-mechanical method of determining the "radius" of the normal hydrogen atom and to a new viewpoint regarding the position of the electron in the atom.

10-5. Quantized Particle in an Impenetrable Box

The idea that an atomic or subatomic particle is to be described in terms of its de Broglie wavelength brings about many interesting changes of viewpoint. For instance, a particle moving about in a box with impenetrable walls would bounce back and forth very much like a molecule of gas in a room. From the classical viewpoint, such a particle could have any particular momentum since there would be no restrictions on the momentum or on the energy, but once we bring the wave description of the particle into the problem, we introduce restrictions.

Consider first the solution of the problem by a simple application of de Broglie waves, and assume that a particle is moving back and forth in the x direction with uniform velocity v in a box of small dimensions with impenetrable walls. According to the de Broglie formula, the particle has a wavelength $\lambda = h/mv$, depending on its mass and velocity. Since the box is assumed to be impenetrable the probability of finding the particle beyond the surface of the wall is zero, and the amplitude of the wave on which the probability depends must drop to zero at the walls. For a particle to set up a stationary wave pattern in such a box, representing continual motion back and forth between opposite sides, it appears that the only possible stationary wave patterns for which the displacement falls to zero at the boundaries of the box are exactly those of a vibrating string fixed at the ends. The various modes of vibration form a series in which the length of the string is an integral number of half wavelengths. Consequently, the various simple wave patterns for a particle are those for which the various possible wavelengths (Fig. 10-2) are

$$\lambda = \frac{2d}{n} \qquad [10\text{-}14]$$

where d is the width of the box and n may have any integral value from 1 to ∞.

From the above it appears that for the particle moving back and forth in the box only those momenta are possible for which the de Broglie wavelengths are given by Eq. 10-14. This introduces a new concept into the question of the motion of a particle. Previously there had been no thought of quantizing linear motion, but, in the example given, momentum is quantized, and likewise only particular discrete states of kinetic energy are possible for such a particle.

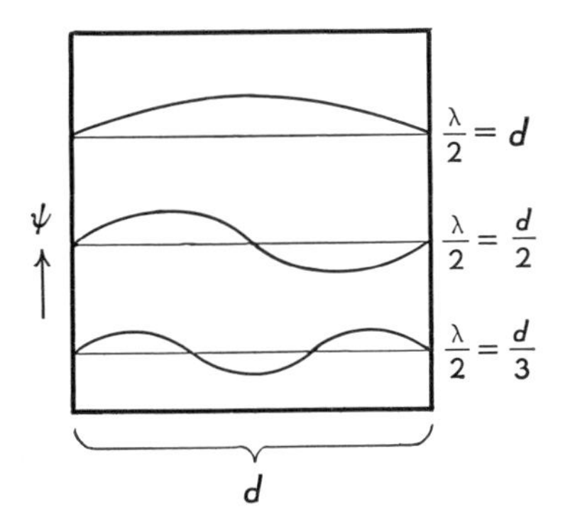

Fig. 10-2. Possible de Broglie wavelengths of amplitude ψ in an impenetrable box of side d, same as possible modes of vibration of a stretched string.

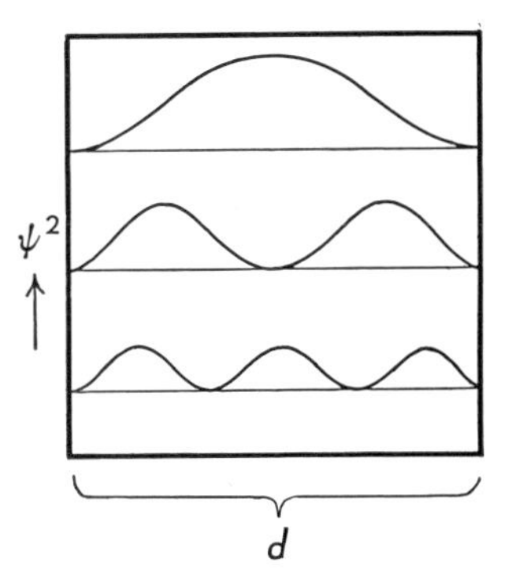

Fig. 10-3. Probability (ψ^2) curves for the wavelengths of Fig. 10-2. Unlike the ψ curve, the values of ψ^2 are always positive.

There is a very good reason why with the objects of everyday life such quantization is not noticed. If we should try to apply the idea to the motion of a macroscopic particle as small as a just barely visible particle of dust, which of course is enormously more massive than an atomic particle, we would find that unless this particle were given an unreasonably small velocity the wavelength would be so small that no effects of quantization of motion would be noticeable. A similar conclusion is reached in trying to apply the wave equation to the enormous number of individual atoms of the dust particle. The result would be very much the same as if the individual waves averaged out to approximately zero for the whole group, and we are justified in saying that, as we leave the atomic realm and approach the realm of ordinary events, quantum concepts lose themselves by merging into classical concepts. This merging of quantum concepts into the classical concepts of everyday life was expressed by Bohr in his **principle of correspondence.**

The question of where a quantized particle is most likely to be found at a given moment, although not of particular interest in the idealized example of the impenetrable box, is of much interest when the atom is discussed from the wave-mechanical viewpoint. According to Born, the square of the wave function, that is, the square of the displacement term ψ at a given position gives the relative probability of finding the particle at that position. The curves of Fig. 10-2 represent the values of ψ, and the curves of Fig. 10-3 represent values of ψ^2. The result is apparently quite different from that of classical mechanics. From the classical viewpoint, since the particle moves with constant velocity, it spends equal times in equal spaces along its path, and the probability of finding it along its path is constant. From the wave picture, although by the artificially imposed conditions the probability must drop to zero at the sides of an impenetrable box, we may be surprised to find that for the higher energy states the probability curve drops to zero at points between. This need not disturb us unduly since the conditions of the experiment are highly artificial, and in this example the wave serves chiefly to introduce quantization of momenta. Besides, the standing wave pattern in the box may be thought of as composed of two oppositely directed "running" waves of sharply defined wavelength $\lambda = h/mv$, and as previously noted (§ 6-7) such a wave train of uniform amplitude does not serve to locate an electron at all.

However, in most problems it is necessary to adopt the wave-mechanical methods based on the application of the Schrödinger equation rather than the simple de Broglie wave formula alone. Then the situation may be quite different. If the amplitudes of the different loops of the wave vary along the wave pattern as, for instance, in a wave group or wave packet, the probability of finding the electron is evidently a maximum where the amplitude is a maximum. With the aid of the Schrödinger equation still another and even more important result appears. Boundaries which would be impenetrable according to classical physics become penetrable to some degree at least, and the resulting predictions regarding atomic phenomena are in agreement with observations. For an introduction to these matters, let us consider the application of the Schrödinger equation to a simple harmonic oscillator.

10-6. Simple Harmonic Linear Oscillator

An ideal, simple harmonic oscillator is approximated by a ball vibrating at the end of a spring or by a pendulum swinging back and forth with not too large amplitude. By definition the motion is simple harmonic if the restoring force is proportional at each instant to the displacement from the center of path. The velocity of such an object is a maximum at its center of path. Consequently, from the classical viewpoint the probability in any small time interval of finding the body at its center of path is a minimum, and such an oscillator spends more of its time near the ends of its path than at any other points.

The probability of finding the oscillator at a given point in its path according to classical theory is represented by the curve *ABC* in Fig. 10-4. Just at the end of its path where the velocity has dropped momentarily to zero and is in the process of reversing direction, the probability curve goes off to infinity. This represents a defect in the mathematical description since all aspects of the motion are finite. Such defects in the mathematical description of nature are not uncommon, and it might be considered surprising that natural phenomena submit to mathematical description as well as they do. Defects may sometimes occur in wave-mechanical descriptions, but it is well to remember that classical descriptions are not always free of them. Let us now imagine an atomic particle moving back and forth with simple harmonic motion under the action of a central force. No longer do we have free motion of the particle up to a sharply defined barrier, described as a potential energy barrier, which rises discontinuously to its full value at a given distance. A particle surrounded by such a barrier is said to be in a **rectangular potential well,** and the potential barrier may be represented graphically by a vertical wall. The harmonic oscillator, on the other hand, may be described as being in a **parabolic potential well.**

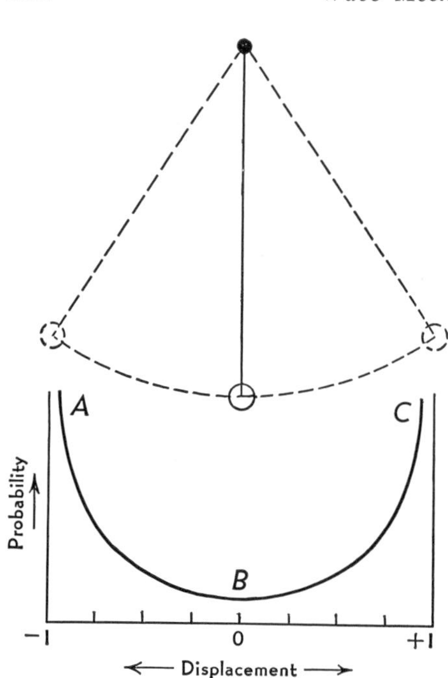

Fig. 10-4. Curve *ABC* represents probability of finding oscillating particle at points along its path according to classical physics. Amplitude is assumed so small that oscillations are essentially linear and harmonic.

In solving atomic problems by the methods of wave mechanics still other types of potential wells may be assumed for special purposes.

To see that the simple harmonic oscillator may be described as being in a parabolic potential well, consider the work done in displacing the oscillator a distance x. Just as with a stretched spring, the average force is $kx/2$, and the work is $kx^2/2$, where k is the force per unit stretch of the spring or per unit displacement of the oscillator. The energy required for the oscillator to reach a distance x from the center of attraction, or in other words to "climb" the barrier for that distance, is proportional to the square of the distance; thus we may describe the oscillator as being in a potential well the walls of which rise parabolically with increased distance.

To apply the Schrödinger equation (Eq. 10-12) to the problem of the linear oscillator it is first necessary to substitute for V, the potential energy, the particular value $\frac{1}{2}kx^2$, representing this oscillator. The solution of the resulting equation is too involved for inclusion here, but the consequences are of great interest. They show that the simple harmonic linear oscillator, according to wave mechanics, is a quantized oscillator whereas the classical oscillator is not. Therefore it can have only certain discrete amounts of energy, and only certain wave patterns will fit into its length of path, just as only particular wave patterns could be fitted into the box of the previous section. That the present wave patterns do not fall to zero at the end of the path but "tail off" gradually indicates a definite, though frequently small, probability that the oscillating particle may be found beyond the classical limit. The explanation of this with a simpler type of barrier will be given in the next section. The wave-mechanical solution of the problem then differs from the classical solution in that it leads to three important and different results: the quantization of the oscillator, a different method of locating the oscillator, and the probability that the oscillator may be found beyond the classical limit.

The probability of finding the linear oscillator at different positions of its path is again accepted as being represented by ψ^2. For such a quantized harmonic oscillator the ψ^2 probability curve is, as before, a series of peaks depending upon the wave pattern, one for the first possible energy state, two peaks for the second, and so on. Just as with a classical oscillator, we would expect the probability of finding the particle to be greater toward the ends of the path, and this is seen to be true for the higher energy states where there are enough peaks of the curve to establish a trend (Fig. 10-5). Again, as in Fig. 10-3, the minima of the curve need not necessarily be interpreted as forbidden positions unless such interpretation serves a useful purpose, and the

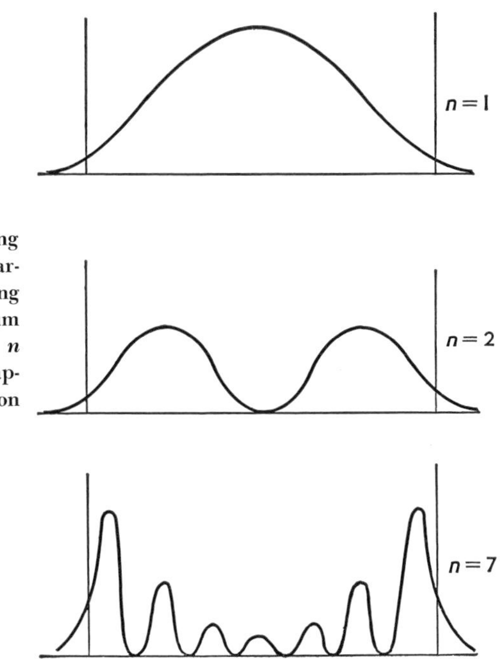

Fig. 10-5. Curves representing probability of finding linear harmonic oscillator at points along its path according to quantum mechanics. For high values of *n* the average of the curve approaches the classical distribution of Fig. 10-4.

average value of the curve may be more meaningful since it approaches the classical probability curve for the higher energy states.

10-7. Reflection at a Barrier and the Penetrable Barrier

Solutions of problems reached by wave-mechanical methods and by classical methods have many striking differences. An important example is that of what happens to a moving electron (or other electrically charged particle) approaching a region of reverse electric field. Such a field is best described in terms of its potential distribution and is called a potential barrier.

According to classical electrical theory, the electron approaching such a barrier will either pass the barrier or be turned back, depending on whether its energy is greater than the reverse potential difference of the field or less than it (Fig. 10-6). A 90-volt electron approaching a

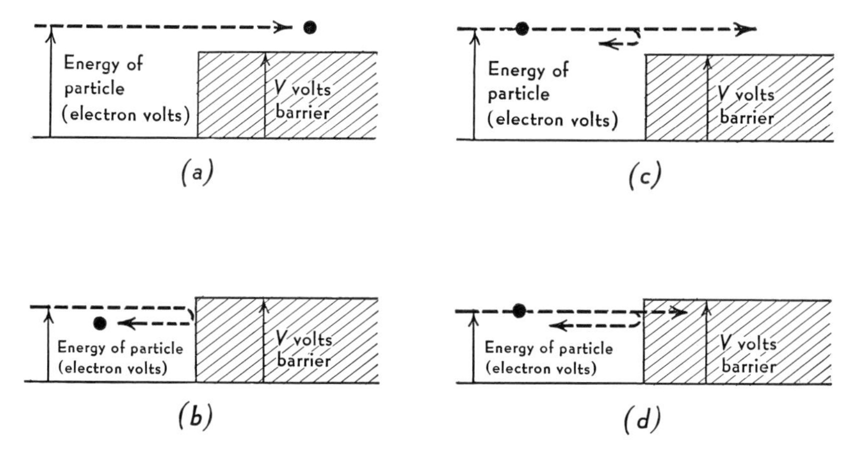

Fig. 10-6. ***a*, Total transmission; *b*, total reflection of electrons according to classical theory; *c*, partial transmission (some probability of reflection); *d*, partial reflection (some probability of transmission) according to wave mechanics.**

100-volt barrier can never pass it according to classical theory, and a 110-volt electron will always pass it. In the latter case the electron is said to surmount the barrier. In classical theory there is no such thing as penetration of a barrier.

According to wave-mechanical analysis the results are quite different. Without going into the solution of the Schrödinger equation for these two examples, we shall confine ourselves to the brief assertion that the equation clearly predicts that some electrons with sufficient energy to surmount the barrier may suffer reflection and that some with insufficient energy to overcome the barrier may penetrate the boundary of the barrier (Fig. 10-5). If the barrier is infinitely wide, those which penetrate will eventually be turned back, but if the barrier is of finite width there will always be some probability that the electron or other particle will penetrate the whole barrier region and escape completely. Partial reflection (and transmission) at the face of a barrier, according to the wave picture, has a close analogy in ordinary optics where partial reflection (and transmission) always occurs when light is incident upon the boundary between two different media. These findings have important applications in nuclear physics.

When electrically charged particles are bounded by actual electric fields the ideal model of an impenetrable barrier usually does not apply, and the barrier becomes a penetrable one. It is in this situation that wave mechanics has scored one of its most important triumphs. Consider an electrically charged particle moving back and forth in a confined region or "box" bounded by an electric field. The walls become a potential barrier. In the region inside the "walls," that is, between the barriers, the potential energy V of the particle is less than the total energy E, and the Schrödinger equation may then be written

$$\frac{d^2\psi}{dx^2} = -k^2\psi \qquad [10\text{-}15]$$

where

$$k^2 = \frac{8\pi^2 m}{h^2}(E - V) \qquad [10\text{-}16]$$

This is the familiar equation of a sine or cosine wave function, and in its simplest form the solution for the sine term may be written

$$\psi = \psi \sin kx$$

If the electric field is continuous over the surface of the wall, and if the potential barrier is infinitely high and infinitely thick at each point, there is no way in which the particle can completely escape from its confinement. If it passes the boundary of the barrier it is continually pushed back and must at some time return.

If the barrier is not infinitely high a particle with sufficient energy may escape by surmounting it, or if the barrier is not infinitely thick the particle may occasionally pass completely through the barrier and keep on going. Since it is quite possible that in the atomic world not all barriers are constant and continuous there may be other unknown possibilities of penetration, but wave mechanics seems to take care of most possibilities. In any event the probability of such penetration is of great importance. The question now arises as to what happens to the solution of the Schrödinger wave equation if the quantity V in Eq. 10-16 is larger in magnitude than E. In such a case the sign of the right-hand term is reversed, and the equation becomes

$$\frac{d^2\psi}{dx^2} = +k^2\psi \qquad [10\text{-}17]$$

The solution of this equation is well known, and the useful part takes the form

$$\psi = \psi\epsilon^{-kx} \qquad [10\text{-}18]$$

showing that ψ is represented by a decreasing exponential curve.

It becomes evident, if we assume a particle moving back and forth between the walls which we now call potential barriers, that a solution may be obtained for the wave equation involving not only the region between the barriers but also the region beyond where the barrier begins. Obviously the standing wave patterns given in Fig. 10-2 apply only to an impenetrable barrier, and only for such a barrier does the wave function drop to zero at the surface of the barrier, but if the barrier is not impenetrable there must be some probability of finding an electron at or beyond the surface of the barrier, as indicated by the logarithmic decay curve which represents the solution beyond the face of the barrier.

We now have a mathematical problem in which there are two kinds of solutions of the Schrödinger equation, one kind showing a simple sine wave pattern inside the barrier, the other kind showing a logarithmic decay curve outside the barrier. Physical intuition tells us that for a complete solution involving the space both inside and outside the barrier these curves must be continuous. This is no more than partial fulfillment of the familiar condition for mathematical functions, when applied to physical quantities, that they be single-valued, finite, and continuous. To avoid mathematical intricacies we may fulfill all these conditions by doing a job of patchwork in putting the two curves together graphically, so that where they join at the barrier they both have the same value and the same slope. This is represented in Fig. 10-7. Here we have fitted the two curves together, thus giving us a ψ graph from which a ψ^2 graph may be obtained showing the probability of finding the electron (or other subatomic particle) at any position in the "box" or outside.

As before, the probability distribution inside the barrier is represented by the square of the ψ values of the wave patterns that fit into the "box." Outside the "box," however, the value of ψ drops off logarithmically, and the ψ^2 curve representing the probability drops off similarly. Although mathematically the curve does not reach zero until an infinite distance, practically the value becomes too small to be appreciable within a fairly short distance.

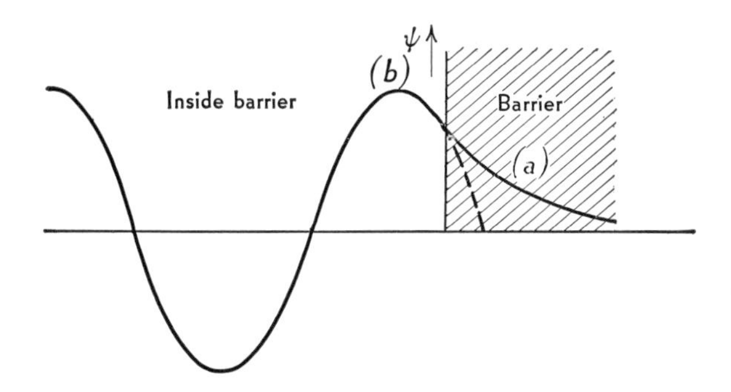

Fig. 10-7. Exponential curve: *a*, fitted to wave function ψ; *b*, inside barrier.

The case of penetration of a narrow finite barrier is represented by Fig. 10-8. Here, for instance, a few electrons from a beam may completely penetrate the barrier. When an electron emerges on the other side its velocity is less, as represented by an increased de Broglie wavelength, and the probability of finding such an electron outside the barrier is also less than inside since the amplitude ψ (and consequently ψ^2) is less outside.

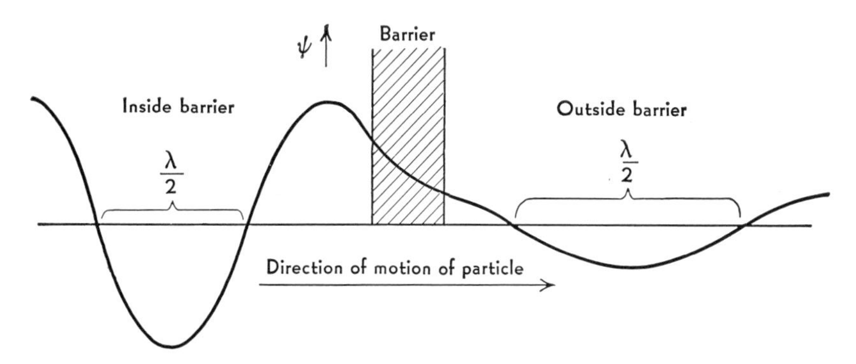

Fig. 10-8. Penetration of a barrier of limited extent by a particle, according to wave mechanics.

10-8. Application of the Schrödinger Equation to the Hydrogen Atom

One of the great values of the Schrödinger equation lies in the fact that it may be applied to atoms heavier than hydrogen and with more electrons than in hydrogen. It is at exactly this point that the Bohr-Sommerfeld theory failed completely. Before discussing the application of the Schrödinger equation to more complex atoms it is first desirable to see how successful it has been in describing the character of the hydrogen atom.

The only disposable quantities in the Schrödinger equation are the total energy E, and the potential energy V, the difference $(E - V)$ of course being the kinetic energy of the particle. In the hydrogen atom it is the potential energy that we may now specify for the electron in terms of the central field of force around the nucleus of the hydrogen atom. Putting into the Schrödinger equation the expression $-e^2/r$ for the potential energy of the electron in the hydrogen atom in terms of its distance r from the nucleus and the product of the charges of nucleus and electron, we have the Schrödinger equation in three dimensions in the following form:

$$\nabla^2\psi + \frac{8\pi^2 m}{h^2}\left(E + \frac{e^2}{r}\right)\psi = 0 \qquad [10\text{-}19]$$

This is a differential equation the solution of which is beyond the scope of this textbook, but those who are mathematically minded can find it in more advanced works. It does involve transforming the equation into spherical coordinates and then separating it into three equations, one for each of the usual spherical coordinates φ, θ, and r. These can be solved one at a time and a combined solution finally arrived at.

When this is done it is found that there are certain possible functions of each of the three variables which are solutions of the original Schrödinger equation. These are called characteristic functions or *eigenfunctions,* and each of them involves a constant which may take only integral values. The constant m, which we call the magnetic quantum number, is associated with the variable angle φ. The constant l, which we call the reduced azimuthal quantum number, is associated with the variable angle θ. The constant n is the total quantum number and is associated with the variable radius r. Thus the quantum numbers which were arrived at in the gradual development of the Bohr-Sommerfeld theory, including space quantization, are herewith arrived at in the solution of the Schrödinger equation. When numerical values are given to the constants the functions lead to particular values of the solution called *eigenvalues* or characteristic values.

We may now associate l with the k of the Bohr-Sommerfeld theory, with the provision that $l = k - 1$. This was done earlier in the description of the alkali metal spectra. From the solution of the Schrödinger equation we find that n can have any integral value from 1 to ∞; l can only have integral values from 0 to $n - 1$, and m can only have integral values from $-l$ to $+l$, including zero. These, together with the spin quantum number s, are just what are required to describe observed phenomena. That these quantum numbers should come with surprising mathematical elegance from the solution of the Schrödinger equation is strong evidence of the fundamental validity of the equation and its value in attacking atomic problems.

The Schrödinger equation as given does not involve the spinning electron directly, nor does it include anything of the viewpoint of relativity. Dirac introduced relativity into the basic theory and found equations which were still more complete, since they are invariant for the Lorentz transformation. These equations now included terms which could be identified as representing the spin of the electron, and a complete theory was established.

It is common to speak of the angular momentum quantum number l as if the angular momentum were l times the unit $h/2\pi$ where l takes only integral values. Actually, however, in the solution of the Schrödinger equation the quantity $\sqrt{l(l+1)}$ appears instead of just l, and its use is required by the theory instead of simply l as the multiplier by which the amount of angular momentum is determined. For convenience, however, it is common to speak of l as if it were to be used directly whereas when a computation is made it is actually $\sqrt{l(l+1)}$ which is needed. The same mathematical relationship is generally true of the other quantum numbers obtained by wave mechanics. For instance, when the quantum numbers s and j are indicated the actual values for computing energies are $\sqrt{s(s+1)}$ and $\sqrt{j(j+1)}$ where s and j, like l, can only take integral values. These are the values required by the solutions of the wave-mechanical equations if they are to have physical significance. They are the characteristic values or eigenvalues belonging to the more general characteristic functions or eigenfunctions.

The solution of the Schrödinger equation for hydrogen not only furnishes a valid set of quantum numbers and gives valuable information about quantized states in hydrogen, but it leads to exactly the same energy levels as did the simple Bohr theory. This is a great triumph for the new theory, but there remains the question of the location of an electron in a hydrogen atom.

If now, in the case of the hydrogen atom, we solve the equation for ψ and plot the value of ψ for different distances from the nucleus when $n = 1$ and $l = 0$ we obtain curve 1*a*, Fig. 10-9. When $n = 2$ and when $n = 3$, with $l = 0$, we obtain curves 2*a* and 3*a*. We cannot plot ψ^2 directly to get the probable space distribution around the nucleus according to Born's suggestion, since ψ^2 applies to equal volumes of space and the available space about the nucleus increases as the square

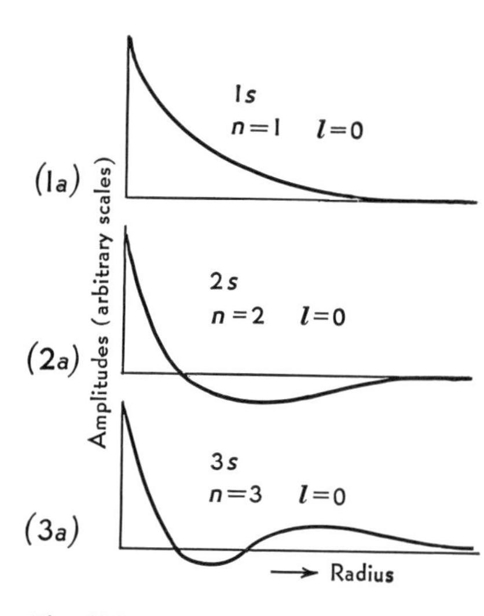

Fig. 10-9. Plots of ψ for variations of distance r from nucleus of hydrogen atom for different energy states.

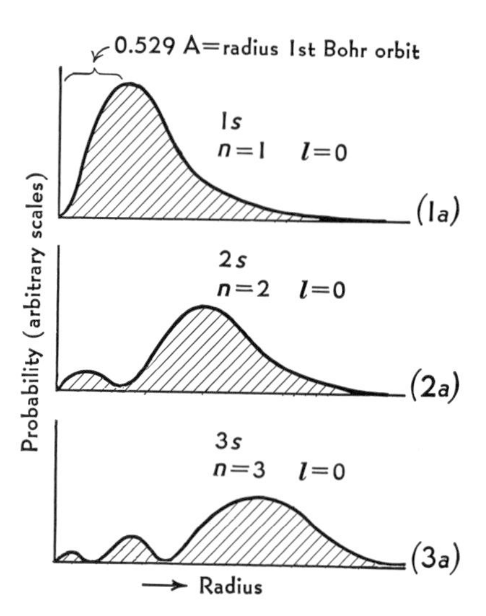

Fig. 10-10. Plots of radial probability $4\pi r^2\psi^2$ for variations of distance r from nucleus of hydrogen atom for same energy states as Fig. 10-9.

of the radius. In other words, for each unit distance from the nucleus, the volume of the shell of unit thickness increases as the area of the shell. To get the probability function we must multiply ψ^2 in its radial variation by $4\pi r^2$ and thus get the curves of Fig. 10-10, where 1*a*, 2*a*, and 3*a* represent the probable location of the electron in hydrogen for the states given. The maxima and minima of the curves now serve a useful function. At certain distances from the nucleus the probability of finding the electron is at a maximum, and at points between these maxima the probability falls to a minimum. These probability regions may be thought of as taking the place of the old-fashioned Bohr orbits. This is strikingly confirmed when we note that the distance from the nucleus to the top of the probability peak for $n = 1$ comes out the same as the radius of the first orbit obtained by Bohr's original method.

It may at first disturb the student that the electron in the hydrogen atom cannot always be pinned down to a particular orbit, sharply defined at any instant by a specific path each point of which is at a definite distance from the nucleus. However, the new concept is in harmony with the principle of indeterminacy. After all, the Bohr orbits were a little too sharply defined in light of the complementarity of the wave and particle aspects. It is not the distance of the electron from the nucleus or the orbital radius which is sharply defined; rather, the various energy states of the atom are sharply defined, as they need to be to account for the distinct frequencies of spectral lines. However, if energies are sharply defined, so also momenta will be, and momentum is conjugate to position. The more sharply the momentum is defined the less sharply is the position defined, and in the atom the ability to locate the electron is sacrificed in the interests of sharply defined spectral lines.

With the introduction of the new quantum theory Heisenberg insisted that all physical theories should be based only upon observable quantities, or at least quantities that are in principle observable, rather than upon more purely hypothetical quantities. For instance, we observe spectral lines and measure their frequencies. We do not observe the orbits of electrons. This is an example of the modern operational viewpoint in science, which holds that physical meaning comes from interpretation of the operations performed in measuring observable quantities. Every once in a while when scientific theories become cluttered with too many artificial concepts emphasis must be put on a return to reality, and the modern emphasis on "observables" in atomic theory represents such an intellectual "house cleaning."

10-9. Application to Complex Atoms

As has been seen, Schrödinger's equation can be applied very directly to hydrogen or, for that matter, to any hydrogenic-type atom, but for the more complex atoms the application is more difficult. For instance, the potential-energy function which was put into the Schrödinger equation for hydrogen was simply $V = -e^2/r$, but for helium, where there are two electrons, there are at least three terms, $-Ze^2/r_1$

for one electron, $-Ze^2/r_2$ for the second electron where $Z = 2$ for helium, and e^2/r_{12} for the interaction between the two electrons where r_{12} is their distance apart. Thus

$$V = -\frac{Ze^2}{r_1} - \frac{Ze^2}{r_2} + \frac{e^2}{r_{12}} \qquad [10\text{-}20]$$

Not only the number of charges on the nucleus and their effect on each electron but also the effect of each electron on every other electron must be considered. When there are many electrons this becomes an extremely complicated problem, for which even for helium there is no simple and direct solution. However, approximate solutions can be reached by several methods. When this is done for a heavy atom, and when ψ^2, the probability, is plotted for the total electron population, it is found to follow a curve such as is shown in Fig. 10-11. From this

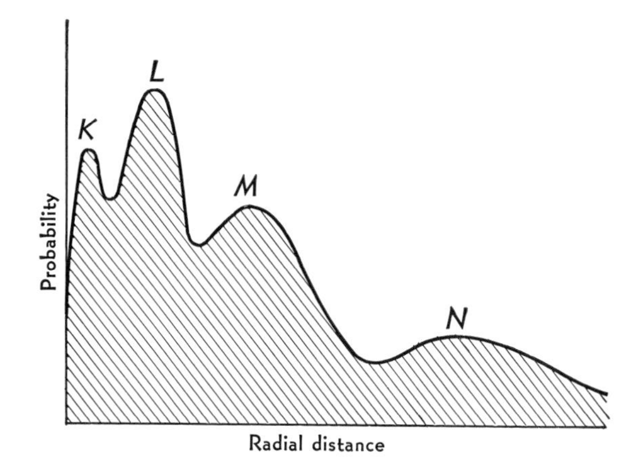

Fig. 10-11. Approximate radial electron population probability for a heavy atom, obtained by one of several wave-mechanical methods. The curve is the sum of all the separate curves for the individual electrons in the atom.

the average population density of the electrons around the nucleus is greatest in the immediate vicinity of the nucleus. The curve also shows definite maxima corresponding to *K*, *L*, *M*, and other electron shells after which it drops to a negligible value. Whereas the Schrödinger equation in solving the problems of complex atoms may not be the last word on the subject, it has proved through the method of approximation to be a useful tool, and the equation has made it possible to deal with complex atoms in a manner that the Bohr-Sommerfeld theory was completely incapable of doing.

10-10. Applications of Wave Mechanics

The applications of wave mechanics are of great importance in nuclear physics. Not only is the electron belonging to a hydrogen atom confined in a kind of potential box, but particles in the nucleus of an atom are surrounded by a very high potential barrier. This barrier may be surmounted by particles of sufficient energy, or it may be penetrated according to the laws of probability expressed by the Born interpretation of the Schrödinger equation.

Wave mechanics has been applied in the present chapter to atomic particles, but under certain conditions it can be applied to matter in bulk. It has been applied to the description of phenomena in gases where the particles are far enough apart so that they do not interfere particularly with one another. It has been applied to the "free" electrons in metals to explain metallic conduction, and it has been applied to crystals to explain phenomena of semiconductors. The many successes of the theory, some of which we will encounter in subsequent chapters, form an impressive array strongly favoring the validity of its basic relations.

SUGGESTED READING

M. Born, *Atomic Physics,* 5th ed. (New York, Steckert-Haffner, 1951).
F. K. Richtmyer, E. H. Kennard, and T. Lauritsen, *Introduction to Modern Physics,* 5th ed. (New York, McGraw-Hill, 1955).
R. W. Gurney, *Elementary Quantum Mechanics* (London, Cambridge Univ. Press, 1934).
W. Heitler, *Elementary Wave Mechanics* (Oxford, Clarendon Press, 1945).
S. Dushman, *The Elements of Quantum Mechanics* (New York, Wiley, 1938).

CHAPTER 11

MOLECULAR MOTIONS, QUANTA, AND SPECTRA

11-1. Picture of a Gas

Man has always tended to make his scientific concepts and theories as concrete as possible by means of pictures. Classical physics, which borrows its ideas directly from everyday life, was able to do this far better than can be done with the concepts of modern quantum physics many of which are not picturable. Although classical physics had great difficulty in the attempt to make a working model of an electric or magnetic field, it was at its best in the effort to picture a gas. Before the advent of the electrical theory of the atom, an atom in its simplest form was pictured as a perfectly elastic sphere. Molecules were two or more of these joined together in a dumbbell, or more extended, arrangement. Such models are still useful for some purposes, even though we now know that they far less directly represent the actual state of affairs.

Consider a gas composed of monatomic molecules (single atoms). Air, of course, is a mixture of gases mostly composed of diatomic molecules, such as oxygen (O_2) and nitrogen (N_2) and triatomic molecules of carbon dioxide (CO_2). A gas at 0° C and 76 cm of mercury pressure contains 27 billion billion (2.7×10^{19}) molecules per cubic centimeter. According to the kinetic theory of gases these molecules are moving randomly in all directions, incessantly colliding with one another and with the walls of any containing vessel. In order to explain the absence of any observable decrease in pressure as time goes on, the collisions are assumed to be perfectly elastic. Imagine that the dimensions of such a cubic centimeter of a monatomic gas are magnified a little more than a hundred million times. One cubic centimeter would then become a volume a thousand miles on a side. The molecules would be as large as ping-pong balls and on the same scale would be somewhat heavier. They would be, on the average, about 3 ft apart. Between collisions they would travel an average distance of about 300 ft, and there would be 4.5 billion collisions per second. A similarly magnified man living in such an atmosphere could walk through the cloud of "molecules," pushing them aside, perhaps not even realizing there was anything in the way.

Returning to the unmagnified dimensions of a normal gas, the actual diameters of air molecules are a few angstrom units ($1 \text{ A} = 10^{-8}$ cm). Their average distance apart is about 33 A, and their speeds are in the neighborhood of a quarter of a mile per second. Between collisions they travel an average distance (mean free path) of approximately a hundred-thousandth of a centimeter, and they make 4.5 billion collisions per second, just as in the enlarged model.

The enlarged mechanical model is of help in forming a rough picture of a gas, but it has many limitations. The atoms or molecules of a real gas are not tiny spheres with smooth surfaces. They are electrical systems in which the terms *surface* and *diameter* do not have the same definite connotation as in the everyday world. To treat atoms as spheres is only a rough approximation. We need to define carefully such terms as the diameter of an atom. For many purposes this may be taken to be the distance between centers of two similar atoms when they are at their distance of nearest approach. Thus we avoid talking about the "surface" of an atom. Nevertheless, even this definition may not be entirely precise and may not always agree with definitions based on other experimental procedures. The remarkable thing is that many experiments involving quite different operations give corroborating evidence of atomic and molecular sizes, numbers, and velocities and thus give to these entities a high degree of reality. Table 11-1 shows

TABLE 11-1. MOLECULAR DIAMETERS (CM)

Method	Hydrogen	Oxygen	Nitrogen	Carbon Dioxide
From viscosity	2.40×10^{-8}	2.98×10^{-8}	3.15×10^{-8}	3.34×10^{-8}
From Van der Waal's equation	2.34	2.92	3.15	3.12
From heat conductivity	2.32	—	3.53	3.40

how closely the experimentally determined diameters agree, though obtained by widely divergent sets of operations.

11-2. Pressure of a Gas

From the above simple mechanical model of an ideal gas based on what we may call the Newtonian atom, it is possible to develop a fairly adequate theory of gas pressure as being due to repeated collisions of gas molecules with one another and with the walls of the containing vessel. To do this we need do no more than apply Newton's laws of motion to these invisible particles, just as we would to objects of common experience. We shall find, however, that not all molecular phenomena can be dealt with so simply and that certain well-known phenomena cannot be described by classical theory but involve the quantum theory.

The successful application of classical Newtonian mechanics to the molecular realm, in the description of the simpler aspects of molecular motions and their effects, was an extension of the field of usefulness of these laws which could not have been wholly foreseen. (Neither could the failure to describe some of the less simple phenomena have been foreseen.) As an example of the successful use of these laws consider the derivation of the formula for the pressure of a gas in terms of molecular masses, velocities, and the number N per unit volume, where the pressure P is

$$P = \frac{1}{3} Nmv^2 \qquad [11\text{-}1]$$

The macroscopic gas law of Boyle states that, at constant temperature, pressures and volumes are inversely proportional.

$$\frac{P_1}{P_2} = \frac{V_2}{V_1} \qquad (T = \text{constant}) \qquad [11\text{-}2]$$

This law says nothing about the particles of the gas or their characteristics, whereas Eq. 11-1 does, since it gives the pressure in terms of the molecular quantities, mass, velocity, and number.

Imagine a box containing a gas at pressure P. Let the box have dimensions a, b, c (Fig. 11-1). The right-hand face of the box has an area ab. The volume is abc. Since the pressure is the same on all sides of the box we may assume that, on the average, one-third of all the molecules in the box are in effect moving along each of the three di-

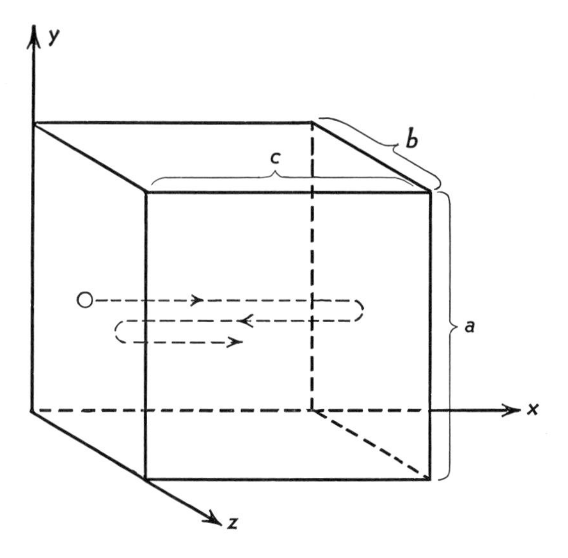

Fig. 11-1. Simplified diagram for deriving the formula for gas pressure.

mensions of the box. If there are N molecules per unit volume, the total number of molecules in the box is N times the volume abc, or

$$N(abc) = \text{total number of molecules in box}$$

$$\frac{N}{3}(abc) = \text{number moving along one dimension}$$

If m is the mass of a molecule and v is its velocity, by Newton's third law the momentum transferred to the side of the box when the molecule is stopped is mv, and upon elastic rebound from the wall with reversal of velocity a further amount of momentum mv ("back kick") is contributed to the wall making a total of $2mv$ per collision.

$$mv = \text{momentum of molecule}$$

$$2mv = \text{momentum given to wall per collision}$$

For simplicity we assume molecules to move back and forth between the sides of the box without collision, but if collisions are taken into account exactly the same formula is obtained. A molecule moving along the x axis of Fig. 11-1 would move back and forth once, or a distance of $2c$, for each collision with side ab. Consequently

$$\frac{v}{2c} = \text{number of collisions per sec per molecule with side } ab$$

Multiplying this by the number of molecules moving in this direction

$$\frac{N}{3}(abc)\frac{v}{2c} = \text{total number of collisions per sec with side } ab$$

Multiplying this by the momentum per collision

$$\frac{N}{3}(abc)\frac{v}{2c}(2mv) = \text{total momentum per sec given to side } ab$$

and this is the rate of change of momentum. However, by Newton's second law, rate of change of momentum is force, and consequently the force on side ab is

$$F = \frac{N}{3}mv^2(ab)$$

To get the pressure we divide by the area ab of the side of the box, and

$$P = \frac{N}{3}mv^2 \qquad [11\text{-}1]$$

in which either mks or cgs units may be used. Experimental tests show that this ideal formula is quite successful and that a real gas may often behave in a manner close to the ideal. However, this is by no means always true, and the formula involves certain simplifying assumptions that must be clearly recognized.

11-3. Simplifying Assumptions for an Ideal Gas

It is the normal scientific procedure in analyzing observed physical phenomena to abstract from them the most prominent features on which measurements can be made. The isolation of these features from a complex interrelationship commonly involves idealization if not over-simplification. The philosophical implications of such a process make an interesting study in themselves. The kinetic theory of gases is a typical example of a synthetic theory in which ideal characteristics are introduced as required and modified until a satisfactory description of observed phenomena is attained.

An ideal gas is one in which the molecules are assumed to be so small that they do not occupy appreciable volume. Collisions are assumed to be perfectly elastic. It is assumed that no forces of attraction or repulsion are exerted between molecules. Modifications of these assumptions must be made to adequately describe certain observed phenomena of real gases.

The assumption made in deriving Eq. 11-1 that all molecules have exactly the same speed is only an approximation for a real gas. There is no one speed for all molecules but rather a distribution of speeds. Although the same formula is arrived at if the distribution of speeds is taken into consideration, the speed v in the formula turns out to be the **root-mean-square (rms) speed,** that is, the individual speeds of the molecules are each squared, after which the average or mean of these squares is found and the square root is taken (see § 11-6).

11-4. Gas Laws

Boyle's law is the law of an ideal gas. At very high pressures and small volumes this law is inaccurate and for a real gas must be corrected as was done by Van der Waals in his equation

$$\left(P + \frac{a}{V^2}\right)(V - b) = RT \qquad [11\text{-}3]$$

It is not the total volume occupied by the gas that is compressed but the volume between the molecules $(V - b)$ where b is the volume of the molecules. The pressure is also corrected for any forces between molecules by the term a/V^2. Not only does this equation take care of deviations from Boyle's law at high pressures, but from these deviations the volume of a gas molecule and consequently its diameter can be computed (Table 11-1).

By combining Boyle's law with Charles's law, $P_1/P_2 = T_1/T_2$, which expresses the variation of pressure of a gas with absolute temperature when the volume is constant, the well-known general law for an ideal gas is obtained.

$$\frac{PV}{T} = \text{constant} = R \qquad [11\text{-}4]$$

or

$$PV = RT \qquad [11\text{-}4a]$$

where R is called the gas constant. When the amount of a gas is 1 gram-molecular weight the volume at standard temperature and pressure is 22,415 cm^3. This is the same for all gases. The value of R for this amount of gas is written R_0 and is the same for all gases.

$$R_0 \text{ (per gm-mol wt)} = 8.31 \text{ joules/°K}$$
$$= 8.31 \times 10^7 \text{ ergs/°K}$$
$$= 1.99 \text{ cal/°K}$$

If a kilogram-molecular weight is used, as is sometimes done in the mks system, $R_0 = 8310$ joules/°K, and the volume of that amount of gas is 22.415 m^3.

Upon substituting the value of P from Eq. 11-1 in Eq. 11-4*a* when R is R_0, we have

$$RT = \frac{1}{3} Nmv^2V \qquad [11\text{-}5]$$

For $V = 22{,}415$ cm^3 the total number of molecules NV is Avogadro's number N_0. Consequently, upon solving this equation for the average kinetic energy of a gas molecule, we have

$$\frac{1}{2} mv^2 = \frac{3}{2} \frac{R_0}{N_0} T \qquad [11\text{-}6]$$

Writing k for R_0/N_0

$$\frac{1}{2} mv^2 = \frac{3}{2} kT \qquad [11\text{-}7]$$

The quantity k is the famous Boltzmann constant. It is the gas constant per molecule, and

$$k = \frac{R_0}{N_0} = \frac{8.31}{6.25 \times 10^{23}} = 1.38 \times 10^{-23} \text{ joule/°K mol}$$
$$= 1.38 \times 10^{-16} \text{ erg/°K mol} \qquad [11\text{-}8]$$

If Eq. 11-7 is to give average energies per molecule, the v^2 in the equation must be the average of all individual speeds squared.

From Avogadro's conclusion (§ 2-10) that equal volumes of different gases at the same temperature and pressure contain the same numbers of molecules, and from Eq. 11-7, it can be seen that the average kinetic energy of the molecules should be the same for all gases at the same temperature since k is a constant. Indeed, this may be considered as a defining equation for the meaning of temperature. According to the classical picture absolute zero would then be that temperature at which the molecules do not possess any kinetic energy of random motion. Kinetic energy of random motion and absolute temperature are not only directly proportional, but indeed it is the average kinetic energy of random motion of the molecules of a gas that determines the temperature of the gas. Quantum considerations now require a certain minimum residual energy called zero-point energy at absolute zero, but at higher temperatures the classical relation still holds.

11-5. Molecular Speeds

Inserting the value of the pressure P (Eq. 11-1) into Boyle's law for any given volume of gas V, we have

$$PV = \left(\frac{1}{3} Nmv^2\right) V \qquad [11\text{-}9]$$

but NmV is the total mass M of the gas, and consequently

$$\begin{aligned} P &= \frac{1}{3}\frac{M}{V} v^2 \\ &= \frac{1}{3} dv^2 \end{aligned} \qquad [11\text{-}10]$$

where d is the density of the gas, from which the rms speed is

$$v = \sqrt{\frac{3P}{d}} \qquad [11\text{-}11]$$

When the macroscopic quantities of pressure and density are known we may compute the molecular speed, as in the following example.

Example For oxygen gas at 76 cm of mercury pressure and 20° C temperature the speed is obtained as follows, with cgs units:

Density of oxygen = 0.0014 (gm/cm³)

Pressure = $76 \times 13.6 \times 980 = 1.01 \times 10^6$ dynes/cm²

$$\begin{aligned} v &= \sqrt{\frac{3P}{d}} = \sqrt{\frac{3(1.01 \times 10^6)}{0.0014}} \\ &= 46{,}500 \text{ cm/sec} \\ &= 465 \text{ m/sec} \cong 1/4 \text{ mi/sec} \end{aligned}$$

If mks units are substituted in the preceding example, the pressure is

1.01×10^5 newtons/m^2, and the density is 1.4 kg/m^3 giving the same answer, of course.

If a gas is composed of a mixture of two or more different kinds of molecules the average kinetic energy at a given temperature is the same for all molecules (law of equipartition of energy). Consequently for two molecules of masses m_1 and m_2 having speeds v_1 and v_2, respectively, on the average,

$$\frac{1}{2} m_1 v_1^2 = \frac{1}{2} m_2 v_2^2$$

but since the masses are different the speeds must also be different, and the velocities are seen to be inversely proportional to the square roots of the masses.

$$\frac{v_1}{v_2} = \sqrt{\frac{m_2}{m_1}} \qquad [11\text{-}12]$$

For instance, since a hydrogen molecule is nearly 1/16 the mass of an oxygen molecule it will travel on the average with a speed 4 times that of oxygen as just computed, or $\sim$1 mi/sec.

11-6. Maxwellian Distribution of Speeds

As previously stated in the derivation of Eq. 11-1, the assumption that all molecules have the same speeds is only a first approximation. After the work of Maxwell and Boltzmann it became well recognized that the collisions of molecules of a gas will temporarily increase the speeds of some and decrease the speeds of others. Theory showed, however, that it was improbable that any one molecule would continually lose speed in a very long series of collisions without gaining speed in some collisions, or that a molecule would continually gain without losing. This results in a distribution of speeds clustered about a most probable value.

Since no molecule can have a speed less than zero and since there is no similar upper limit, the shape of the distribution curve indicates that the average speed will be a little larger than the most probable speed, which is the speed possessed by the maximum number of molecules. Since kinetic energy depends on speed squared, the average kinetic energy depends not on average speed but upon the average or arithmetic mean of the squares of the speeds. The square root of this average is called the root-mean-square or rms speed (§ 11-3), and it is neither the most probable speed nor the average speed but is a little larger even than the latter.

The formula for the rms speed in terms of a distribution of speeds will now be obtained. The total kinetic energy of the molecules of a gas is N times the average kinetic energy where N is the number of molecules. It is also equal to the sum of the separate kinetic energies, as given on the right of the following equation,

$$N\left(\frac{1}{2}mv^2\right) = \frac{1}{2}mv_1^2 + \frac{1}{2}mv_2^2 + \frac{1}{2}mv_3^2 + \cdots \frac{1}{2}mv_n^2 \qquad [11\text{-}13]$$

Since m is the same in all terms, this reduces to

$$v(\text{rms}) = \sqrt{\frac{v_1^2 + v_2^2 + v_3^2 + \cdots v_n^2}{N}} \qquad [11\text{-}14]$$

where the right-hand term under the radical of Eq. 11-14 is the mean-square speed. The root-mean-square speed $v(\text{rms})$ is then the square root of this term.

To obtain the corrected value of the pressure from Eq. 11-1 when there is a distribution of speeds, it is not necessary to change the formula; it is only necessary to put into this formula the rms speed. Similarly Eq. 11-11 gives the rms speed which is actually 1.08 times the average speed. However, in some formulas consideration of the distribution of speeds requires a small change in the formula itself.

Maxwell derived the formula for the distribution of speeds of molecules in a gas when that distribution is caused by the random motions and chance collisions of molecules. It is called a Maxwellian distribution. Since it is based on classical statistics or the probability theory (Chap. 12) involving large numbers of particles it is also called the classical statistical distribution of speeds. The equation obtained by Maxwell is

$$N_v = 4N\sqrt{\frac{m^3}{8\pi k^3 T^3}}\, v^2 \epsilon^{-mv^2/2kT} \qquad [11\text{-}15]$$

where N_v is the number of molecules having a particular speed v, N is the total number of molecules of mass m, k is the Boltzmann constant, ϵ is the base of the natural system of logarithms, and T is the absolute temperature. The graph of this distribution is given in Fig. 11-2,

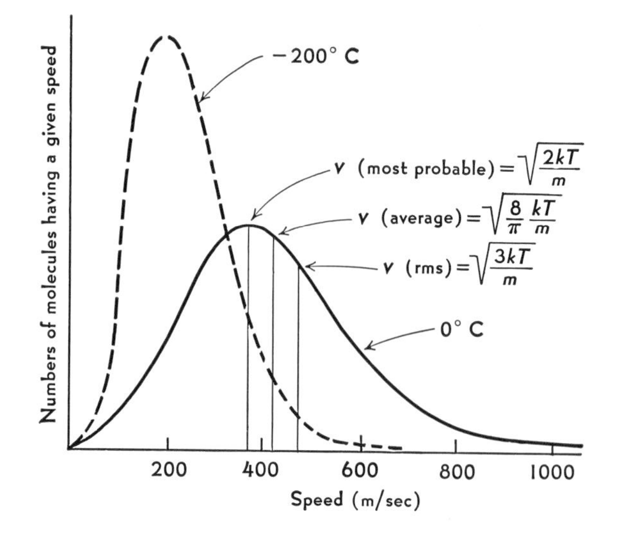

Fig. 11-2. The curves representing a Maxwell distribution of speeds at two different temperatures.

where the three speeds (most probable, average, and rms) are indicated. The summation of all the molecules represented by the curve is the total number of molecules in the gas.

We learn from this distribution law that only 1.61 per cent of the molecules of gas have speeds less than 1/4 the average speed, and only 1.71 per cent have speeds as much as or more than twice the average. The chance that a molecule may gain a very high speed by successive collisions is extremely small, and less than one in a hundred million would have speeds of as much as or more than 4 times the average.

The validity of the Maxwellian distribution of speeds can be checked experimentally in several different ways and has recently been confirmed in great detail by Nobel prize winner Kusch. One of the most direct methods was initiated by Stern in 1920 and was carried further by Zartman in 1931. Atoms of a metal are evaporated from a vapor source (Fig. 11-3), and pass through a series of slits limiting the beam to a narrow width. A rotating cylinder above the slits has a slit at S. As the cylinder rotates, a group of atoms pass the slit S into the cylinder and continue to move in a straight line to the top of the cylinder where they are deposited on a curved plate P_1P_3. The atoms with highest speeds hit the plate at P_1. However, the cylinder is rotating at a known speed, and slower atoms reach the plate later, for instance, at P_2. The density of the deposited film at any position is proportional to

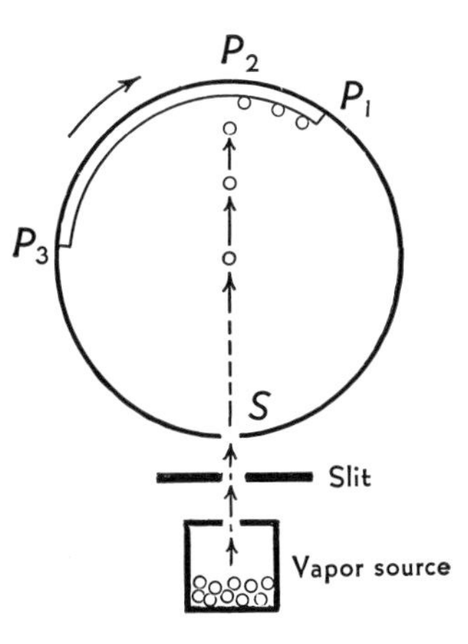

Fig. 11-3. Sketch of apparatus for determining distribution of atomic speeds. Atoms from vapor source (small furnace) enter rotating cylinder at slit *S* in a group moving vertically upward. Those with highest speeds hit recording plate first and are carried to P_1 by rotating cylinder. Slower atoms hit later at points such as P_2.

the number of atoms having speeds enabling them to cross the diameter of the cylinder while the cylinder has turned through a known angle. The results of the experiment are found to be in agreement with Maxwell's theory within the limits of experimental error.

The many successes of the Maxwell distribution law have established its value as an accurate description of this aspect of molecular phenomena. We shall find, however, that other types of distribution law involving quantum concepts are required in other fields, as for instance for the random speeds of free electrons in a metal (Chap. 13).

11-7. Viscosity and Thermal Conductivity

The phenomena of viscosity and of thermal conductivity are discussed in elementary textbooks from the macroscopic viewpoint, and useful formulas are set up whereby computations can be made when the coefficient of viscosity or the coefficient of thermal conductivity for a given substance is known. However, these formulas say nothing about the atomic processes which produce these effects. Let us examine these phenomena from the viewpoint of the kinetic theory of gases.

The resisting force of viscosity offered to an object moving through a gas is commonly said to be the result of the internal friction of the gas, but obviously such internal friction is not the same as ordinary friction between two solids. In forming a picture of what happens we assume that some molecules of the gas cling to the surface of the moving object, in a fashion "wetting" the surface, or that they are otherwise "dragged" with the surface. These gas molecules are in collision with others in a region near the surface and at each collision impart a component of momentum in the direction of motion of the object.

The total momentum per second in the forward direction given to the molecules of gas by a moving object is the force in that direction exerted by the object. By Newton's third law the molecules of gas will react on the moving body to give a force of equal magnitude in the opposite direction. This is the resisting force of fluid friction (viscosity), and it evidently must depend on the number of collisions of the molecules per second and the average momentum transfer per collision. These quantities depend upon molecular velocities, molecular masses, and mean free paths. The mean free path involves the molecular diameter, and the approximate formula for the average mean free path λ of a gas molecule was derived in Chap. 4 (§ 4-5). When corrected for a Maxwellian distribution of speeds it became

$$\lambda = \frac{1}{\sqrt{2}\, N\pi d^2} \qquad [4\text{-}3]$$

On the basis of these quantities the formula for the coefficient of viscosity η may be derived from kinetic theory. Although the derivation is too lengthy to be included here the resulting formula is

$$\eta = \frac{mv}{3\pi d^2} \qquad [11\text{-}16]$$

where v is the random rms velocity of the molecules of mass m, and d is the diameter of the molecule.

If the coefficient of viscosity η of a gas is carefully measured and if m and v are known, the formula may be solved for the molecular diameter. Some values obtained by this method are given in Table 11-1.

The thermal conductivity of a gas is likewise due to collisions in which the kinetic energy of molecules at a higher temperature is transferred to molecules at a lower temperature. Thus thermal conductivity involves masses, diameters, and mean free paths of molecules, and is closely related to the viscosity. The formulas for these two phenomena involve so many quantities common to both that the coefficient of thermal conductivity k may be written in terms of the coefficient of viscosity η as follows:

$$\eta = c_v k \qquad [11\text{-}17]$$

where c_v is the specific heat of the gas at constant volume.

11-8. Reality of Molecules and Atoms, and Brownian Motions

Although the Greek "atomists" Leucippus and Democritus believed the world to be composed of an infinite number of atoms of infinite variety, their belief was based on little more than imagination. Centuries later, when the idea of atoms was revived in more scientific form by Gassendi and Boyle, there was still no very direct evidence, and not until late in the nineteenth century was there general acceptance of the existence of atoms.

The question of the existence of atoms brings up many philosophical problems, including the question of what is meant by existence or the reality of anything. Scientists are coming to lean more and more heavily on the operational viewpoint as exemplified by the foundations of relativity. What is represented by a measured quantity must be judged in terms of the operations involved in making the measurement. Our concepts of atoms and molecules must depend on the related quantities that we measure and the methods by which we measure them.

We measure more or less directly such quantities as masses, velocities, mean free paths, diameters, and so on, and when many measurements of a quantity agree closely, though made from quite different experimental approaches, we organize them into conceptual patterns that we feel represent something in nature. When we say we believe in the *reality* of atoms and molecules, what we mean is that we have verified the usefulness of this concept in organizing observed phenomena and in predicting new phenomena. Most scientists would go so far as to say that they believe that atoms and molecules have an independent existence in nature aside from our concepts of them and that many features of these entities are closely paralleled by our concepts of them, but such a belief is not susceptible of direct proof.

We may further ask: can something that we do not see directly have the same degree of reality as the objects we see about us every day? It would be difficult to deny that there are different levels of reality, but a chance observation by Thomas Brown in 1827 brought the motions of molecules very close to the realm of direct observation. He noticed that finely divided particles suspended in a liquid do not remain at rest but if observed through a microscope are seen to dance back and forth with an irregular motion (Fig. 11-4). It was soon recognized that this motion was similar to the random motions that the molecules of a gas were supposed to undergo. However, there had

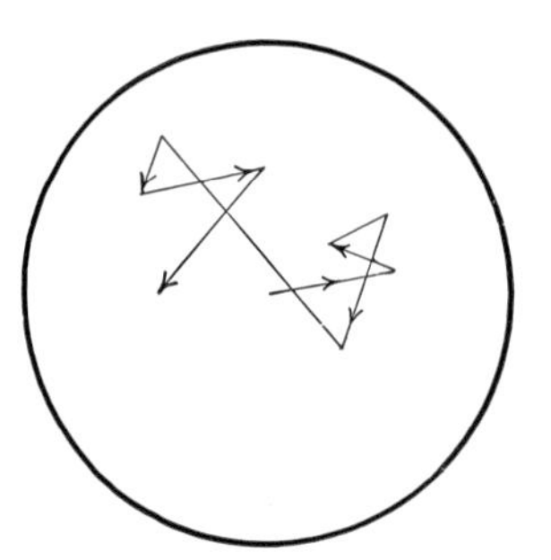

Fig. 11-4. Path of a particle undergoing Brownian motion.

been no direct proof of this random motion of gas molecules or that molecules of a liquid partook of a similar motion. The full explanation of these Brownian motions was not given until 1905, when Einstein and Smoluchowski independently developed a complete theory based on the idea that a tiny particle is bombarded on all sides by the molecules of the liquid in their random motions, but that at any instant the forces produced on opposite sides may not balance, and that motion results. The theory predicted the displacement of the particle after a given time interval.

Perrin tested the theory experimentally under many different conditions. Among other things he found that the average kinetic energy of a Brownian particle is the same as computed for the gas molecules (equipartition of energy), thus "verifying" that the Brownian motion of these relatively large particles is the direct result of random bombardment by large numbers of molecules. Knowing the average energy per molecule and the temperature, he could also arrive at Avogadro's number for which he obtained the value $N_0 = 6.85 \times 10^{23}$. Considering the great experimental difficulties, this was quite close to the presently accepted value of 6.025×10^{23}. Similar measurements were soon made on Brownian motions in gases by Millikan and others. The importance of this work for modern physics becomes apparent when it is noted that not only were Brownian motions explained but the whole kinetic theory received unquestionable confirmation, and along with the first direct determination of Avogadro's number came confirmation of Avogadro's hypothesis proposed nearly a century earlier.

11-9. Degrees of Freedom, Rotation, and Vibration

So far, in our discussion of gas molecules, we have assumed the molecules to be monatomic, i.e., consisting of one atom each, as for instance in the rare gases (He, Ne, A, Kr, Xe) and mercury vapor (Hg). Such molecules are said to have three degrees of freedom since they are free to move independently in any one of the three directions of space (Fig. 11-5), and there is no evidence that they are set in rotation by collisions; to be more precise, if they possess intrinsic rotation, there is no evidence that this rotation is changed by collisions.

Diatomic molecules such as hydrogen (H_2), oxygen (O_2), and nitrogen (N_2) each are composed of two atoms held together by mutual attraction. Molecules such as these, in which the forces holding the atoms together act between like atoms, are called homopolar molecules. The intermolecular forces between unlike atoms may be either homopolar or ionic in nature.

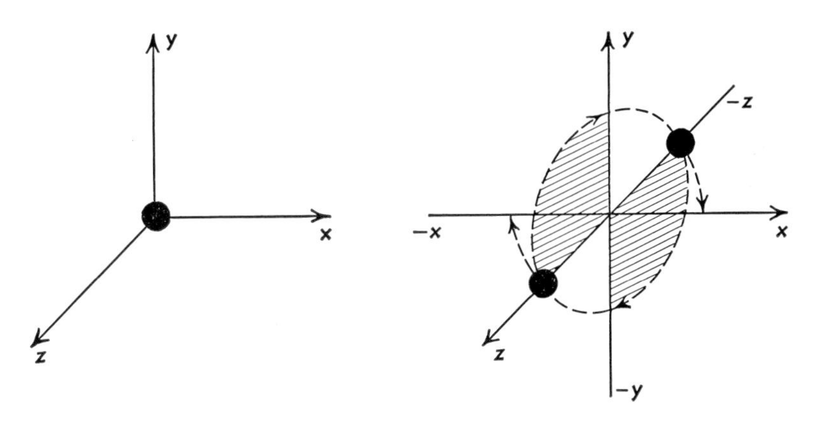

Fig. 11-5. Degrees of freedom of atom. Atom can move rectilinearly in any of three directions of space but is not able to accept energy of rotation about any axis. Consequently, such an atom is said to possess three degrees of freedom.

Fig. 11-6. Degrees of freedom of diatomic molecule. Molecule can move rectilinearly in any of three directions of space. It can also rotate about molecular axes *x* and *y* but not about atomic axis *z*.

A diatomic molecule may be represented ideally as two spheres held together to form a kind of dumbbell arrangement (Fig. 11-6); there is good evidence that it may be set in rotation by collision. However, we must assume that a diatomic molecule cannot absorb energy of rotation about the axis joining the atomic centers any more than a single atom can about its axis. This leaves it free to rotate independently about either or both of the other two axes in space. Consequently it has three degrees of freedom of linear motion, plus two of rotation, or five degrees of freedom in all. That the degrees of freedom of a diatomic molecule are five instead of three was inferred from measurements of the energy absorbed by such a gas per degree change in temperature, namely, from measurement of specific heats.

When a molecule accepts more energy than can be accounted for by the degrees of freedom thus far described, it becomes necessary to infer more degrees of freedom, and there is unquestioned evidence that internal vibrations may occur in a molecule. The picture of an ideal diatomic molecule composed of two atoms held rigidly at a fixed distance apart is oversimplified. Certainly the atoms must be held in equilibrium positions relative to one another such that if the atoms are pushed closer together there is a net force outward, or if they are pulled further apart there is a net force inward. Such an arrangement would permit vibrations along the line of centers. In molecules of more than two atoms there are possibilities of other more complicated types of vibrations.

11-10. Quantum Theory of Molecular Heats of Gases

So far in the present chapter it has been found possible to describe molecular phenomena in terms of classical mechanics, supplemented by probability considerations involving a distribution of velocities. However, not all molecular phenomena can be so easily described. In the study of specific heats of a gas at low temperatures classical methods lead to wrong results. Since we have witnessed the increased importance and application of the basic principles of the quantum theory, perhaps we should not be surprised to find that such considerations are now required and yield valid results.

The molecular heat, or specific-heat capacity per gram-molecular weight of a gas at constant volume (designated as c_v), is proportional to the heat absorbed per molecule of a gas for a rise of temperature of 1 degree. It is commonly measured in calories per gram-molecular weight per degree Kelvin. This would be N_0 times the average energy per molecule where N_0 is Avogadro's number in the appropriate units. If measured at constant pressure the molecular heat c_p is of course larger than that for constant volume c_v by the amount of work done in change of volume.

When the molecules of a gas undergo an increase in energy this energy is divided between the different degrees of freedom. In a monatomic gas any increase of energy goes to increase the kinetic energy of translational motion. It is this energy which determines the temperature of a gas. In polyatomic molecules energy also goes into producing rotations and vibrations. Whatever the form, the total energy divided individually among the molecules of a gas is called the internal energy of the gas, but only the fraction represented by translational motion determines the temperature.

From Eq. 11-6 it is seen that

$$N_0\left(\frac{1}{2}mv^2\right) = \frac{3}{2}R_0T = \frac{3}{2}\left(\frac{1.99 \text{ cal}}{°\text{K}}\right)T$$

where $(3/2)R_0$ is the kinetic energy per degree per gram-molecular weight for an ideal monatomic gas having three degrees of freedom. Consequently by the equipartition law each degree of freedom would require $(1/2)R_0$ or 0.99 calorie per gram-molecular weight. For a monatomic gas 3/2(1.99) gives for c_v 2.99 cal per °K per gram-molecular weight. For a diatomic molecule with five degrees of freedom the energy per gram-molecular weight per °K would be 5/2(1.99) or 4.98 cal. Measured values for real gases (Table 11-2) indicate that the agreement with theory is for the most part quite good at ordinary temperatures. At extremes of temperature deviations occur that are in disagreement with classical theory. The most striking example is that of hydrogen, the specific heat of which becomes less as the temperature is reduced and finally reaches a lower level, indicating that the molecule has lost two degrees of freedom and now behaves like a monatomic molecule with only 3/5 the specific heat it had at normal temperatures. Other types of molecules show the effect to a lesser extent. Classical theory is helpless to explain these deviations, but quantum concepts offer the basis for a fairly simple explanation.

TABLE 11-2. MOLECULAR HEATS AT 15° C

Molecule	C_v Experimental	C_v Theoretical	Degrees of Freedom
Helium (He) (monatomic)	2.98	2.99	3
Mercury (Hg) (monatomic)	2.98	2.99	3
Hydrogen (H_2) (diatomic)	4.83	4.98	5
Nitrogen (N_2) (diatomic)	4.94	4.98	5
Oxygen (O_2) (diatomic)	4.97	4.98	5

There are no restrictions on the free translational motion of a molecule in a straight line that would require quantization. The rotational motion of a molecule, however, like the orbital motion of an electron in an atom, is a repeated motion, the restrictions on which require quantization. Such quantization is attained, as in the Bohr orbits, by permitting only amounts of angular momentum equal to integral multiples of $h/2\pi$ or $I\omega = mvr = nh/2\pi$. The same result is reached on the basis of the earlier wave theory by restricting the rotational motion to that for which the effective circumference $2\pi r$ is an integral number of de Broglie wavelengths. This quantization means that a molecule can only rotate with particular values of angular velocity and consequently with particular amounts of energy of rotational motion.

The angular momentum for a body of rotational inertia I and angular velocity ω is $I\omega$. The kinetic energy of rotation is $\frac{1}{2}I\omega^2$. To set up a quantized state in which the angular momentum $I\omega = nh/2\pi$ which is the usual quantum condition, there must be an equivalent energy change. Since angular momentum is quantized, so also will energy be quantized. Squaring both sides of the equation for the quantization of angular momentum (Eq. 8-10) and dividing by $2I$, it follows that to give a molecule 1 unit of angular momentum the energy must be increased by an amount $h^2/8\pi^2I$. For molecules composed of light atoms the small rotational inertia I makes the energy a relatively large quantity even for the first state where n equals 1, and the angular velocity must likewise be large.

At low temperatures the collisions of molecules may not be sufficiently energetic to excite even the first quantum state of rotation, and according to quantum theory either this degree of angular momentum is excited or none are. At a sufficiently high temperature higher quantum states of angular momentum may be excited, and these will consequently represent higher energy states. For instance, at room temperature an oxygen molecule may have 20 units of angular momentum, whereas a hydrogen molecule having about 1/40 the rotational inertia of an oxygen atom must spin far faster for the same amount of angular momentum and, on the average, at room temperature may have only 2 or 3 units of angular momentum.

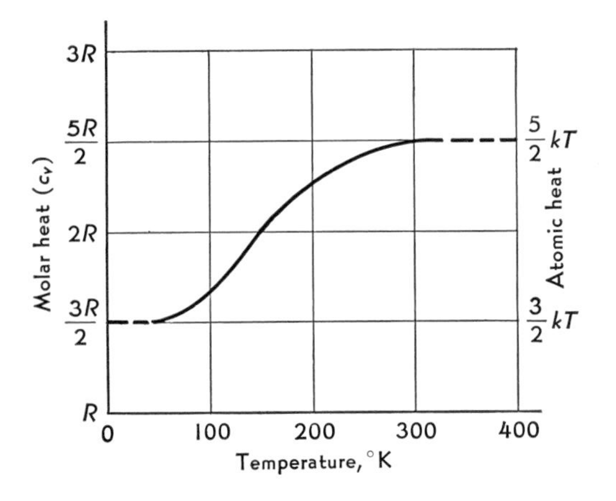

Fig. 11-7. Specific heat of hydrogen at different temperatures.

As the temperature of a gas is reduced the probability of exciting rotational energy states becomes less, and for hydrogen a marked decrease is observed in the molecular heat, as indicated in Fig. 11-7. From the curve it is seen that below about 70° K no rotational states can be set up. The hydrogen molecule thus loses its two degrees of freedom representing rotations, and the diatomic hydrogen molecule then behaves like a single atom or monatomic molecule. For heavier molecules the effect is much less and is only detectable, if at all, at much lower temperatures than for hydrogen.

Thus it is that quantum physics achieves another triumph in the explanation of the variation of specific heats with temperature. The methods of the earlier quantum theory here outlined have now been supplanted by the more elegant mathematical methods of wave mechanics based on the Schrödinger equation, but the results achieved are essentially the same.

11-11. Quantum Theory of Molecular Spectra

For a long time after the discovery of spectra it was not understood why the spectra produced by molecules consist of series of what at first appeared to be broad bands, covering a considerable frequency range, whereas the spectra of atoms consist of separate and distinct lines. Progress was made when it was found by observation with instruments of higher resolving power that the broad bands, from which the name *band spectra* was derived, are in reality closely packed groups of individual lines.

A satisfactory explanation of the origin of the lines forming a band and of the bands themselves was not obtained until, with the aid of quantum theory, a scheme of possible energy levels was set up for an individual molecule. In an atom, energy absorption or emission occurs, as we have previously seen, by electron transitions by which the atom passes from one energy state to another. A molecule, however, has possibilities of absorbing energy by the excitation of rotational states and vibrational states, and also by electron transitions. The resultant energy state of a molecule depends on the total energy, and this may involve one, two, or all three types of excitation. Emission of energy occurs when the molecule undergoes a transition to a lower energy state, which again involves one or more of these factors.

In the previous section the idea was developed that a diatomic molecule will have one or more quantized rotational energy states excited if the temperature of the gas is high enough to assure the occurrence of collisions of sufficient violence. When such molecules return to a state of lower rotational energy, a quantum of radiation is emitted giving a line in what is called the **rotation spectrum** of the molecule. The quantum conditions for the excitation of the various rotational energy states were also given, leading to an energy in the nth state of

$$E_{\text{rot}} = \frac{n_r^2 h^2}{8\pi^2 I} \qquad n_r = 1, 2, 3, \cdots \qquad [11\text{-}18]$$

where n_r is an integer called the **rotational quantum number.** Wave-mechanical analysis confirms this relation generally but substitutes for n_r the quantity $\sqrt{n_r(n_r + 1)}$. The energy of the nth rotational level now becomes

$$E_{\text{rot}} = n_r(n_r + 1) \frac{h^2}{8\pi^2 I} \qquad [11\text{-}19]$$

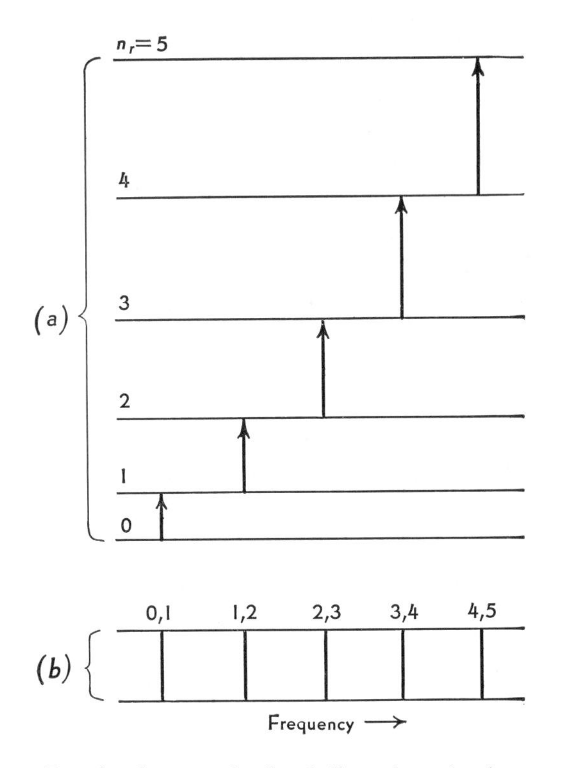

Fig. 11-8. *a*, **Rotational energy levels of diatomic molecule; arrows represent transitions in which energy is absorbed;** *b*, **rotational spectrum showing absorption lines (equally spaced) for transitions shown in** *a*.

and the selection rule is that n_r can only change by ± 1. A set of energy levels for different values of n_r is represented in Fig. 11-8*a*. Since rotation spectra are usually studied by absorption methods the arrows for the transitions are directed from lower to higher energy states. The spectral lines corresponding to these transitions are shown in Fig. 11-8*b* and are seen to be equally spaced, since each energy level represents the same increase in energy with respect to the preceding level.

Since these rotational states are excited at moderately low temperatures they represent small energy differences, and by the quantum relation $W = hf$ the lines will represent small frequency difference and be close together. At such low temperatures there is not sufficient energy per collision to excite vibrational states or electronic transitions, and the spectra are called pure rotation spectra. Because of the low frequencies involved the lines occur in what is called the far infrared region of the spectrum, far beyond the long-wave limit of the visible spectrum. The lines are hard to detect, and not many successful studies have been made of such emission spectra, but such as have been made confirm the theory. A much greater advance has resulted from the more recent studies of absorption spectra by methods using microwaves (§ 11-13).

At higher temperatures vibrational energy states are excited in addition to rotational states. Whereas rotation spectra may be observed separately, vibration spectra cannot be so observed. Vibrational energy-level transitions always occur in connection with rotational energy-level changes, giving rise to what are called **rotation-vibration spectra.**

If f is the frequency of vibration of the molecule in a given state we can write for the vibrational energy in any level where n_v is the number of the level, or the **vibrational quantum number,**

$$E_{\text{vib}} = n_v h f_v \qquad [11\text{-}20]$$

This type of quantization, however, belongs to the older quantum theory, and wave-mechanical theory predicts the energy to be

$$E_{\text{vib}} = \left(n_v + \frac{1}{2}\right) h f_v \qquad [11\text{-}21]$$

An interesting feature of the newer scheme is that it predicts a residual amount of energy for $n_v = 0$. This is a typical feature of wave mechanics, and the energy in any rotation-vibration state is then

$$E = E_{\text{vib}} + E_{\text{rot}} = \left(n_v + \frac{1}{2}\right) h f_v + n_r(n_r + 1)\,\frac{h^2}{8\pi^2 I} \qquad [11\text{-}22]$$

The frequency f of emitted (or absorbed) radiation in a transition from one level to another is then given by

$$hf = (E'_{\text{vib}} - E_{\text{vib}}) + (E'_{\text{rot}} - E_{\text{rot}}) \qquad [11\text{-}23]$$

where the primed quantities represent higher (or lower) energy states. Since vibrational levels represent much larger energy changes than rotational energy levels, there will be a series of rotational energy levels for each vibrational energy level. The energy-level scheme for a diatomic molecule such as HCl is shown in Fig. 11-9*a*, where sets of

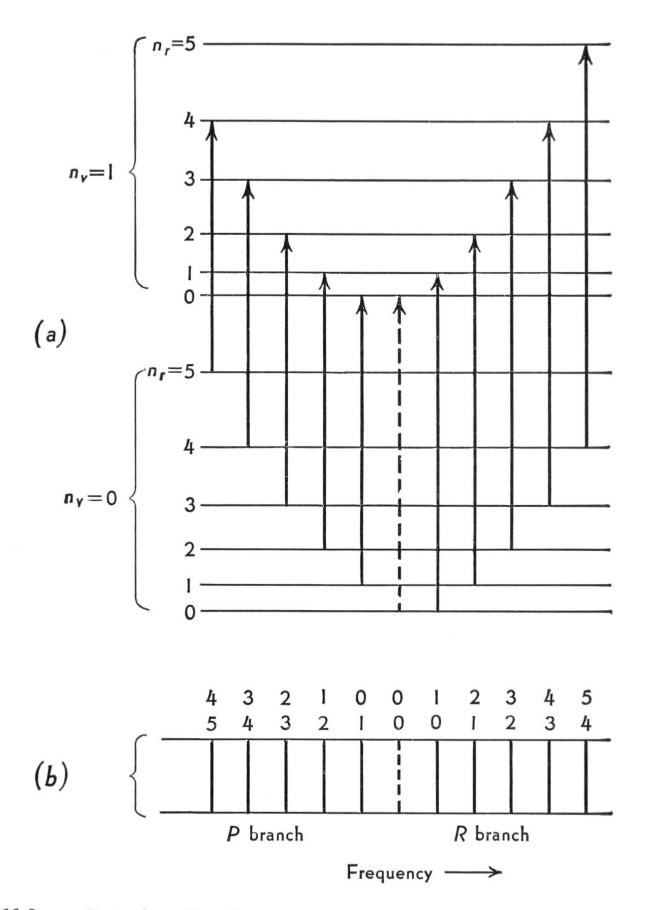

Fig. 11-9. ***a*, Rotation-vibration energy levels of diatomic molecule such as HCl, showing transitions between rotational levels belonging to the first two vibrational levels; *b*, absorption lines of the rotation-vibration spectrum for the transitions shown in *a*.**

rotational levels for different vibrational levels are shown, together with the possible transitions leading to groups of lines in two branches, known as the P and R branches, Fig. 11-9*b*. Since n_r can change by only ± 1 the transition $0 \rightarrow 0$ is excluded and leads to a missing line characteristic of this type of spectra. This is the line that would be given for zero change in the rotational quantum number. Since it is not observed we conclude that the usual selection rule which excludes such a change is valid and that changes in vibrational energy are always accompanied by changes in rotational energy.

Rotation-vibration spectra are found in the near-infrared region, and intensities of lines can be measured by photometric methods, giving the type of curve represented in Fig. 11-10, where the position of the missing line is plainly evident.

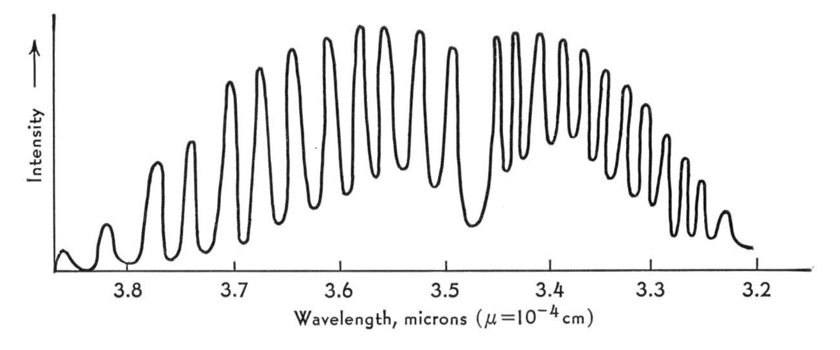

Fig. 11-10. Typical photometric measurement of intensities of rotation-vibration absorption spectrum of HCl. Note missing line for forbidden $0 \rightarrow 0$ transition.

If the available energy is sufficient to excite an electron transition as well as rotation-vibration states, the energy of the electron transition hf_e must be added to that of the other transitions, giving generally for a rotation-vibration-electronic line in the spectrum,

$$hf = hf_e + (E'_{\text{vib}} - E_{\text{vib}}) + (E'_{\text{rot}} - E_{\text{rot}}) \qquad [11\text{-}24]$$

From this the frequency of emitted (or absorbed) radiation is given by dividing both sides of the equation by h.

The effect of electronic transitions is to give groups of closely packed lines converging to a "head" on one side of the band, and this accounts for the common structure of molecular spectra in the visible region. Such spectra are called **rotation-vibration-electronic spectra.** An energy-level diagram involving all three types of levels, electronic, vibrational, and rotational, is shown in Fig. 11-11. For each electronic level there is a group of vibrational levels, and for each vibrational level there is a group of rotational levels. The transitions of the diagram are for electronic and rotational changes. The spacings of the rotational levels are different for the two electronic levels since electronic excitation may be expected to change the rotational inertia I of the molecule. Below the energy-level diagram the emitted (or absorbed)

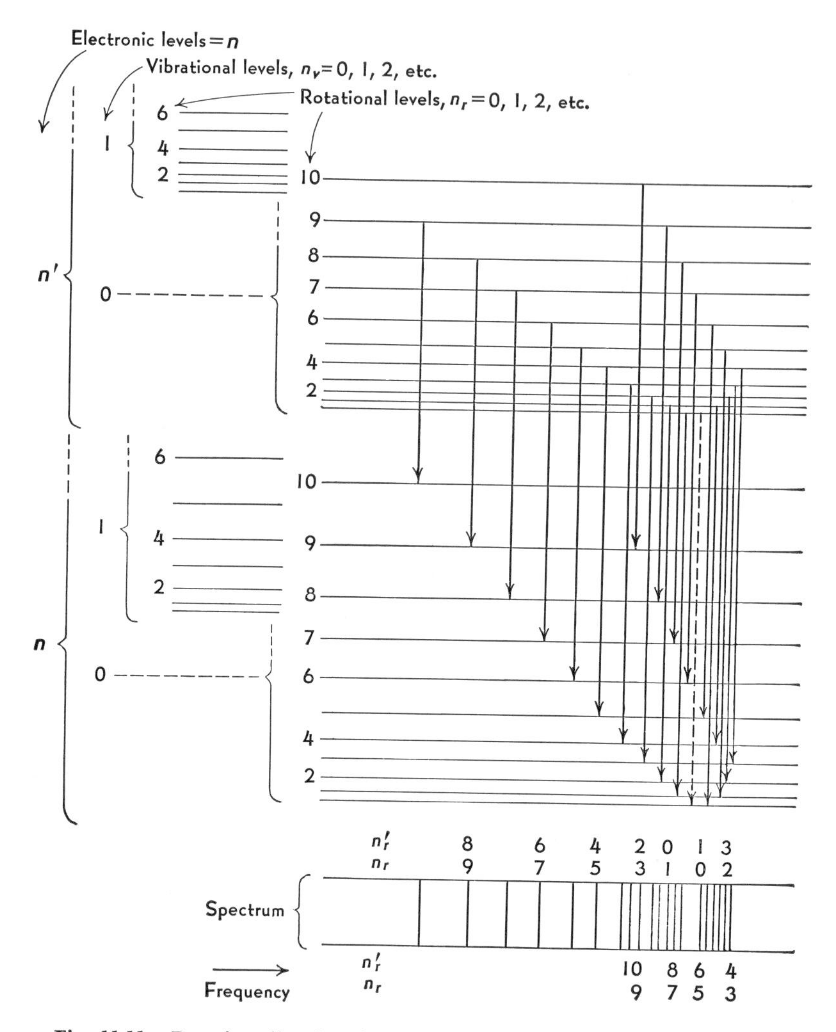

Fig. 11-11. Rotation-vibration-electronic energy levels, showing how transitions form typical "electronic" band with lines converging to a "head" at the high-frequency limit.

lines are indicated with a gap for the $0 \rightarrow 0$ transition for n_r and only those transitions permitted for which n_r changes by ± 1. Transitions may also take place between various levels of different energy and between different electronic states, so that in a characteristic molecu-

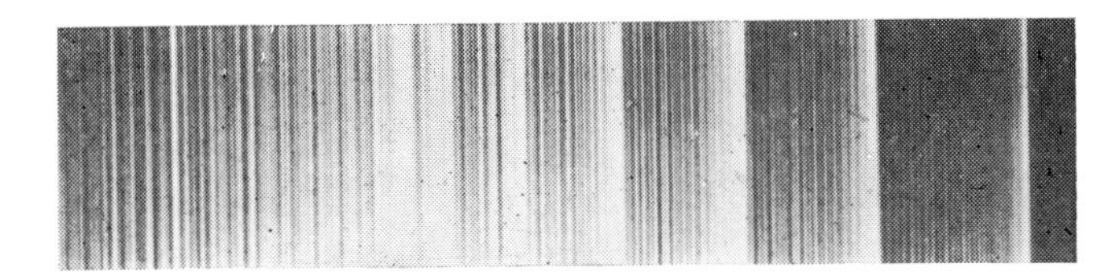

Fig. 11-12. Typical molecular spectrum showing bands in the spectrum of cyanogen.

lar spectrum many bands of lines may be observed, the lines always crowding in one direction toward a "head" for each band, as in Fig. 11-12.

11-12. Raman Spectra

Certain additional faint lines on either side of an observed spectral line (Fig. 11-13) may be detected by special means when the observed light is scattered by suitable molecules. These Raman lines were first detected by Raman in India in 1928, for which he received the Nobel

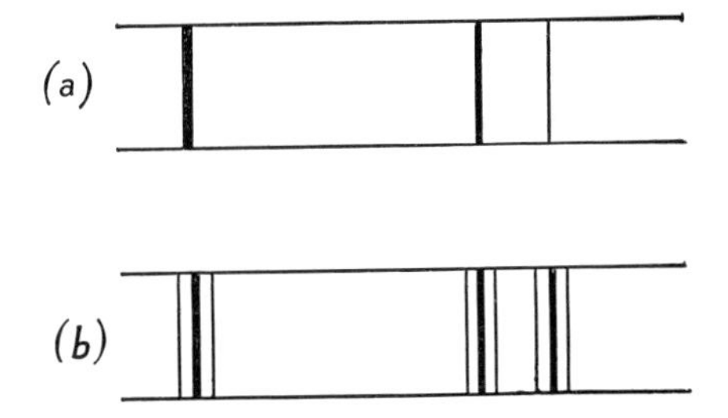

Fig. 11-13. Raman lines: *a*, incident light before scattering; *b*, scattered light shows Raman lines on each side of lines of incident light.

prize. The special method adopted was to make an extremely long exposure of the lines on a photographic film, greatly overexposing the primary lines.

The method of producing the Raman effect is to illuminate with an intense beam of light a molecular solution, the Raman spectrum of which it is desired to study. The beam may be produced by a mercury arc, and the beam of light may be limited to a single wavelength (monochromatic). The light scattered in all directions by the solution is then passed through a spectrograph and focused on photographic film, after which the exposure is made.

The explanation of the appearance of the extra lines involves the quantum theory. The lines of lower frequency than that of the incident photons are produced by scattering from molecules, which go into a higher energy state and take a small quantum of energy E_q from the incident photon of energy hf_0, thus by the quantum hypothesis lowering the energy of the photon and consequently lowering frequency to a new value f given by the relation

$$hf = hf_0 - E_q$$

A similar relation holds for gain of energy in the scattering process:

$$hf = hf_0 + E_q$$

where the observed scattered frequency is higher than that of the incident light. At the moment of scattering the excited molecule contributes a small quantum of energy E_q to the incident photon, which then becomes a photon of higher frequency. Lines of higher frequency are usually less intense since they are due to scattering from molecules already in an excited state.

11-13. Microwave Spectroscopy

A new branch of spectroscopy, microwave spectroscopy, has in recent years fairly leaped into prominence. Microwaves are electromagnetic waves less than a meter in length produced by electronic means. During World War II methods of producing such waves were greatly improved, and where originally used for radar, they have now become very important in research in several fields.

Molecules often possess energy levels so closely spaced that the radiation frequencies are far below any detectable infrared radiation. They lie in a region continuous with the infrared, embracing wavelengths from a fraction of a centimeter to 15 or 20 cm in length. Whereas infrared spectroscopy would be unable to separate the observed frequencies even if they could be detected, it is possible to separate them easily by means of electronic circuits. Since any emitted radiation at such frequencies would be masked by the ever-present thermal radiation of other bodies, microwave spectra are always absorption spectra. The frequencies detected are those removed from an incident beam by molecular absorption. By such methods much new information is now being obtained concerning molecular energy states.

PROBLEMS

1. If there are 2.7×10^{19} molecules per cm^3 in a gas at standard pressure and temperature, find their average distance apart at any instant.

Ans. 33.3×10^{-8} cm.

2. If all the human beings in the world could be turned into gas molecules, how much volume would they occupy at standard pressure and temperature? (Assume 3 billion inhabitants in the world.)

Ans. 1.1×10^{-10} cm^3.

3. If all the molecules of gas in 1 cm^3 at standard pressure and temperature could be turned into human beings, how many duplicate worlds like ours would be required to hold them at the present population level? (See problem 2.)

Ans. 9×10^9 worlds.

4. If a hydrogen atom could be magnified until its diameter was 2 miles, how big would the magnified nucleus be? (Assume the nucleus is 10^{-13} cm in radius.)

Ans. 0.20 ft.

5. By means of the equation $P = \frac{1}{3}Nmv^2$ find the root-mean-square velocity of a nitrogen molecule at standard temperature and pressure. (Density of nitrogen is 1.25 kg/m^3.)

Ans. 493 m/sec.

6. Mercury vapor particles in air at 0° C and 76 cm mercury pressure would have what velocity if oxygen molecules have a velocity of 465 m/sec?

Ans. 186 m/sec.

7. What is the average energy of random motion in electron volts of an oxygen molecule at 0° C and 76 cm of mercury pressure?

Ans. 3.58×10^{-2} ev.

8. An oxygen molecule having a velocity of 465 m/sec hits head-on an oxygen atom momentarily at rest. What is the velocity of the molecule after collision? (Assume the simple laws of collision.)

Ans. 155 m/sec.

9. Rocket measurements at high altitudes indicate that the air pressure at an altitude of 150 kilometers is 3×10^{-6} mm of mercury. Assuming air is mostly nitrogen, compute the mean free path.

Ans. 2120 cm.

10. If the density of air at an altitude of 50 kilometers is 1.3×10^{-3} kg/m^3 and if the pressure is 0.75 mm of mercury, what would the mean free path of a nitrogen molecule be? ($T = 273°$ K, as in next problem.)

Ans. 8.4×10^{-3} cm.

11. Atmospheric pressure varies with altitude h according to the equation

$$p = p_0 \epsilon^{-(mg/kT)h}$$

where p_0 is the pressure at the earth's surface and m is the mass of a molecule. Find the pressure at an elevation of 5 km. (Assume that air is chiefly nitrogen, the temperature is 300° K, and the pressure at the earth's surface is 76 cm of mercury.)

Ans. 43.5 cm of mercury.

SUGGESTED READING

F. K. Richtmyer, E. H. Kennard, and T. Lauritsen, *Introduction to Modern Physics*, 5th ed. (New York, McGraw-Hill, 1955).

E. Bloch, *The Kinetic Theory of Gases*, 2nd ed. (London, Methuen, 1930).

L. B. Loeb, *Kinetic Theory of Gases*, 2nd ed. (New York, McGraw-Hill, 1934).

CHAPTER 12

RADIATION AND BOSE STATISTICS

12-1. Introduction

At first thought it might seem that there is little or no direct relation between the kinetic theory of random motions of molecules of a gas and the manner in which the energy radiated from a hot body is distributed over a range of wavelengths. Nevertheless, a possible relation was noticed late in the nineteenth century, and with the later development of Planck's quantum theory of radiation in terms of photons with particle-like characteristics the relation became more evident. It also became apparent, however, that the particular type of statistical theory which is based on ideas of chance collisions and the ensuing variations in speeds of gas molecules does not apply directly to photons. The radiation in a closed region may be thought of as a "photon gas," but the photons do not collide and exchange energy as gas molecules do. It will be the object of this chapter to show how statistical laws had to be revised to account for radiation phenomena and how, with the introduction of quantization, the fundamental problem of radiation was solved. As a preliminary, it will be desirable to review briefly the classical laws of radiation and note where they failed.

12-2. Early Work on Radiation

At the end of the nineteenth century radio waves, x-rays, and gamma rays had just been discovered and had not been studied to any extent. Scientists had been concerned with investigations of the ultraviolet and infrared regions near the visible part of the spectrum and of thermal radiation from hot bodies further in the infrared. It had been recognized that the best absorbers of radiation are also the best radiators and that the poorest absorbers are the poorest radiators (Kirchhoff's law). In other words, absorption coefficients for various bodies are in the same proportion as emission coefficients. Since no ordinary object could be a perfect absorber of radiant energy, so also, according to this law, it could not be a perfect radiator. Such a perfect absorber or radiator is called an **ideal black body,** and the idea of an ideal black body not only became the basis for theories of radiation, but it also became desirable to approximate one as nearly as possible in the laboratory.

The standard black body, as now generally accepted, consists of a hollow sphere with an opening or hole by which radiation may enter or leave. It is this opening which acts as the radiator or absorber (Fig. 12-1). When the inside of the spherical shell is coated with a good ab-

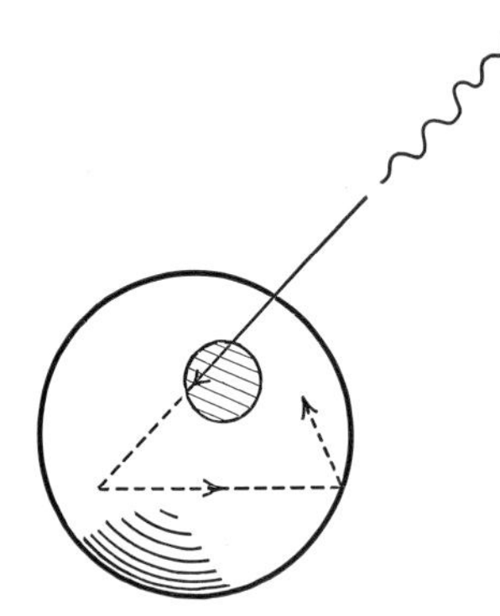

Fig. 12-1. The opening in a hollow sphere, coated with lamp black on the inside, is one type of standard black body.

sorber such as lamp black, very little radiation entering the hole and hitting an inner surface is reflected. After multiple reflections within the enclosure very little is left to escape from the opening. The opening consequently acts very nearly as an ideal black body and absorbs nearly 100 per cent of the energy falling on it. If the sphere is raised to a high temperature the emission may be studied, and the opening then acts as a nearly perfect radiator.

The amount of radiation per unit area per unit time from the surface of any object depends upon two factors, the absolute temperature and the emissive capacity of that surface. Dependence of radiation on temperature is given by the **Stefan-Boltzmann law** which states that *the rate of radiation from an ideal black body is proportional to the fourth power of the absolute temperature.* This law was derived experimentally by Stefan and confirmed theoretically from thermodynamic considerations by Boltzmann. If the emissive capacity of an ideal black body per unit area of surface is designated by E, the total energy radiated per second is given by the Stefan-Boltzmann law

$$\text{Ideal black-body radiation} = ET^4 \qquad [12\text{-}1]$$

where E is numerically equal to the energy emitted per second per unit area of the surface when $T = 1°$ K.

$$E = 5.67 \times 10^{-8} \text{ joule/sec m}^2 \, (1° \text{ K})^4$$
$$= 1.36 \times 10^{-12} \text{ cal/sec cm}^2 \, (1° \text{ K})^4$$

Since the rate of emission of any ordinary surface is less than the rate for an ideal black body, the rate of radiation ET^4 must be multiplied by the fraction of black-body radiation that the surface can emit. This fraction e is called the emissivity of the surface (Table 12-1), and the rate of radiation for any surface of emissivity e is

$$\text{Radiation rate} = eET^4 \qquad [12\text{-}2]$$

TABLE 12-1. SAMPLE EMISSIVITIES AT 100° C

Surface	e
Ideal black body	1.00
Flat black paint	0.90
White cloth	0.85
Aluminum paint	0.30
Silver (polished)	0.06

The radiation law of Eq. 12-2 implies that any object at a temperature above absolute zero must be radiating energy. Indeed, all objects are radiating energy all the time at rates depending on their absolute temperatures. This was recognized by Prevost, who formulated his theory of heat exchange in 1792. In any enclosed space in which the total amount of heat energy is constant, hot bodies radiate more than they receive and tend to cool off whereas cool bodies receive more than they radiate and tend to become warmer. This process continues until temperature equilibrium is reached, after which further exchanges do not change the temperature.

12-3. Black-Body Radiation and Wien's Displacement Law

Radiation from a black body in particular, and from any body in general, does not occur at a single frequency but covers a range of frequencies (or wavelengths) with a maximum rate of energy emission at a frequency which depends upon the temperature. Curves representing the energy radiated at each frequency (or wavelength) are shown in Fig. 12-2. Such curves have been measured experimentally for a variety of conditions. The measurements may be made by means of a type of spectrometer that will separate the various wavelengths. The energy radiated in a narrow band of wavelengths may be detected and measured by a thermocouple coated with lamp black to make it a good absorber.

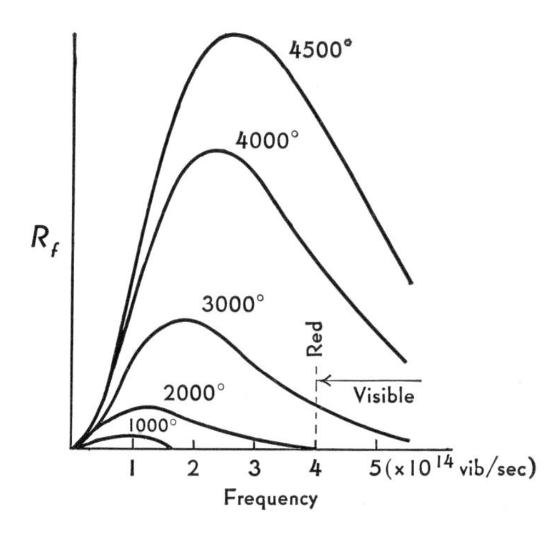

Fig. 12-2. Energy-distribution curves for different temperatures showing the energy R_f radiated at any frequency f by an ideal black body.

Solid bodies heated to 700° C begin to give off visible light as the peak of the radiation curve shifts toward shorter wavelengths (higher frequencies); as the temperature is increased the height of the curve is increased. Thus, as the temperature of an object is raised and it becomes "red-hot," the curve shifts so that it begins to include the frequencies of the red end of the visible spectrum. If the temperature is further raised the shift is toward still higher frequencies, including some of the orange and yellow, and the appearance of the object changes from dull red to bright red or to an orange-red. If the temperature is raised sufficiently the emission curve shifts to include the blue end of the spectrum, and the object becomes white-hot or even blue-white in extreme cases.

Wien found that the frequency at which maximum energy is radiated per second is proportional to the absolute temperature. This is called **Wien's displacement law,** and the frequency of the maximum for any absolute temperature T is

$$f(\text{sec}^{-1}) = 5.88 \times 10^{10} T \text{ °K} \qquad [12\text{-}3]$$

For all ordinary sources of light the peak of the radiation curve lies considerably below the visible region. This might have been guessed from the knowledge that an incandescent lamp bulb is a better "stove" than lamp, with 95 per cent or more of its radiation in the thermal rather than in the visible region. For the sun the peak of the curve comes near the middle of the visible region, but for the intensely hot blue-white stars it may be in the ultraviolet region.

These radiation curves, regardless of height, all follow the same general pattern which is closely confirmed by experiment, but the height of the energy-frequency curve rises rapidly with increasing temperature, and the peak or maximum of the curve is proportional to the third power of the absolute temperature (T^3). Since the area under the curve represents the total energy radiated, which according to the Stefan-Boltzmann law is proportional to T^4, the effective width of the curve must vary as the first power of the temperature.

12-4. The Failure of the Classical Radiation Theory

The Wien radiation formula The basic radiation problem would have been considered solved if it had been possible to write a formula giving the correct shape of the radiation curve. Wien attempted in 1896 to obtain the correct formula by noting the similarity between the radiation curve and Maxwell's distribution law for the speeds of molecules in a gas. By means of classical methods of computing the energy of a wave of given frequency he tried to distribute these energies just as the energies of the molecules of the gas are distributed. By this process he arrived at the formula for the rate of energy emission per unit area R_f at a given frequency in terms of the frequency f, the absolute temperature T, the base of the natural system of logarithms ϵ, and constants c_1 and c_2.

$$R_f = c_1 \frac{f^3}{\epsilon^{c_2 f/kT}} \qquad [12\text{-}4]$$

The formula was successful in describing the shape of the curve except at the low-frequency end of the curve, where it was increasingly in error.

The Rayleigh-Jeans formula Lord Rayleigh shortly afterward took up the search for the correct radiation formula, and the mathematics was further developed in 1905 by Jeans. The method is of great historical interest and importance, not because it gave the correct formula, which it failed to do, but because it foreshadowed events to come in quantum theory and wave mechanics. Instead of borrowing the Maxwellian distribution directly, Rayleigh borrowed the idea of the equal division of energy between degrees of freedom in a gas, applying it to the radiation in a perfectly black enclosure. To do this he applied classical methods to find just those wavelengths which could form standing waves in the enclosure, and he called each of these modes of vibration a "degree of freedom."

The radiation law obtained by this method was almost a total failure throughout most of the frequency range of the radiation curve except far out toward the long wavelength end. Here, where the Wien formula failed, the Rayleigh formula had its only success. Thus, classical methods failed to yield a single formula that could completely describe the entire radiation curve. The dilemma was a serious one.

12-5. Origin of the Quantum Theory and Planck's Radiation Formula

To Max Planck in 1900, as to others, it seemed that the one major problem concerned with thermal radiation remaining to be solved was the dilemma presented above. Planck sought a formula that would fit the radiation curve from the shortest wavelength to the longest, and his mathematical search was successful with the development of the following formula for R_f, the rate of radiation of energy per unit area at frequency f and temperature $T°$ K,

$$R_f = \frac{8\pi h}{c^3} \frac{f^3}{\epsilon^{hf/kT} - 1} \qquad [12\text{-}5]$$

h being the Planck constant and k the Boltzmann gas constant. This equation is of the same form as the Wien equation (Eq. 12-4) except for the -1 in the denominator. At high frequencies this term is negligible, but at low frequencies it is just what is needed to make the equation fit the experimental curve where the Wien equation fails. Planck's formula now described the radiation process correctly, but a question arose as to the physical interpretation of his results. Not only did the classical theory of the continuous emission of radiation by a simple classical oscillator give the wrong results, but obviously the radiation could hardly be emitted as a continuous form of wave motion, for no atomic oscillator could be considered as having an unlimited supply of energy to radiate. Planck obtained his formula by exceedingly clever mathematical reasoning, and at first he considered that the discontinuity which he had put into his formula was a mere mathematical artifice. Then he saw the possible physical significance if he took the bold and revolutionary step of assuming that the energy of each oscillator responsible for thermal radiation and absorption was quantized and that the energy of an oscillator could only change discontinuously by a definite amount or quantum. He assumed the energy E_q of a quantum to be given by the product of a constant h and the frequency of the radiation. This was the origin of the quantum theory and

$$E_q = hf \qquad [6\text{-}1]$$

Over a period of years, however, this quantization has been found to represent something inherent in the nature of things, and, as we have seen in previous chapters, it is now a fundamental concept throughout the entire realm of radiation in its applications to atomic physics.

12-6. The Breakdown of Classical Causality

The failure of classical statistics in dealing with certain groups of phenomena led to the development of newer types of statistical theory, by means of which great progress has been made in the description of phenomena involving photons or electrons in large numbers. Before going into the newer developments it is desirable to examine a little more closely some of the steps by which the statistical theory of the behavior of large numbers of particles entered physics in the first place and at the same time to look at some of the broader implications of classical theory.

Classical mechanics was based on the exact measurement of the positions and velocities of objects at a given instant. The classical idea of causality, as applied to mechanics, then led to the conclusion that if at any instant such information were available, including knowledge of the forces acting on the particles, it would be possible to predict the positions and velocities of the particles at any future time. Indeed, if the whole universe were subject to such deterministic laws it would be possible in theory at least to predict any future state of things.

Yet, when such ideas were applied to the enormous numbers of molecules in even one cubic centimeter of gas, it became absurd to think of making detailed observations on each particle. Scientists therefore turned to the theories of chance and probability, applying them to the large numbers of objects in such an assemblage. It was thus in the study of the assemblage of particles in a gas that the probability theory first entered physics, simply because there were too many particles to distinguish individually. This did not overthrow the classical idea of causality but transferred its application from single molecules to large groups. Although it is not feasible to predict the exact position and velocity of a given molecule in such an assemblage, we can still predict with full assurance (except for minor fluctuations which themselves can be predicted) states of a large group such as pressure and the root-mean-square velocity for a gas under known conditions of volume and temperature. Determinism of single particles was given up for determinism of the states of large groups of particles simply because of the impossibility of dealing with such large numbers of individual particles, even though in principle the behavior of each was determinate.

The final breakdown of the classical concept of individual causality in the atomic realm, with its implied rigid determinism, came from another source. It came because of inherent limitations in the descriptions of waves and particles and because of the complementary character of the descriptions. These limitations were expressed in Heisenberg's principle (§ 6-6), according to which it became understood that detailed observations of momentum would prevent detailed observations of position. Since detailed observations of both at the same time were required by classical physics in order to make a definite prediction, such determinations for individual particles now became impossible. Here is a restriction due not to large numbers nor to the inaccuracy of our measurements but to something fundamental in nature itself and in the measuring process. Still, this breakdown does not extend to large groups of particles, and the states of the groups can still be predicted accurately, in their macroscopic aspects, by probability methods.

The classical probability methods that apply to gas molecules are found not to apply to photons and electrons, and new types of statistics, the Bose and the Fermi, based on quantum considerations have been developed. These will be discussed in the present chapter and in the one following. Thus, despite limitations in the subatomic realm, science by means of the new statistics preserves the classical causality of assemblages or states, and where it had appeared that a serious barrier to scientific progress had been reached science found ways to surmount the barrier.

12-7. The Classical Maxwell-Boltzmann Statistics*

Before considering the newer statistical methods let us look again at classical statistics. Maxwell and Boltzmann applied probability methods to the molecules of a gas in order to find just how the velocities of the particles could be affected by successive collisions and how many molecules could be expected to have a given velocity range at a given temperature when equilibrium was reached. Since some molecules momentarily gain velocity by collision and others momentarily lose velocity, equilibrium is that state in which in a given time interval the gains in velocity balance the losses. Maxwell derived his famous velocity distribution law from an application of what were considered to be the laws of pure chance. A more rigorous deduction was made later by Boltzmann, in which actual effects of collisions as determining the distribution of velocities in equilibrium were more explicitly involved. Consequently the law of distribution is sometimes called the *Maxwell-Boltzmann law.*

From the viewpoint of the probabilities involved it is well to start with the idea of the random deviations of bullets aimed at a target

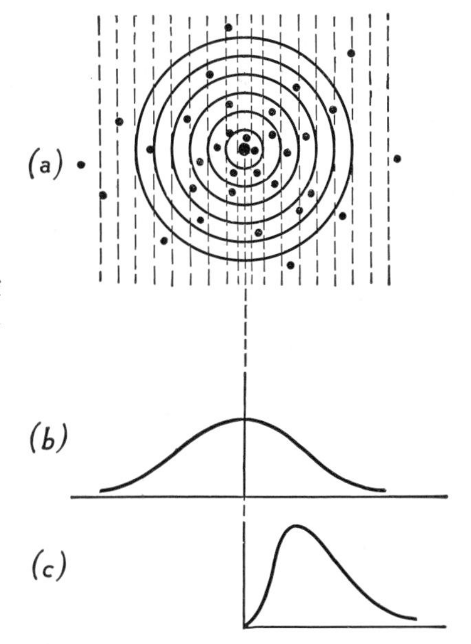

Fig. 12-3. ***a*, Random distribution of shots at a target; *b*, lateral distribution curve; *c*, radial distribution curve.**

* Optional.

(Fig. 12-3*a*). Unless unknown factors are involved this is presumed to represent a chance distribution grouped about the center of the target. If the number of shots that deviate to the right or the left by a certain amount is plotted, that is, the numbers in the vertical spaces, the curve of Fig. 12-3*b* is obtained. This is quite closely described by the so-called Gauss curve of errors the mathematical form of which is

$$y = a\epsilon^{-bx^2} \qquad [12\text{-}6]$$

where a is the height of the curve for $x = 0$, and b is a constant. However, let us now assume that it is desired to know how many shots miss the center of the target by a given amount regardless of direction. Very few if any hit the exact center, and very few if any miss the target by a large amount. The numbers to be plotted are the numbers in the concentric rings. The desired equation is obtained by multiplying the distribution equation 12-6 by the area of each ring surrounding the center. The product is the number of shots in each ring of the same width, and the values when plotted give the curve of Fig. 12-3*c*.

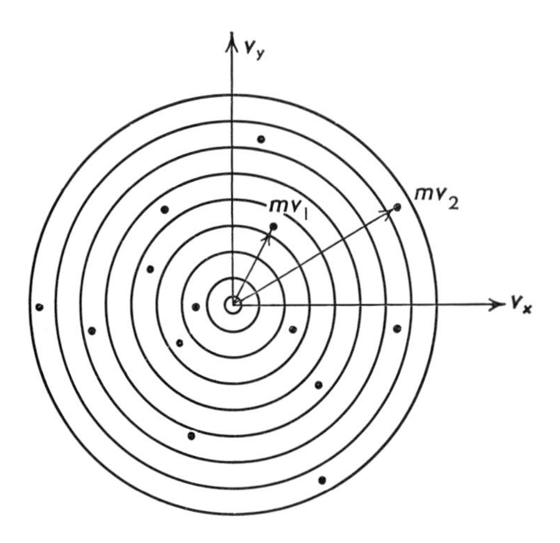

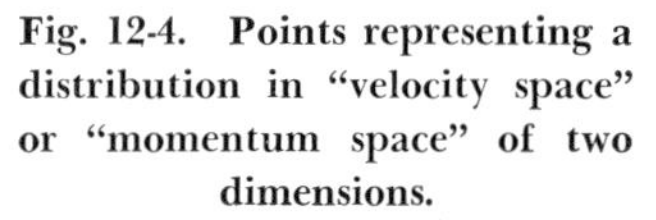
Fig. 12-4. Points representing a distribution in "velocity space" or "momentum space" of two dimensions.

Let us transform the picture and apply it to the molecules of a gas. The points representing hits on the target (Fig. 12-4) may now be interpreted as velocity points in "velocity space," each point representing the velocity of a molecule. The direction of an arrow drawn from the center of the target to the point represents the direction of the velocity, and the length of the arrow represents the magnitude of the velocity. The distribution of points then represents a velocity distribution. Maxwell and Boltzmann found that, instead of Eq. 12-6, the distribution law for velocity components v in one direction such as x is

$$y = a\epsilon^{-bv^2} = a\epsilon^{-mv^2/2kT} \qquad [12\text{-}7]$$

where the constant b is $m/2kT$, and $\frac{1}{2}mv^2$ is the kinetic energy of the molecule. The quantity kT is the Boltzmann constant k multiplied by the absolute temperature, and it also represents energy. The distribution then is actually an energy distribution, but from it the velocities may be obtained.

However, velocities may take any direction in space, so that we must now imagine the points in velocity space surrounding the center on all sides in three dimensions. The number of molecules having a given speed v irrespective of direction is represented by the number of points in a thin shell surrounding the center of the coordinate system. The number of points in such a shell is proportional to the volume of the shell. Take the radius of any shell to be v for that shell. The volume of this shell is $4\pi v^2 \Delta v$ where Δv is the thickness of the shell. Multiplying Eq. 12-7 by this, we have for the number of molecules Δn possessing velocities of a magnitude between v and $v + \Delta v$, regardless of direction,

$$\Delta n = 4\pi a\epsilon^{-mv^2/2kT}\, v^2 \Delta v \qquad [12\text{-}8]$$

This is the exact form of the Maxwell distribution law, and it only remains to evaluate the constant a, a matter too lengthy for inclusion here, to obtain the complete form of the equation

$$\Delta n = 4N\sqrt{\frac{m^3}{8\pi k^3 T^3}}\, v^2 \epsilon^{-mv^2/2kT}\, \Delta v \qquad [12\text{-}9]$$

where N is the total number of molecules in the gas. This is the same as Eq. 11-15.

Since the directions of motion have been disregarded it is now desirable to speak of this formula as representing a distribution of speeds. If, for each point in velocity space representing the velocities of an assemblage of molecules, we multiply the velocity of each molecule by its mass we can think of the array of points existing in a new region called **momentum space.** The idea of representing the momenta of gas molecules by vectors measured to points in a space called momentum space is of much importance in what follows.

The Maxwell distribution law can also be derived by starting with the classical definition of the most probable state of a given arrangement. Classical statistics defines the thermodynamic probability W of a given arrangement of particles as

$$W = \frac{N!}{N_1!\,N_2!\,N_3!\cdots N_m!} \qquad [12\text{-}10]$$

where N is the total number of molecules, N_1 is the number in a given group, and $N!$ is the factorial of N. The thermodynamic probability of a given state of an assemblage has values from 1 up and must be distinguished from the ordinary probability of an event represented by values from 0 to 1 where 1 stands for certainty.

The factorial of the number of particles such as N_1 in each group is divided into $N!$, the factorial of the total, because the particles in any group are assumed to be indistinguishable and any two in a group may change places without affecting the arrangement. If all the molecules were in one group we would have the value unity, and this would be the least probable arrangement. If all the molecules were divided as evenly as possible between all possible groups the value of the probability W would be a maximum, and this would be considered the most probable arrangement.

This definition, as it stands, applies directly to the distribution of molecules of a gas in space, as, for instance, the air in a room. Although statistical theories properly apply only to very large numbers, an example with small numbers may make things clearer. Figure 12-5 shows four boxes and four marbles. In distribution *a* they are all in one box, and the probability is 1. Since $0! = 1$ these are omitted.

$$W = \frac{4!}{4!} = 1$$

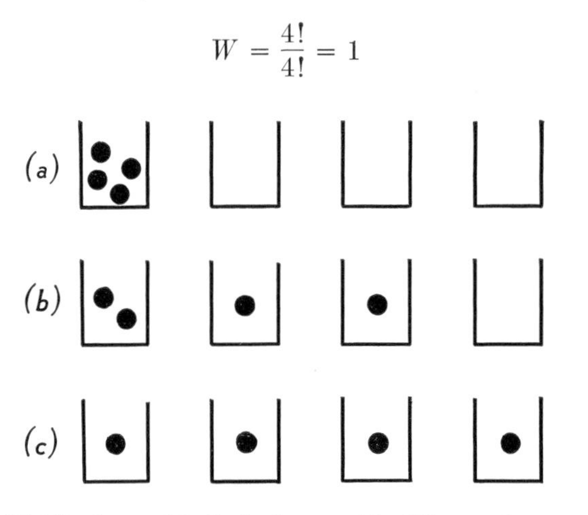

Fig. 12-5. Distributions of balls in boxes with different degrees of probability: *a*, least probable; *b*, intermediate; *c*, most probable.

In *b*, where two are in one box and the other two are in separate boxes, the probability is

$$W = \frac{4!}{2!\,1!\,1!} = 12$$

In *c*, where the distribution is uniform, the probability is

$$W = \frac{4!}{1!\,1!\,1!\,1!} = 24$$

Consequently the first distribution is least probable and the last is most probable. From this we may say that it is far more probable that gas molecules will, on the average, be fairly evenly distributed about a room than that they will all be found on one side or in the middle of the room, since all parts of the room are equally probable.

If we try to apply such probability considerations to a velocity distribution, the boxes can represent velocity groups, but we know from the Maxwellian distribution curve (Fig. 11-2) that not all velocities are equally probable in a given volume of gas at constant temperature and that the velocities tend to cluster about a most probable value in a manner similar to rifle shots fired at a target. Consideration of this fact leads to the introduction of the factor $\epsilon^{-mv_2/2kT}$ (Eq. 12-7) into the distribution formula. This is the same factor as in the Gauss curve of errors, where *b* is now $m/2kT$ and depends on molecular mass and energy, as previously indicated. Since the unavailable energy (entropy) of a gas is a maximum for the most probable state, the probability of a state may be related to the energy and temperature, and the constants of the distribution formula can be evaluated. The derivation of Maxwell's equation by this method is not significant here, but it is important to notice how the classical definition of probability must now be changed in the realm of photons and electrons where quantum considerations arise.

12-8. Bose Statistics*

Twenty-four years after the origin of the quantum theory, Bose (1924) (in India) and Einstein independently developed a new system of statistics involving certain quantum restrictions, the new theory being applicable to radiation photons. This was called the Bose-Einstein statistics, now shortened to Bose. They noted, as had Rayleigh and

* Optional.

others, that there was a strong resemblance between the shape of the energy-distribution curve for the radiation from a black body (Fig. 12-2) and the Maxwell distribution curve for the speeds of molecules in a gas at a given temperature (Fig. 11-2).

Whereas Maxwell and Boltzmann had applied classical statistics (probability theory) to gas molecules, Bose now found it necessary to do two revolutionary things in order to apply statistical theory to photons. The definition of "most probable" had to be changed, and quantization had to be introduced. With such changes Bose was able to deduce the Planck radiation law.

In order to have a distribution representing ideal black-body radiation at a temperature T, it is assumed that the radiation is inside an enclosure, the inner walls of which are perfectly black. Then, under equilibrium conditions the walls emit as much radiation as they absorb in unit time, and the radiation in the enclosure will be ideal black-body radiation.

It must be remembered that the photons in such an enclosure are different in important ways from gas molecules. Photons all travel in free space with the same speed regardless of frequency, and it is the frequencies (or energies) which are distributed. On the other hand, gas molecules have a distribution of speeds, though all have the same mass. A convenient connecting link between the two is the concept of momentum. Since the masses of all gas molecules in a simple ideal gas are the same, the velocity distribution is just as well described as being a momentum distribution. The relation to radiation photons now becomes apparent. Despite the constant speed of all photons there can be a momentum distribution since frequencies may vary and since the momentum of a photon (§ 6-2) is hf/c or h/λ. Thus a momentum distribution for photons would mean a frequency (or wavelength) distribution, which is exactly what is observed.

To determine such a momentum (or frequency) distribution Bose found it necessary to alter the classical definition of probability in the following manner. He defined the probability W^* not in terms of particles (now photons) in a given state but in terms of the numbers of states having a given number of particles in it, and the states must be quantized.

$$W^* = \frac{Z!}{Z_0!\, Z_1!\, Z_2!\, Z_3! \cdots Z_m!} \qquad [12\text{-}11]$$

where Z is the total number of states, Z_0 is the number of states having no particles in it, Z_1 the number having one particle, Z_2 the number having two, and so on. This is justified at least by the validity of the results. In terms of the previous example, with the provision that the boxes in Fig. 12-5 represent frequency states, we see that in *a*

$$W^* = \frac{4!}{3!\,1!} = 4$$

In *b*

$$W^* = \frac{4!}{1!\,2!\,1!} = 12$$

In *c*

$$W^* = \frac{4!}{4!} = 1$$

Thus, according to the new definition of probability, neither extreme is most probable, but the state in between (*b*) is.

To obtain the Bose formula for the momentum distribution of photons in radiation the new definition of "most probable" is necessary. Quantization is introduced by the assumption that photons cannot have just any arbitrary amount of linear momentum but must have values determined by the Planck constant h. This can be done graphically by dividing momentum space (§ 12-7) about the center of our erstwhile target into small compartments, each with volume h^3. For such an element of volume, at a particular distance from the center of coordinates in any direction, all photons will have the same amount of momentum, that is, they will have the value for the element of volume at that distance. To move radially outward to another compartment or element of volume would involve a quantized change of momentum, not a continuous change as in classical theory.

The reason for choosing h^3 as the unit of volume is somewhat involved, but a fairly simple statement can be made. Since, according to Heisenberg's principle, h is approximately the limit of precision of simultaneous measurement of momentum and position in one direction of space such as x, the product of the limits in three dimensions would be h^3. The three dimensions of space x, y, z and the three directions of momentum p_x, p_y, p_z together make up a mathematical space of six dimensions called **phase space** but in the present discussion we restrict ourselves for simplicity to momentum space. Suffice it to say that, in moving outward in momentum space from one cell to the next, the momentum increases by one quantum, and the numbering of the cells represents a set of quantum numbers instead of continuous changes of momentum, as in classical physics.

The number of elements of volume in a shell surrounding the center of coordinates, multiplied by the appropriate factor representing the new probability distribution, gives the number of photons having a particular amount of momentum. Transforming this into an energy distribution, the number of photons having energies within unit energy range is

$$N = B \frac{hf^3}{\epsilon^{hf/kT} - 1} \qquad [12\text{-}12]$$

where hf is the energy of the photon. The variable term now has the same form as in the Planck radiation formula (Eq. 12-4), and by evaluating the constant and finding the energy radiated per unit area the Planck formula is obtained. This law, as previously stated, accurately describes the form of the radiation curve for all wavelengths at a given temperature and thus solves the fundamental radiation problem.

One of the most satisfying aspects of this theory is that the same result may be obtained by wave mechanics by considering the wavelengths of the photons moving back and forth between the walls of a perfectly reflecting box or enclosure. Quantization enters since the wavelengths are limited to just those which form standing wave patterns in the box with nodes at the sides of the box. This is similar to the Rayleigh-Jeans method except that the classical idea of equal division of energy between "degrees of freedom" is now replaced by a different distribution function involving quantum restrictions.

The progress made in describing radiation phenomena in terms of Bose statistics represents another victory for the quantum theory, and it means the extension of quantum concepts in a new way to a new field. Probability theory, which entered physics by way of the kinetic theory of gases, has now invaded the realm of radiation after being appropriately modified. The capacity for exact scientific description has been extended from the world of atomic phenomena, where radiation was described in terms of individual atomic or molecular transitions, to the world of large-scale radiation phenomena, where large assemblages of photons are dealt with, thus forging another link in the chain of underlying relatedness of all phenomena. Similar progress has been made in studying the behavior of electrons in solid matter, as will be seen in the next chapter. It should also be noted that Bose statistics has applications to particle physics, as will be found in the study of nuclear particles.

SUGGESTED READING

M. W. ZEMANSKY, *Heat and Thermodynamics,* 2nd ed. (New York, McGraw-Hill, 1943).
W. SEARS, *Thermodynamics* (Cambridge, Addison-Wesley, 1953).
M. PLANCK, *Theory of Heat* (New York, Macmillan, 1949).
E. FERMI, "Quantum Theory of Radiation," *Reviews of Modern Physics, 4* 87 (1932).

CHAPTER 13

THE SOLID STATE AND FERMI STATISTICS

13-1. Thermal and Electric Conductivity

Electrons can best be studied when they are removed from solid matter, as for instance in an electric discharge. The use of some form of probe to investigate the inner secrets of a solid defeats itself by displacing the solid. Measurements of current and voltage drop along a conductor enable us to confirm Ohm's law, but that is a macroscopic law and tells us nothing about how electrons pass through the conductor or indeed whether or not there are any electrons in it. Nevertheless, man craves answers to many such questions, and much has been learned in recent years about electrons in solids and how these electrons behave.

The question of how an electric current is produced and maintained in a conductor has always been an intriguing one. The discovery of the electron and the recognition of the electrical nature of the atom were a great step forward, but many puzzling aspects remained to be solved. For example, when thermal energy is conducted along a metal rod the electrons play an important part, yet in the case of the specific heat of a metal they apparently play no appreciable part in the process although classical theory had predicted otherwise. The reason for this was for a long time unaccountable. In the study of substances called semiconductors, the evidence indicated that electrons are much more restricted in their motions than they are in conductors, and in certain conditions not electrons but positive carriers called "holes" move to carry current. This was contrary to common theory.

It had long been known that the best conductors of electricity were also the best conductors of heat. In 1850, Wiedemann and Franz found that the ratio of thermal to electric conductivity K/σ is almost the same for all good conductors at a constant temperature. It was later found that the ratio is directly proportional to the absolute temperature over a considerable range.

From the constancy of this ratio for different materials at a constant temperature it was concluded by Lorentz, Richardson, and others at the beginning of the twentieth century that both kinds of conductivity are due primarily to the "free" electrons present in the conductor. From a simple application of what was then the new electron theory, Richardson derived a formula for the ratio of thermal to electric conductivity.

$$\frac{K}{\sigma} = \frac{3k^2}{e^2} T \qquad [13\text{-}1]$$

where k is the Boltzmann constant of molecular theory, e is the charge of the electron, and T is the absolute temperature. The basic assumption was that there are "free" electrons in a conductor, that they behave like the molecules of a gas, moving with unceasing random motion, and that they thus constitute what has been called an "electron gas." A drift of the electron gas in one direction or another would then constitute an electric current, and the transfer of any increase in the energy of random motion in any direction would be thermal conduction. Each form of conductivity was assumed to depend on the number of free electrons per cubic centimeter and upon the mean free path of each in the conductor. These qualities, which would have been difficult if not impossible to measure, fortunately canceled in the ratio. Putting in known values of e, k, and T, the theoretical value of the ratio was found to agree fairly well with experimental results.

Notwithstanding this agreement, the theory, which at first had looked so reasonable, encountered many difficulties. The attempt to introduce a Maxwellian distribution of electron speeds into the theoretical derivation made the agreement with experiment poorer instead of better. Worst of all, the theory went into a state of collapse for years when it was noted that the free electrons apparently make little or no contribution to the specific heats of the metals concerned. Since they had just been proposed as the carriers of thermal energy like gas molecules, this seemed to be an utter contradiction.

The impasse thus presented was resolved only with the application of entirely new ideas arising from the developments of the newer quantum theory. Along with the possibility of describing the electron in terms of its de Broglie wavelength came the development in 1927 by Fermi and by Dirac of what are called the Fermi-Dirac statistics (or Fermi for short), applicable to electrons in a metal. This represented as radical a departure from classical ideas as did the Bose statistics and indeed can be considered a modification of the Bose statistics.

13-2. Fermi Statistics and Distribution of Speeds*

The difficulty of applying a Maxwellian distribution (§ 12-7) to the electron speeds in a metal might be foreseen in view of the absence of appreciable constraints on the molecules of a gas, whereas electrons in a conductor must certainly suffer some constraints even though we loosely speak of them as "free." Whatever constraints there may be, they need no detailed consideration and are covered by application of the basic concepts of quantization, including the Pauli exclusion principle. A complete statement of the derivation and results of the Fermi distribution would be much too lengthy and involved for discussion here, but certain main features may be set forth that illustrate the manner in which quantum considerations have contributed to the new theory and to the important achievements of the theory.

In deriving the distribution of speeds in an ideal gas, Boltzmann introduced the concept of molecular chaos. This implied independence of motion and freedom from constraints, so far as possible. There was, of course, at that time no idea of quantization, and the mathematical formula (distribution function) was a "smooth" function "permitting" molecules to have any gradation of velocity or momentum and consequently any gradation of energy. Bose, on the other hand, as we have just seen (Chap. 12), in applying statistical considerations to the photons representing black-body radiation in equilibrium with the radiator, was obliged to introduce quantization, so that photons could have only particular amounts of momentum. However, in Bose's theory there was no limit to the number of photons that could have the same momentum. The fact that one photon had a particular momentum did not exclude some other photon from having the same amount.

Fermi found it necessary at this point to make a radical addition to the Bose theory to make it applicable to the electrons in a metal. In a single atom the Pauli exclusion principle does not permit two

* Optional.

electrons to have the same quantum numbers. Might it not be, since all metals are crystalline and since a crystal represents an extremely orderly arrangement of atoms, that a similar form of regimentation and restriction must be applied to such crystals, just as had previously been applied to the atom? The success of the Fermi theory now amply justifies the method adopted. In brief, the assumptions are as follows.

Quantization of momenta is accepted, as in the Bose theory, as is his method of defining the probability of a distribution of momenta. Upon all this, however, is superposed the Pauli exclusion principle. Whereas in the Bose theory any number of photons could occupy the same compartment in momentum space having a volume h^3, now only two electrons are permitted to have the same momentum, that is, only two are permitted to occupy the same compartment, and they must have opposite spins. Since each compartment in momentum space represents a different number of quanta of momentum and since in each compartment only two electrons are permitted, one with spin quantum number $+\frac{1}{2}$ and the other with spin quantum number $-\frac{1}{2}$, the Pauli exclusion principle is satisfied, and no two electrons have the same set of quantum numbers. Thus we see that, according to the Fermi theory, electrons in a metal are quantized in such a way that they possess an extraordinary degree of individualism and are so constrained in their behavior that no two can act exactly alike.

Fermi distribution of speeds According to the Maxwell-Boltzmann theory, if electrons were to behave like gas molecules they would all behave on the average very much the same. As the temperature of a block of metal is lowered, the kinetic energy of random motion should decrease steadily until at absolute zero such motion should cease, and all free electrons would then have reached the same zero energy state. According to the Fermi theory, however, a quite different situation exists. Momenta are quantized, and only two electrons (with opposite spins) can have a given amount. As the temperature is decreased, electrons would settle down by quantized steps to lower momentum values, that is, to compartments in momentum space nearer the origin at which the momentum is zero, avoiding of course values of momentum (compartments) pre-empted by other electrons.

Consequently, as the temperature is reduced the electrons settle down into their compartments in momentum space like bees in a hive. At absolute zero they would be clustered as closely as possible about the origin of momentum space, filling all compartments and leaving no vacant compartments within the limits of the group. Owing to the very large number of free electrons in a metal, however, the outermost filled compartments in momentum space, even at absolute zero, are a considerable distance from the origin and represent a relatively large amount of energy. This is called zero-point energy and is in direct contrast with the Maxwellian conception of zero energy at the absolute zero of temperature.

The Fermi theory leads to an interesting and important result when we consider what happens with rising temperature. Since at absolute zero there are no unfilled momentum compartments except on the outer edge of the group, where in our representation the electrons already have considerable amounts of momentum, the average electron, upon being offered extra momentum, has "no place to go" and cannot accept it unless the amount is sufficient to raise it to an unfilled compartment. Consequently only the electrons of highest momentum, that is, those adjacent to unfilled cells, can respond to ordinary temperature

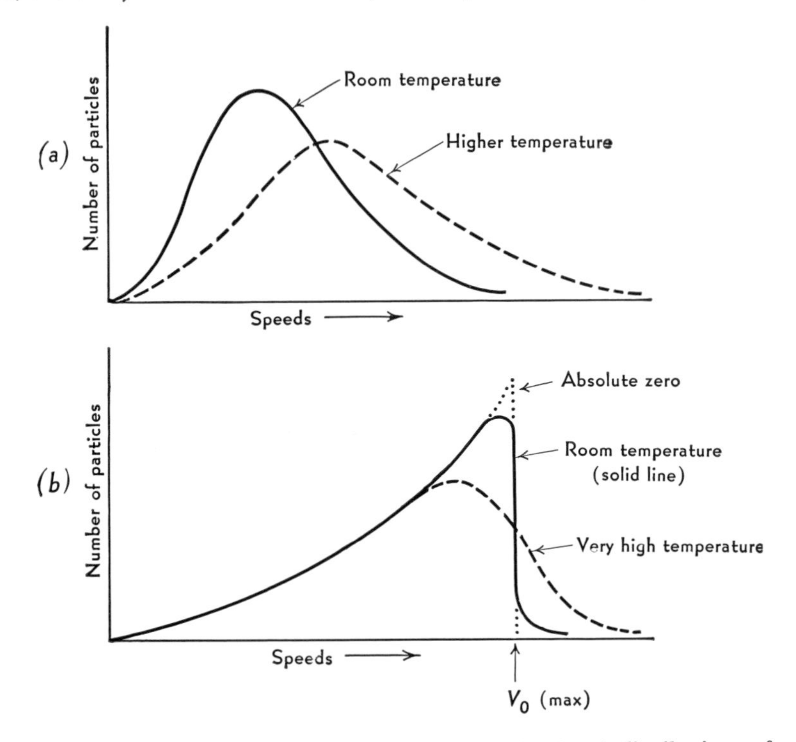

Fig. 13-1. Comparison of: *a*, Maxwellian, and *b*, Fermi distributions of speeds at different temperatures. Dotted line in *b* shows Fermi distribution for absolute zero, with the maximum speed for that temperature indicated. Dashed line in *b* shows how Fermi distribution approaches a Maxwellian one at sufficiently high temperatures.

changes and move to outer compartments. This is the result of the quantum restriction, and the picture is changed quite completely from that of the Maxwellian theory.

Fermi statistics lead to the following distribution law for the velocities of the particles of a "Fermi gas":

$$N_v = \frac{8\pi m^3}{h^3} \frac{v^2}{\epsilon^{\frac{1}{2}mv^2 - w_m/kT} + 1}$$

where N_v is the number of particles of mass m having a velocity v, and w_m is the maximum energy that a particle can have at absolute zero.

Figure 13-1 shows a graph representing a comparison of a, the distribution of speeds of particles in a Maxwell gas, and b, particles in a Fermi gas. The solid line in b indicates the Fermi distribution of speeds at room temperature. The modification of this curve to show the speeds at absolute zero is indicated by the dotted lines, with the notably sharp cut-off where the curve drops perpendicularly to zero at the upper end of the range. The dashed line in each figure presents the distribution for a higher temperature. As the temperature is increased, the curve becomes more rounded, departing further from the sharp upper limit of the distribution at absolute zero. The rounding of the curve represents the shift of some electrons to higher states.

Note on conservation of statistics In the subsequent chapters on nuclear physics, reference will be made to Fermi and Bose statistics and their applications to atomic nuclei and to the particles of which those nuclei are composed. When the wave functions of nuclear particles are set up it is found that there are two different classes, if the spin of the particles is included in the equations. In one group the sign of the equation changes from plus to minus when the signs of the coordinates are changed. In the other group the sign does not change. The former equations are associated with Fermi statistics, and the latter are associated with Bose statistics. Nuclei composed of an even number of particles are described by Bose statistics, whereas nuclei composed of an odd number of particles are described by Fermi statistics. Single electrons, protons, or neutrons "obey" Fermi statistics. The statistics of any particles involved in a nuclear transformation are found to remain the same during any nuclear transformation. This invariance is called the conservation of statistics, and the statistics of a particle or group of particles are just as important as other quantities such as mass, charge, and spin.

13-3. Specific Heats of Metals

According to the Maxwell theory, the large number of free electrons able to participate in a rise in temperature by sharing the increased kinetic energy would make the energy increase considerable. Consequently, the specific heat of any conductor should be much larger because of the presence of free electrons than that of a substance not possessing such free electrons. With the Fermi distribution this is not true.

In Fig. 13-2 below, the Fermi curve is turned 90°, and the different shape of the curve results from plotting energies instead of speeds.

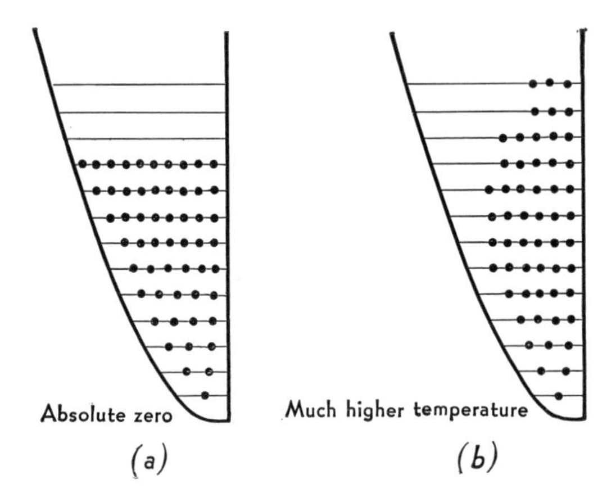

Fig. 13-2. Representation of Fermi distribution: *a*, at absolute zero with all levels filled up to the maximum; *b*, an approximation of how some electrons move to higher energy states at a very much higher temperature.

Higher energy states now appear higher up on the diagram, and the horizontal lines represent a few of the many possible energy levels. At *a* the diagram shows how, for absolute zero, all energy levels are occupied up to a certain maximum. At *b* the diagram indicates how, for a much higher temperature, some electrons in the upper levels have been able to accept energy and move to still higher levels. Owing to the quantum restrictions most of the electrons have not been able to participate in the temperature rise. Their contribution to the specific heats of metals is then relatively small, only something like 1 per cent of what it would be in the Maxwell theory.

This is just what was required to clear up the difficulty with specific heats. If all the valence electrons belonging to an atom were free, and if all such free electrons acted like gas molecules, it would be necessary to assign to them a heat capacity of $3k/2$ per electron per degree. However, experiments indicated that the specific heats of most metals are quite close to the value assigned to the thermal agitation of the atoms themselves. Consequently it is impossible to explain experimental results on the assumption that electrons absorb the amount of thermal energy they would, according to Maxwell-Boltzmann statistics, if they behaved like the molecules of an ordinary gas. Now, by the Fermi theory, such absorption is seen to be negligible, and the theory thus is remarkably successful in the matter of specific heats.

13-4. Electric Conduction in Metals

The success of the Fermi theory in describing specific heats of metals would be one-sided indeed if the new theory ruined what had appeared to be a satisfactory explanation of electric conduction on the basis of an electron gas with a Maxwellian distribution of speeds.

Lorentz had based his original theory of electric conduction on what seemed to be a reasonable assumption that all valence electrons are free and that electron mean free paths in metals are of the order of magnitude of the spacing between atoms in the metallic crystal. The restriction on free motion by the Fermi theory to about 1 per cent of the electrons would now imply that mean free paths are of the order of a hundred times the distance between atoms.

Sommerfeld, applying Fermi statistics to the problem of electric conduction, arrived at an equation similar to that of Lorentz, but he had had to arbitrarily assume the existence of such long mean free paths. However, with this assumption the theory successfully described conductivity in metals, and Pauli extended the theory to give a satisfactory description of the feeble paramagnetism exhibited by metals.

The long mean free paths seemed unreasonable, but here again the new wave mechanics came to the rescue. Instead of picturing electrons as particles colliding with the atoms of the crystal lattice of a metal such as copper, Bloch and others pictured moving electrons in terms of de Broglie waves of wavelength $\lambda = h/mv$. The passage of such waves through a lattice of atoms could now be treated mathematically by methods like those used in describing the passage of light waves through a similarly complicated lattice. This in turn involved diffraction of waves and a quite different treatment from that based on the particle picture. With some important extensions to the theory the longer mean free paths were justified, and the theory now gives a more adequate description of the behavior of nonconductors and semiconductors as well as conductors.

13-5. Conductors, Semiconductors, and Insulators

In the earlier theories of conduction of electricity by metals, it was thought that electrons moved inside the metal in a region of uniform field in which they were uniformly accelerated between collisions. This was soon recognized as only a crude approximation. From a large-scale viewpoint a conductor of finite length, on which an emf is impressed, does have a certain average fall of potential per unit length, but the electrons in the conductor belong distinctly to the atomic realm where there must evidently be variations of potential from atom to atom even without an impressed emf. A more exact theory of conduction would have to take these variations into consideration.

The simplest arrangement is the regularly spaced arrangement of atoms of a crystal lattice. To get from one atom to another an electron has to go up over a potential hill. In Fig. 13-3 the approximate variation of potential energy of an electron with distance is shown for a one-dimensional model crystal with no applied emf. If the Schrödinger

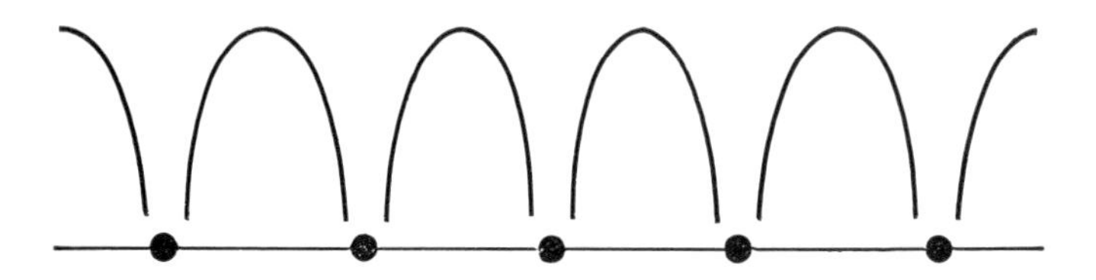

Fig. 13-3. Smoothed-over variation of potential energy along a one-dimensional crystal lattice for five atoms.

wave equation is to be solved for this potential distribution, the complicated function representing variation of potential energy with distance must be put into the equation (Eq. 10-12) instead of V. This makes the equation a very difficult one to solve, requiring intricate methods of approximation. By a more simple method of attack certain salient features may be revealed.

The kinetic energy $(E - V)$ in the Schrödinger equation may be set equal to $p^2/2m$ where p is the classical momentum. From the equation for the de Broglie wavelength $\lambda = h/mv$, the momentum mv is h/λ. From this the kinetic energy $p^2/2m$ is $h^2/2m\lambda^2$. If $1/\lambda$ is defined as the de Broglie wave number represented by ν,

$$E - V = \frac{h^2}{2m}\nu^2 \qquad [13\text{-}2]$$

If V is constant throughout the metal, as was assumed in the Pauli-Sommerfeld theory, the total energy E varies as the square of ν. This leads to the parabola of Fig. 13-4*a*, showing how E varies continuously with ν. However, if the potential energy V is assumed to vary as in Fig. 13-3, the energy E is no longer a continuous function of ν.

Mathematical analysis of this situation by Strutt, More, Brillouin, and others has shown that in general the energy curve jumps discontinuously for particular values of the de Broglie wavelength, as shown

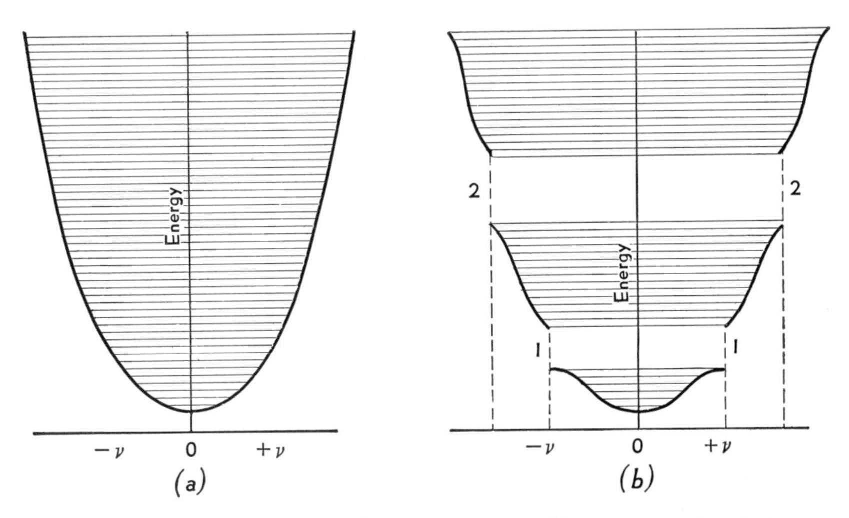

Fig. 13-4. Energy vs wave number curve: *a*, not taking account of variation in potential between atoms; *b*, assuming a potential variation between atoms similar to Fig. 13-3.

in Fig. 13-4*b* at positions 1,1, 2,2, etc. This is interpreted as meaning that not all energies for an electron are possible. At each discontinuity a band of energies is forbidden. Between these are the allowable energy bands (shaded regions in *b*).

A valence electron is "free" to move through the atomic lattice, but it experiences periodic variations of energy. It is more likely to be found between two atoms where it is repelled by electrons on either side, but it may pass from one of these regions to another. According to the solution of the wave equation, in so doing it can only have energies lying in certain allowed bands.

Another way of considering the problem is to think of a block of conductor as a "giant molecule" which may contain as many as 10^{23} valence electrons per cm^3. Just as each electron in a single atom is in a particular quantized state, according to the Pauli principle, so also all the electrons in a block of conductor are in quantized states. But no longer are these states sharply defined by narrow energy levels. Here the atoms are so close together that mutual interactions occur and fields overlap. What were quite sharp energy levels are now broadened into wide bands. In some substances these bands may overlap, and sometimes they are separated by forbidden energy regions.

With this as a basis it is now possible to describe the main features of conduction in terms of wave-mechanical theory. A more detailed analysis of particular crystals leads to confirmation of the over-all scheme outlined here. In Fig. 13-5 three allowed bands *A*, *B*, and *C*

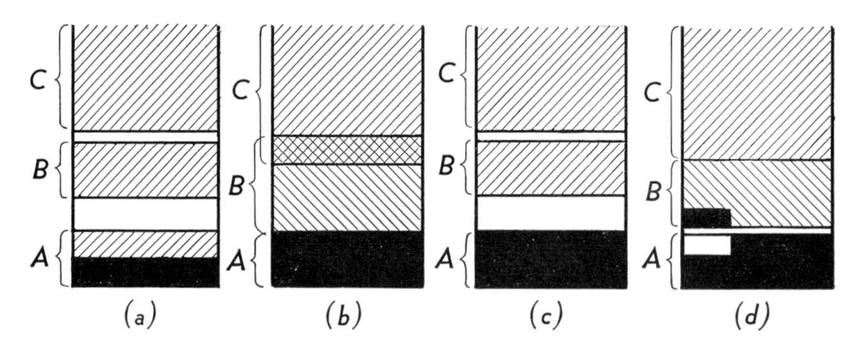

Fig. 13-5. Conduction bands (shaded) for: *a*, a fair conductor (conduction band not filled); *b*, a good conductor; *c*, a good insulator (conduction band filled); *d*, a semiconductor (conduction band filled but small energy interval between bands).

are illustrated. Each band is composed of a large number of closely related, overlapping energy levels. The shaded regions represent the allowed bands; the unshaded regions are the forbidden energy regions. The black regions represent completely filled energy levels. At *a*, the lowest band is not completely filled, and electrons in the filled region (black) can accept energy, raising them as far as the highest level at the top of the *A* band. Such electrons are thereby free to move in this band under an impressed emf, and they then constitute an electric current; the diagram represents a fairly good conductor. At *b*, the allowed bands *A*, *B*, *C* overlap. There are no forbidden regions, electrons can accept a wide range of energies, and the diagram represents a very good conductor. At *c*, the allowed band *A* is completely filled.

No electron in the band can accept energy unless the energy is sufficient to raise it to the next band. Since the forbidden range is wide and represents a large energy change, the diagram represents a good insulator. Only under an extremely high potential gradient could electrons be raised to the next allowed level *B*, and then the insulation would break down and a spark might occur.

With these diagrams the wave-mechanical distinction between a good conductor and a good insulator becomes clear. Another class of substances, semiconductors, is acquiring increasing importance. These are represented at *d*, where the lowest band is filled, or nearly so, but the forbidden region is so narrow that a moderate applied emf or even thermal agitation may raise some electrons to the next allowed band where they are free to accept more energy and move with the field. The vacancies left in the filled band are called **holes,** and when these migrate they move in a direction opposite to the electrons, thus behaving like a flow of positive charge.

Among the semiconductors of special interest are germanium and silicon because they are used in the making of **transistors.** Transistors now take the place of electron tubes in many applications. Their chief features are their small size and very low power consumption. Germanium and silicon atoms each have 4 valence electrons and form crystals in which the electrons represented by dashes (Fig. 13-6*a*) are

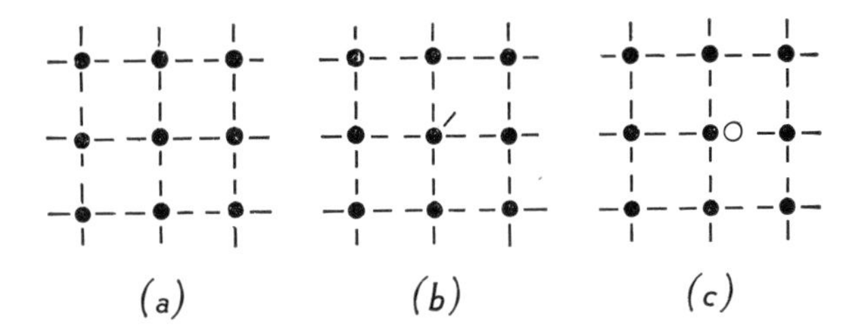

Fig. 13-6. Lattice showing: *a*, arrangement of atoms in a crystal of silicon or germanium; *b*, the same lattice with a donor atom at the center having 5 valence electrons; *c*, the same lattice with an acceptor atom at the center having only 3 valence electrons.

paired. If an impurity atom called a donor with 5 valence electrons, such as aluminum, is introduced into the crystal and appears on the lattice as at *b*, an extra electron for each such atom is produced and may act as a free carrier of current. Such an impure crystal is called an *n*-type crystal. If an impurity atom called an acceptor is introduced with only 3 valence electrons, such as arsenic, as at *c*, a "hole" is produced, and it is free to act as a positive carrier. A crystal with such impurity atoms is called a *p*-type crystal. Both *n*-type and *p*-type crystals may now be prepared artificially.

A junction transistor consists of a very thin slice of *p*-type crystal between two small blocks of *n*-type, forming an *n*-*p*-*n*-type transistor, or a very thin slice of *n*-type crystal between two blocks of *p*-type, forming a *p*-*n*-*p*-type transistor. The thin slice in the middle controls the flow of electrons and holes in much the same way as the grid of a radio or television tube controls the flow of electrons in the tube. This permits such a transistor to take the place of a radio or similar tube in many applications. The so-called point-contact transistor consists of a single crystal in which suitable *p*-type and *n*-type regions have been formed and to which contact is made by metal points.

The simplest application of *p*- and *n*-type crystals is in the crystal diode or rectifier. The rectifying action is represented in Fig. 13-7, where at *a* the difference in potential pulls electrons and holes back from the interface between two sections of crystal, one *p*-type and one

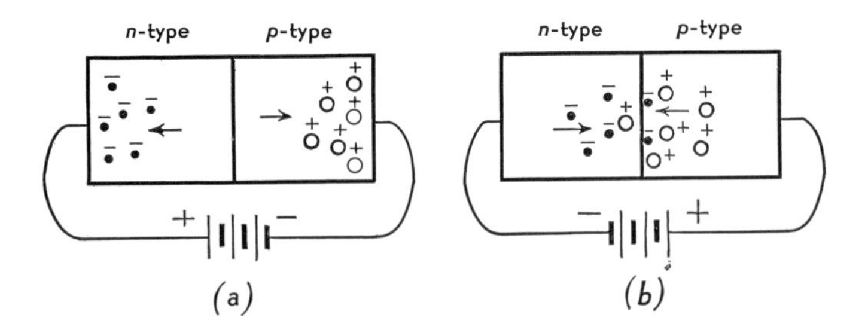

Fig. 13-7. Rectifying action at contact of *p*- and *n*-type crystals; *a*, direction of high resistance; *b*, direction of low resistance.

n-type. At *b*, where the difference in potential is reversed, both holes and electrons are drawn across the interface, and current flows. Natural crystals of germanium or silicon often have adjacent regions with different impurities, and such a region when found by means of a pointed metal contact will give rectification. The development of the three-contact transistor from the two-contact crystal rectifier was an achievement that won the Nobel prize in 1956 for Bardeen, Brattain, and Shockley.

13-6. Thermionic Emission

Careful measurements of the distribution of speeds of electrons emitted by hot filaments show that the speeds closely follow a Maxwellian distribution. It might at first be thought that, although these electrons possess a Fermi distribution of speeds inside the metal, they quickly acquire a Maxwellian distribution of speeds by collision with the gas molecules of the region into which they are ejected. However, it was found that even if the thermionic emission occurs in a very high vacuum, where the chance of hitting gas molecules is negligible, the electrons still apparently have a Maxwellian distribution of speeds. That such electrons belong to a Fermi distribution of speeds inside a metal and to a Maxwellian distribution outside the metal seemed at first contradictory, but further analysis shows that it is not so.

According to classical theory, any electron in the Maxwellian distribution may possibly gain enough energy to pass the potential barrier at the surface of the metal and escape when the temperature of the metal is raised. According to the Fermi distribution, only the electrons at the top of the filled energy levels are likely to accept energy and gain enough to escape. Theory indicates that enough of these electrons are available to account for experimentally measured emission currents. The number of electrons having speeds just sufficient to enable them to escape with small remaining velocities after having passed the surface barrier is large, but the probability that they will actually escape is small. For electrons of higher speeds the probability of emission is greater until maximum emission is reached, at which point the decreasing numbers of electrons of higher energies cause the curve to fall again. Thus the distribution of speeds of emitted electrons turns out to be essentially Maxwellian.

Although, according to the Fermi distribution, only the electrons at the higher energy limit of the group are relatively free to accept energy and move to higher energy levels, the distribution of the speeds of those electrons in a metal which move into energy states above the limiting value for absolute zero closely approximates a Maxwellian distribution in that part of the curve. Indeed, at extremely high temperatures, far beyond anything attainable in the laboratory, nearly all electrons would be shifted to higher energy states, and the whole curve would approach that of a Maxwellian distribution in its general characteristics. It thus becomes evident that the Maxwellian distribution is actually a limiting case of the Fermi distribution.

By purely theoretical procedure, involving wave mechanics and the Fermi distribution function, Dushman arrived at the same equation for thermionic emission as a function of temperature as that obtained much earlier by Richardson on the basis of classical theory (Eq. 3-1). Although wave-mechanical theory introduces the idea that some electrons with sufficient energy to escape may be reflected at the surface of the metal, there is also the possibility that some with less energy

magnetic moment, and when iron crystallizes these domains, in which all the magnetic moments of all the atoms in the domains point in the same direction, form spontaneously and thus the domains magnetize themselves. Several of them, however, tend to form a group in which there is no external effect except in the presence of a magnetic field. When there is no external field and the effects of the domains thus cancel, the substance is said to be "unmagnetized."

An impressed magnetic field causes domains to shift into alignment more or less with the field, and a shift in domain boundaries may cause growth of those domains which are favorably oriented with respect to the field. Thus an over-all magnetic moment is produced, and because of the cooperative effect of all the atoms the effect may be intense.

The magnetic moment of an iron atom is well known to be due to the spin of four unpaired electrons in the 3 *d*-subshell. The cooperative action of atoms in any one domain is difficult to explain on a classical basis, as the electrons in different atoms are presumably too far apart to interact strongly. However, according to quantum mechanics there is exchange of electrons between atoms on the crystal lattice, and theory predicts that because of this the atoms are in a lower energy state when the spins of the unpaired electrons are all parallel. Since the atoms tend to assume the state of lowest energy the domains are self-magnetizing.

13-8. Low-Temperature Physics

In recent years new studies at temperatures near absolute zero have become one of the most important fields of investigation. Two surprising discoveries have been made, that of the superconducting state of some metals and that of the superfluid state of liquid helium. To investigate phenomena at low temperatures, in the field now called *cryogenics,* low-temperature laboratories have been established at a number of universities and at the National Bureau of Standards.

This kind of low-temperature physics became possible after Kamerlingh Onnes at Leyden first liquefied helium in 1909 at −268.9° C and later was able to freeze it at −272.2° C and 26 atmospheres pressure. At lower pressures it does not solidify regardless of temperature. Such temperatures are very near to absolute zero which is −273.16° C. By cooling bodies in liquid helium and then allowing the helium to evaporate, temperatures nearer absolute zero than these may be obtained, and by other special experimental procedures still lower temperatures very close to absolute zero have been attained.

Magnetic cooling In one series of attempts to reach nearer and nearer absolute zero a magnetic method of further reducing the internal energy of a body has been applied. A magnetized state represents a higher energy state than a nonmagnetized state. If a magnetized body is cooled by liquid helium as much as possible and if the magnetizing field is then removed while the body is thermally isolated, the internal energy becomes less and a state of lower temperature is reached. By such means temperatures within a few hundredths of a degree of absolute zero have been reached.

Such considerations lead inevitably to the question, what is the meaning of temperature at such low values and what is the meaning of absolute zero. In the simple gas theory, where absolute temperature is proportional to pressure for a given volume of gas, the absolute zero is pictured as the point of zero random motion of molecules and consequently of zero gas pressure. Before this point is reached any real gas becomes first a liquid and then a solid. It might then be presumed that absolute zero would be the point of zero internal energy, including energy of vibrational or rotational motion. However, according to Fermi statistics the energy would not be zero; the particles would simply be in the lowest available energy states.

To set up a complete temperature scale presents a problem. The measuring of temperature, as deduced from theoretical considerations, must somehow be made to agree with experimental procedure, and in the last analysis actual measured temperatures must be interpreted with due regard to the operational methods for obtaining the measurements. By the classical definition of temperature in terms of the kinetic energy of the particles, there can be no temperature less than absolute zero. Only by changing the definition of temperature, or the operations involved in measuring temperature, can temperatures less than this have meaning.

Low temperatures are usually measured with a hydrogen or helium thermometer down to the neighborhood of the liquefaction point of the gas. Such measurements by means of suitable corrections can be transferred to an ideal gas scale. For lower temperatures the vapor pressure of liquid helium may be taken as the indicator, and for still lower temperatures the magnetic properties of a substance may be used. Since the methods are different in the various temperature ranges, and in the lowest ranges depend on magnetic measurements, the attempt must be made to fit these methods together to obtain a consistent temperature scale from highest to lowest temperatures. This has been done with considerable success, but with new methods and newly extended measurements it is an ever-present problem.

13-9. Superconductivity

The phenomenon of superconductivity was discovered by Kammerlingh Onnes in 1911. While experimenting with mercury at very low temperatures he found that the electric resistance began to drop very rapidly at 4.26° K and that at 4.20° K it had vanished completely. This was a startling discovery.

At ordinary temperatures electric current will exist in a closed circuit only so long as there is an emf to maintain it, such as, for instance, from an electric cell or an induced emf. Consider, for example, a solid conducting ring of metal, as in Fig. 13-8. At ordinary temperatures if a magnet is moved into the center of the ring or removed from the center, a momentary current will occur only so long as the magnetic flux through the conductor is changing. For a superconductor at low temperatures the situation is radically different. It is not too difficult, once the metal ring has been brought to a low temperature, to repeat

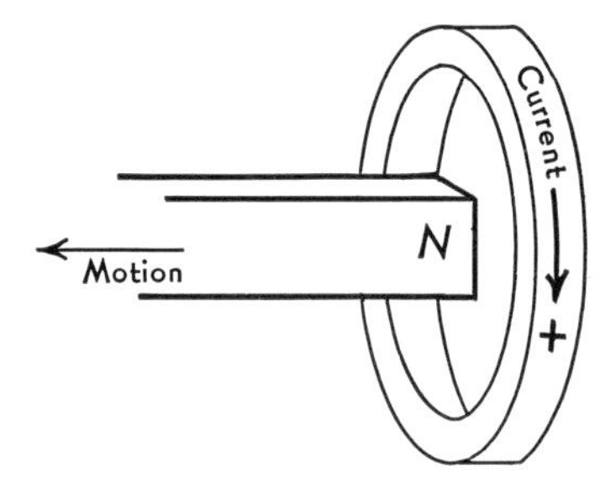

Fig. 13-8. Below the transition temperature, when a magnet is withdrawn from a ring of superconducting metal, the induced current persists indefinitely.

this experiment. Pulling the magnet out of the ring produces an induced current in the ring as before, but now the strength of the current does not diminish after the magnet has been removed. At the end of a minute, or an hour, or a day, or even longer, it still has not diminished by a measurable amount. For as long a time as the ring can be maintained at the proper temperature no measurable decrease in the current can be detected. In a record-breaking time test at the Massachusetts Institute of Technology, a lead ring was said to have carried a current for over a year without appreciable change. Since sensitive methods are used, which could detect a decrease of as little as 0.001 of 1 per cent, it is concluded that the current experiences no resistance at all. This is the state of superconductivity, and it presents an intriguing but baffling problem.

The possibility of superconductivity was not predicted by any theory. In the new theories of electric conduction it had been found necessary to take into consideration the vibrations of the atoms forming the crystal lattice of the conductor. Such vibrations presumably occur at low temperatures and increase in intensity with increasing temperature. On various earlier theories an electron would experience more difficulty in passing through the lattice the more the atoms are vibrating. It would seem as if these atoms were trying to block passage of the electron. Thus the resistance of a conductor would be expected to increase with increasing temperature, and this is confirmed by experiment in the case of pure metals. Conversely the resistance should decrease with decreasing temperature, but it would hardly be expected to do more than approach zero at low temperatures, and nothing in such a theory would indicate that it should vanish completely at a temperature above absolute zero.

Bloch applied wave mechanics to the problem and arrived at the conclusion that electrons could perhaps pass through a crystal lattice without colliding with any atoms if the atoms did not possess thermal vibration. But quantum theory predicts a residual amount of energy at absolute zero, and some vibrations must still occur. Thus a new theory was needed which would explain not only why superconductivity occurs at all, but why it occurs at temperatures above absolute zero, and only in some metals. In 1957 Bardeen, Cooper, and Schrieffer assumed a different type of interacting between electrons and the vibrating atoms in which under certain conditions the vibrations may help instead of hinder the current. An idealized model formulated on this basis shows some of the chief properties of superconductivity and has permitted some exact computations to be made.

The following more or less common metals are now known to be superconducting at temperatures a few degrees above absolute zero: aluminum, lead, zinc, mercury, tin, cadmium, thallium, vanadium, indium, osmium, and at least twelve others which are less common. Since the elements have been rather completely surveyed not many more superconductors may be expected to be found although what may happen at temperatures extremely close to absolute zero is not so well known. One point of interest is that elements, the atoms of which have 3, 5 or 7 valence electrons outside of filled shells, become superconducting most readily, that is at higher temperatures. In addition to the elements a considerable number of alloys and compounds has been found to be superconducting. A compound of niobium (columbium) and tin, becomes superconducting at the relatively high temperature of 18° K and niobium nitride at 15° K. Such substances give promise of important scientific and technical uses particularly in the handling of extremely small electric currents without loss.

Onnes also made the discovery that the superconducting state may be destroyed by the application of a sufficiently intense magnetic field, and it is now known that the lower the temperature is, the more intense must the field be. Even the magnetic field due to the current itself may destroy the superconducting state if the current is large enough. This condition put a limitation on those who hoped to use the superconducting state to produce intense magnetic fields by means of intense currents. Further study leads to the conclusion that in the superconducting state the magnetic permeability is also zero. In other words, in the superconducting state the substance is perfectly diamagnetic and is perfectly opaque to an external field.

13-10. Helium II, a Superfluid

One of the interesting discoveries at very low temperatures has been that of the unusual behavior of helium. Helium is the most difficult of all gases to liquefy. This was first accomplished by Onnes in 1908. Under 1 atmosphere pressure the gas liquefies at 4.22° K. Ordinary liquid helium (He I) behaves like a normal liquid until cooled to 2.19° K. At this temperature it loses its normal properties and acquires most unusual ones. It is then called He II. The transformation temperature at which He I becomes He II is called the lambda-point and at pressures more or less than 1 atmosphere it differs from the value given. At this point the density of the liquid rises to a maximum of about one-seventh that of water. Its thermal conductivity may be increased as much as 10 million times. It transmits sound at two different speeds. It tends to flow toward a source of heat. In flowing through a sufficiently narrow channel its viscosity apparently drops to zero, and it is then said to be in the superfluid state. Such anomalous properties have made this a rich field for experimental research.

SUGGESTED READING

R. L. Sproull, *Modern Physics* (New York, Wiley, 1956).
F. Seitz, *The Physics of Metals* (New York, McGraw-Hill, 1943).
C. Kittel, *Introduction to Solid-State Physics*, 2nd ed. (New York, Wiley, 1956).
R. M. Bozorth, *Ferromagnetism* (New York, Van Nostrand, 1951).
B. T. Matthias, "Superconductivity," *Scientific American*, November, 1957, p. 92.
L. C. Jackson, *Low Temperature Physics*, 2nd ed. (New York, Wiley, 1948).

CHAPTER 14

NATURAL RADIOACTIVITY

14-1. Nuclear Physics

The study of the nucleus and its particles has now become the foremost branch of atomic physics. In the earlier part of the century rapid progress was made in understanding the extranuclear or electronic structure of the atom, but little was known about the nucleus. Nuclear physics actually began with the study of radioactivity before the nucleus was known to exist, but not until Rutherford's famous scattering experiment of 1911 (§ 8-3) was the nucleus "discovered" and the concept of the nuclear atom formulated.

Eight years later Rutherford achieved distinction again, for the first time breaking up an atomic nucleus by bombarding it with high-speed atomic projectiles. From then on the subject of nuclear physics has been developed steadily, with such experimental achievements as the production of artificial or induced radioactivity, transmutations of atoms, and the release of atomic energy. To thus invade the nucleus required the development of new techniques at a new level of refinement. The challenge of the nucleus brought with it the development of powerful particle accelerators capable of furnishing atomic projectiles to disrupt the most resistant nucleus. To correlate the information thus obtained have come the theories of nuclear structure as we know it today.

14-2. Discovery and Early History of Radioactivity

The discovery of radioactivity was made by Henri Becquerel in February, 1896. Its importance was not immediately evident, and the rays were originally called Becquerel rays. Becquerel only knew that he had found a substance that gave off a penetrating, invisible kind of radiation. Interest in such possible effects had been raised to a high pitch by the discovery of x-rays in the preceding year. Becquerel experimented with an ore containing uranium. His interest had been aroused after he found that it fluoresced brilliantly when exposed to ultraviolet light, and his experiment was a simple one. When the mineral was laid on a photographic plate wrapped in black paper, some unknown radiation from it penetrated the wrappings and blackened the plate. This radiation was independent of any fluorescence. It was not affected by exposure to light, and it was not affected by change in temperature. It was a new effect, and the name *radioactivity* was coined to describe it. Soon the search was on for the source of the rays and for other substances that would produce similar effects.

In 1898 Marie Curie and her husband Pierre succeeded in extracting a very small amount of intensely active substance from a ton or more of ore. The new substance was called *polonium* by Madame Curie in honor of her native land, Poland. Some months later she isolated another source of intense radiation and named it *radium*. In 1903 the Curies shared the Nobel prize with Becquerel for the discovery of radioactivity. For isolating radium which turned out to be a new element, and for measuring its atomic weight, Madame Curie herself received the Nobel prize in 1911. Soon a number of other active substances were isolated by the Curies and by other early workers in the field, among them Rutherford and Soddy. These substances were all found to be new elements and are now known to belong to one or more series of radioactive elements, the members of which are closely related.

During the first two decades after the discovery of radioactivity, it was found that the phenomenon of radioactivity was almost but not completely limited to atoms heavier than lead of mass number 206, atomic number 82. The earliest known exceptions were potassium and rubidium. Later other elements including carbon were found to be very feebly radioactive. Such radioactivity is now known to be due to the presence of small amounts of a radioactive isotope mixed with the stable element. In carbon the activity is due to the rare isotope carbon

14, presumed to be formed in the atmosphere by the action of cosmic rays on nitrogen (§ 20-4).

14-3. Nature of Radioactivity and Properties of Rays

The radiations from natural radioactive substances were found to consist of three general types called alpha, beta, and gamma rays. The rays from a sample of radioactive material can be separated into three groups, representing these types, by means of a magnetic field (Fig. 14-1). The rays bent to the right are bent in the proper direction, as Becquerel discovered, to indicate that they are negatively charged particles, and they were named **beta rays.** Measurements of their ratio of charge to mass by deflection methods soon identified them as electrons ejected from the source with extremely large velocities. The rays bent to the left are evidently positively charged particles. These were called **alpha rays,** and to bend their paths requires a very strong magnetic field. A third group of rays, discovered in 1900 by Villard, was found to pass through the strongest magnetic fields undeflected. They were called **gamma rays,** and it was not clear for some years whether they were uncharged particles or a form of wave motion. Now we recognize that gamma rays are electromagnetic waves of very short wavelength, even shorter than ordinary x-rays.

In 1903 Rutherford in England successfully studied the bending of the paths of alpha rays. He found that the rays have a ratio of charge to mass roughly a thousandth of that for beta rays or about half that of a charged hydrogen atom. With characteristic ingenuity he devised a means of counting the individual alpha particles and of measuring the total charge carried by a given number. From this he found the charge per particle, and knowing e/m he could find the mass of the particle. The mass turned out to be four times that of a hydrogen atom. This identified the alpha particle as a doubly charged helium atom. That it was actually the nucleus of a helium atom did not become clear until after the formulation of the concept of the nuclear atom.

Rutherford, still not content, showed by a beautifully simple but direct and convincing experiment that alpha particles actually are charged helium atoms. The rays were allowed to pass through a thin window into an electric-discharge tube (Fig. 14-2) which had previously been evacuated. Then an electric discharge in the tube showed the characteristic spectral lines of helium where none had been observed before. The alpha particles entering the tube had collected outer electrons and had become helium atoms.

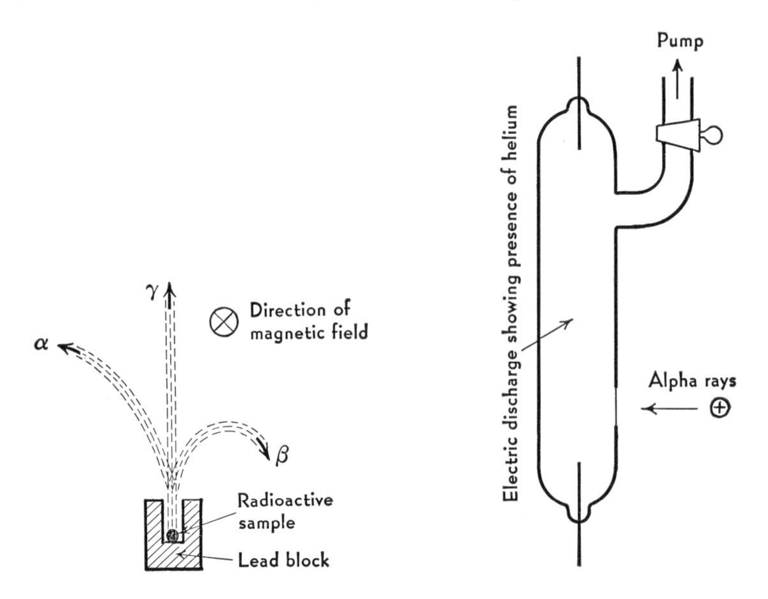

Fig. 14-1. Separation of alpha (α), beta (β), and gamma (γ) rays from a radioactive sample by means of magnetic deflections.

Fig. 14-2. Rutherford's experiment which demonstrated that alpha particles are helium nuclei.

One of the earliest recognized differences between the three types of rays was in their penetrating power. Alpha, beta, and gamma rays are increasingly penetrating in the order named. The exact penetrating capacity depends on the energy with which the rays emerge from the parent atom, but, generally speaking, alpha rays can usually be stopped by a few sheets of paper. Beta rays are approximately 100 times as penetrating, and can usually be stopped by 2 or 3 millimeters of aluminum. They can ordinarily pass through the walls of a glass tube if the tube is not too thick. Most gamma rays are something like 100 times as penetrating as beta rays and may pass through a number of centimeters of metal shielding.

Before the discovery of radioactivity, atoms had been considered largely in Newtonian terms. The complete overthrow of the Newtonian conception that atoms are solid, inert, and everlasting marks one of the great revolutions of modern physics. Instead of lasting forever, the atoms of these new elements were found to undergo spontaneous decay. Instead of being solid, inert particles they were found to be tiny dynamical systems of electrons surrounding a nucleus, involving relatively enormous stretches of space between particles. Instead of being lifeless they were found to be veritable storehouses of energy. Often the energy release during the process of alpha-, beta-, and gamma-ray emission would take place over almost incredibly long periods of time with little decrease in intensity.

The surprising liberation of energy by a radioactive substance was contrary to expectation on any classical basis. Measurements showed that every gram of radium liberates approximately 140 calories of heat per hour, enough energy to raise 1.4 grams of water from the freezing to the boiling point every hour. Furthermore, the decrease in the rate of emission is so little that, after 1600 years, the rate of energy release would only be reduced to one-half. Based on this fact, we say that the half-life of radium is 1600 years.

The energy evolved is actually the energy of the emitted rays. Radium itself emits high-energy alpha particles. Together with its decay products, some of which emit beta and gamma rays, 1 gram of radium releases

Alpha rays	124 cal/hr
Beta rays	6.3 cal/hr
Gamma rays	9.4 cal/hr
Total	139.7 cal/hr

That so much energy could be stored in atoms was not only a revolutionary idea, but one which was very difficult to understand until after 1905, when Einstein proposed that mass could be converted into energy. Though the diminution of mass in a given amount of radioactive material may be hardly noticeable, it is sufficient to account for the energy release.

Among the earliest recognized properties of the rays from radioactive substances, in addition to their penetration and their heating capacity, were their ability to ionize the molecules of a gas through which they pass, their ability to affect a photographic plate, and the ability of the alpha rays in particular to produce tiny flashes of light (scintillations) on a fluorescent screen. It also became more painfully evident, as time went on, that such radiation could produce serious and even fatal burns on the surface of the body and that the more penetrating rays (gamma rays) could produce deeper effects.

14-4. Radioactive Decay and Half-Life

Many experimental measurements show that, whenever large numbers of atoms are dealt with, all radioactive substances follow the same general decay pattern. At the end of a certain length of time half the num-

last few atoms of a radioactive substance may last for a very long period of time, thus bringing the average to more than the half-life.

14-5. Statistical Nature of Radioactive Decay

There is no measurable quantity which can be called the life of a radioactive atom. The lives of human beings can be individually measured, but there is no way of singling out a particular radioactive atom and measuring its life. Indeed, such a measurement would have no useful meaning, even if it were made, for it would apply to no other atom. Measurements of the rate of decay of a radioactive substance are purely statistical averages based on measurements made with very large numbers of atoms. An atom has no memory of past events. Nor does its life expectancy decrease with age, as it does with human beings. A particular atom may have a probability of decay of one in a million in a given length of time. After a thousand years or so, if it has not decayed it still has the same life expectancy or probability of decay. Quantum mechanics can predict the probability of decay of a radioactive atom, but it cannot tell us if the decay in a given atom is a result of favorable conditions that occur only at intervals in a way which we cannot foresee.

14-6. Radioactive Transformation and Series

When the nucleus of an atom emits an alpha or beta ray, sometimes accompanied by a gamma ray, the process is called radioactive decay, and the product nucleus is often found also to be radioactive. For instance, when an atom of radium undergoes decay and emits an alpha particle, the product nucleus is that of an atom of a different element called radon. Radon, it happens, is a gas at ordinary temperature and pressure, and is itself radioactive.

If radium is enclosed in a vessel the space around the radium becomes filled with this radioactive gas, which may be pumped off while the radium produces more. Radon is also an alpha-ray emitter and is found to have a half-life of only 3.8 days. This indicates that the decay goes on at a rate many thousand times as fast as the decay of radium itself. Careful study shows that the residue left by the decay of radon likewise is radioactive, emitting alpha particles, and the residue or product atoms belong to still another element. Originally called radium A it is now known to be one of the isotopes of polonium. Thus radium and radium A are closely related. Radium A is said to be the daughter product of radon, and radon is the daughter product of radium. However, radium is neither the beginning of this series, nor is radium A the end.

The three elements mentioned represent three stages near the center of a chain of 14 successive transformations, known as a radioactive series, in which the decaying atom winds up as a stable, nonradioactive atom of lead. This series begins with the element uranium and with the particular long-lived uranium atom of atomic number 92 and mass number 238. By successive emission of alpha or beta rays, sometimes accompanied by gamma rays, the decaying uranium atoms go through a series of transformations, as shown in Table 14-1.

TABLE 14-1. URANIUM SERIES OF RADIOACTIVE ELEMENTS

Symbol (New)	Symbol (Old)	Element	Half-Life	Emitted Ray
$_{92}U^{238}$	UI	Uranium	4.5×10^9 yr	α
$_{90}Th^{234}$	UX_1	Thorium	24 days	β (γ)
$_{91}Pa^{234}$	UX_2	Protoactinium	1.14 min	β (γ)
$_{92}U^{234}$	UII	Uranium	3×10^5 yr	α
$_{90}Th^{230}$	Io	Thorium	83,000 yr	α (γ)
$_{88}Ra^{226}$	Ra	*Radium*	1,600 yr	α (γ)
$_{86}Em^{222}$	Rn	Radon	3.8 days	α
$_{84}Po^{218}$	RaA	Polonium	3.05 min	α
$_{82}Pb^{214}$	RaB	Lead	26.8 min	β (γ)
$_{83}Bi^{214}$	RaC	Bismuth	19.7 min	β (γ)
$_{84}Po^{214}$	RaC′	Polonium (radium C′)	10^{-5} sec	α (γ)
$_{82}Pb^{210}$	RaD	Lead	22 yr	β
$_{83}Bi^{210}$	RaE	Bismuth	5 days	β (γ)
$_{84}Po^{210}$	RaF	Polonium	140 days	α
$_{82}Pb^{206}$	RaG	Lead	Stable	

There are four chief radioactive series. Three normally begin with elements of atomic number 92 or less, common in nature, and all three series terminate with atoms that are isotopes of lead. These isotopes are stable and consequently end the series. In addition to the uranium-radium series given in Table 14-1, there are the thorium and actinium series represented in Figs. 14-4 and 14-5 by a different but convenient type of diagram. The fourth series (Fig. 14-6) begins with the more recently discovered "man-made" element plutonium, and the end of the series is a stable isotope of bismuth. Although the beginning of the series has now been traced back to plutonium, it is called the neptunium series after the long-lived isotope of neptunium (half-life = 2.2 $\times 10^6$ years), the most stable isotope in the series. Actually small amounts of neptunium and plutonium have been found to exist in some uranium ores.

Symbols and transformations; mass number When an atom of an element such as radium emits an alpha particle the nucleus of the atom loses a particle of charge 2 and approximate mass 4. Its nuclear charge Z (atomic number) is thus reduced by 2 units, and its approximate mass or mass number is reduced by 4 units. The mass number, it will be remembered (§ 2-3), is the nearest integer to the atomic weight of the isotope in question, and it is represented by the symbol A. The symbol for the emitted alpha particle is ${}_2He^4$ where the subscript before the letters representing the element is the atomic number or nuclear charge, and the superscript following the letters is the mass number.

The symbol for the radium nucleus of nuclear charge 88 and mass number 226 is ${}_{88}Ra^{226}$, and by emission of an alpha particle this nucleus becomes transformed into a nucleus having 2 units less charge

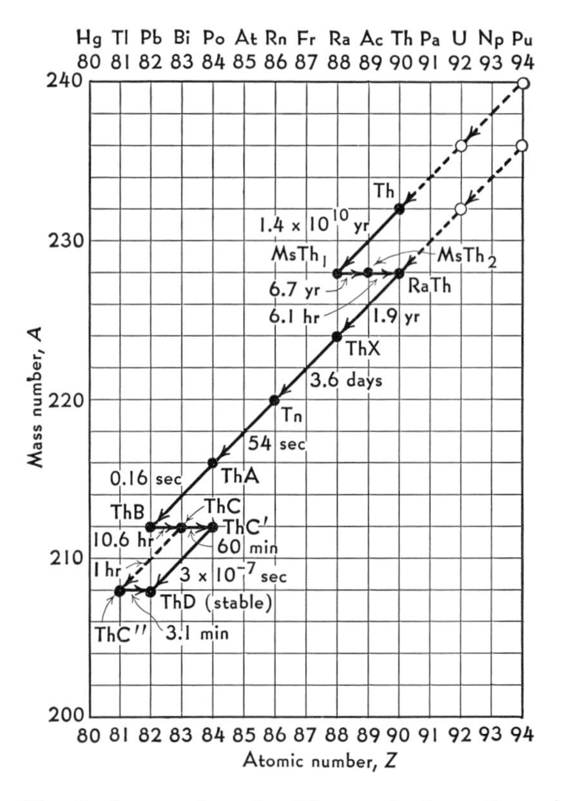

Fig. 14-4. The thorium or 4*n* series. The graph shows the main line of decay for the thorium series, named after its longest-lived member. It will be noticed that ThC may decay in one of two ways. Some earlier members of the series are shown dashed.

and 4 units less mass, named radon, the symbol for which is ${}_{86}Rn^{222}$. The transformation accompanying alpha emission is described symbolically as follows:

$$ {}_{88}Ra^{226} \rightarrow {}_{86}Rn^{222} + {}_{2}He^{4} \qquad [14\text{-}9] $$

The two sides of such a symbolic reaction must balance in total charge and in total mass number. Evidently the subscripts representing nuclear charge balance, since the 88 positive charges of the radium nucleus equals the 86 of the radon nucleus plus the 2 of the alpha particle. Likewise the mass numbers (superscripts) on the right, 222 and 4, add up to the mass number 226 on the left. This is the characteristic manner of writing nuclear transformations, and also the usual way of checking their validity, by balancing the two sides of the reaction as to both mass and nuclear charge.

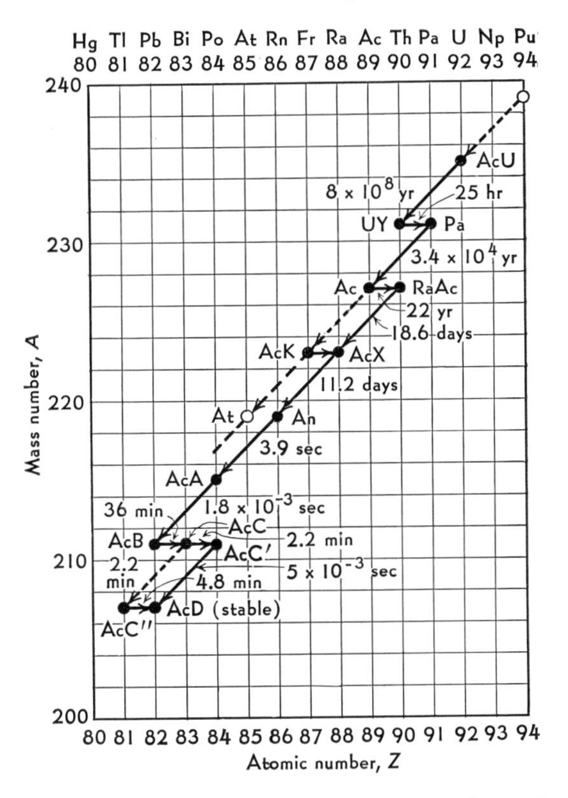

Fig. 14-5. The actinium or $4n + 3$ series. Some alternative modes of decay are indicated by dashed lines. The series may be traced backward beyond AcU (dashed line).

An interesting relation between the four radioactive series may be observed if the mass numbers for the members of any one series are written in the form $4n + m$ (Table 14-2), where n is an integer and m

TABLE 14-2. FOUR HEAVY-ELEMENT DISINTEGRATION SERIES
(Relation of Mass Numbers)

Name of Series	Type	Start	End (stable)
Thorium	$4n + 0$	Th^{232}	Pb^{208}
Neptunium	$4n + 1$	Np^{237}	Bi^{209}
Uranium-radium	$4n + 2$	U^{238}	Pb^{206}
Actinium	$4n + 3$	U^{235}	Pb^{207}

takes the values 0, 1, 2, and 3, respectively, for the four series. The three series with m having values 0, 2, and 3 had long been known, and the prospect that m might take the value 1 led to the discovery of the neptunium series.

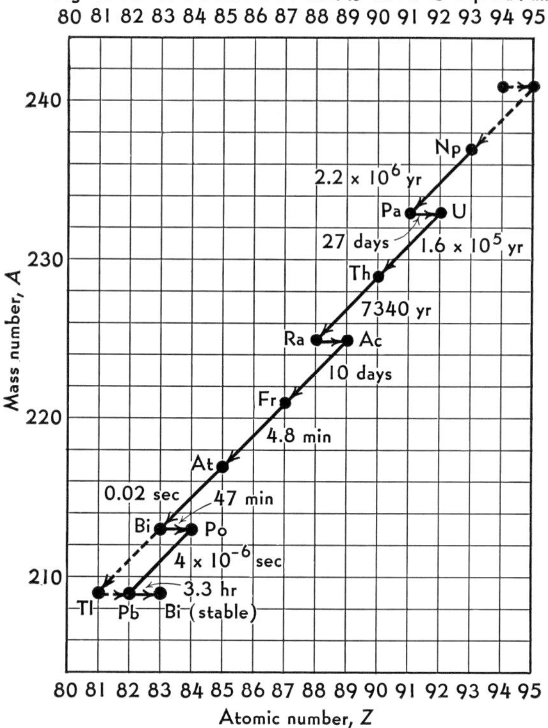

Fig. 14-6. The neptunium or $4n + 1$ series.

Rules of radioactive displacement The emission of an alpha particle by a radioactive nucleus means that the product atom has been shifted in the periodic table two steps in the direction of a lower atomic number (two steps to the left in Fig. 14-4) and four steps in the direction of a lower mass number. However, the emission of a beta particle by a radioactive atom, as for instance by $_{83}Bi^{212}$, represents a decrease in negative charge of the nucleus of 1 unit, which is equivalent to an increase in positive charge of 1 unit. This means that the atomic number is shifted one step in the direction of increasing atomic number (one step to the right in Fig. 14-4), and the mass number is unchanged since the electron has negligible mass. Therefore $_{83}Bi^{212}$ by emission of a beta particle becomes $_{84}Po^{212}$ and is now an isotope of polonium. The rules just given for the shifts in atomic number and in mass number when alpha or beta emission occurs are called the rules of radioactive displacement.

14-7. Radioactive Growth and Decay

If a pure radioactive isotope is isolated at time $t = 0$, it does not remain pure. The decay products begin to form, and while any radioactive substance decays its successive products begin to grow. The growth will continue until a daughter product is in equilibrium with its parent. Equilibrium is reached when the daughter product decays as fast as it is being formed.

Radioactive growth and decay curves are represented in Fig. 14-7. The equation of growth is readily shown to be

$$N = N_0 (1 - \epsilon^{-\lambda t}) \qquad [14\text{-}10]$$

Curve *a* represents decay of a substance, curve *b*, the growth of the daughter substance, assuming that the latter is stable and does not itself decay.

If the daughter isotope also decays, the total number of daughter atoms may be increasing or decreasing at any given moment, and the rate of change in number of the atoms N_2 of the daughter substance is

$$\frac{dN_2}{dt} = \lambda_1 N_1 - \lambda_2 N_2 \qquad [14\text{-}11]$$

when λ_1 and λ_2 are the decay constants of parent and daughter, respectively, and N_1 is the number of atoms of the parent. Then $\lambda_1 N_1$ is the gain in number of daughter atoms per unit time by decay of the parent, and $\lambda_2 N_2$ is the loss per unit time in number of daughter atoms

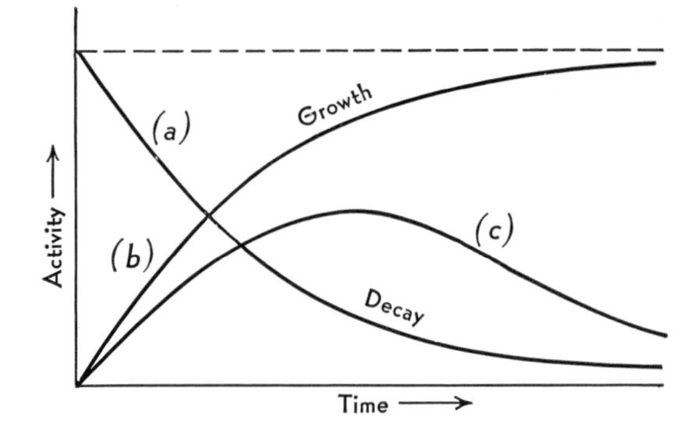

Fig. 14-7. Curves representing: *a*, decay of a radioactive substance; *b*, growth of the daughter element, assuming it to be a stable element with a long-lived parent; *c*, growth and decay of a daughter element which is itself unstable.

owing to its own decay. Let $N_1 = N_{01}\,\epsilon^{-\lambda_1 t}$ where N_{01} is the number of parent atoms at time $t = 0$. Then

$$\frac{dN_2}{dt} + \lambda_2 N_2 = \lambda_1 N_{01}\,\epsilon^{-\lambda_1 t} \qquad [14\text{-}12]$$

By integrating this equation and putting the number of daughter atoms $N_{02} = 0$ for $t = 0$, the number of daughter atoms at any time t is given by

$$N_2 = \frac{\lambda_1}{\lambda_2 - \lambda_1} N_{01}\,(\epsilon^{-\lambda_1 t} - \epsilon^{-\lambda_2 t}) \qquad [14\text{-}13]$$

If the parent substance is so very long-lived that the daughter element may be assumed to be produced at a constant rate, this equation reduces to

$$\lambda_1 N_1 = \lambda_2 N_2 \qquad [14\text{-}14]$$

and is called secular equilibrium. For a series of several product isotopes in equilibrium

$$\lambda_1 N_1 = \lambda_2 N_2 = \lambda_3 N_3 \cdots \qquad [14\text{-}15]$$

where N_1, N_2, N_3 need only be numbers proportional to the numbers of each type of atom present.

14-8. Determinations of Extremely Long and Short Half-Lives

Half-lives of the more common radioactive substances cover an extraordinary range of time, from billions of years to a few microseconds. Some of the more recently discovered unstable particles have half-lives very much less. Whereas the half-lives of many of these may be determined by direct measurements made in the laboratory over periods ranging from minutes to months, half-lives that are extremely long or short must be determined by less direct methods. However, for any substance having a very long half-life a quite simple method has been devised.

If a milligram of uranium is found by laboratory measurement to emit 12.2 alpha particles per second, this is at a rate of 12200 alpha particles per gram per second. If this is put into Eq. 14-2 as ΔN, then Δt becomes 1 sec. From Avogadro's number and the atomic weight, it can easily be determined that there are 2.51×10^{21} atoms in 1 gm of uranium. This is N in the equation, which then becomes

$$12200 = \lambda \times 2.51 \times 10^{21} \times 1$$

from which

$$\lambda = 4.86 \times 10^{-18} \text{ (sec}^{-1}\text{)}$$

and by Eq. 14-8, since 1 year equals 3.156×10^{7} sec, the half-life is

$$T = 4.5 \times 10^{9} \text{ years}$$

Because the end product of the uranium series is lead, the relative amount of lead found in uranium ore in proportion to the uranium present affords a method of computing the age of the ore, assuming that it contained uranium only at the start. This period of time is often spoken of as the "age of the earth," but it is more accurate to call it the age of the earth's crust. Measurements indicate that it may be as much as 3 billion years, if not more.

Extremely short half-lives are more difficult to determine and sometimes are only approximate estimates. An estimate of both long and short half-lives for alpha decay may be obtained from measured ranges of the rays and application of the relation between range and decay constant, known as the Geiger-Nuttall rule (§ 15-5).

14-9. Detection of Rays and Measured Activities

Whereas any pronounced characteristic of a particular type of ray from a radioactive substance may serve in the detection of the rays, the most useful properties are the capacity to produce ions and the capacity to produce scintillations. The electroscope, the ionization chamber, the Wilson cloud chamber, and the Geiger-Müller (G-M) tube depend upon the production of ions. The first two give average effects of considerable numbers of rays but do not enable individual rays to be detected. By means of the last two, single rays are detected. This makes it possible to study individual events, a matter of great importance.

In the early days of the study of them, alpha particles were detected individually by observation with a small magnifier or simple microscope of the tiny "splash" of light or scintillation produced when an alpha particle strikes a fluorescent screen. Beta and gamma rays did not produce observable effects, partly owing to greater penetration. In recent years the scintillation method has been revived and developed into a highly successful method of detecting beta and gamma rays. Certain substances known as phosphors give scintillations which may be detected by photoelectric methods, and the method has achieved unusual success (§ 14-12).

The **actual activity** of a radioactive substance must be distinguished from its apparent or **measured activity.** The latter depends to a large extent upon the efficiency of the detecting device for the particular type of ray. The actual activity A of a specific isotope or nuclide, as the nucleus is called, depends on the number of atoms present and the decay constant, and may be defined as

$$A = \lambda N \qquad [14\text{-}16]$$

Yet, of this number of rays being produced per second, the geometry of the system may be such that only 0.01 or so of the rays is intercepted by the detector. This fraction may be represented by g, and in comparing activities of different samples this must be taken into consideration. Finally the detector itself may respond to only a fraction c of the rays, where c depends upon the efficiency of the detector. The measured activity A' is then

$$A' = cg\lambda N \qquad [14\text{-}17]$$

If measurements are made on rays of the same type with the same detector and the same geometry, the coefficients c and g cancel, and

$$\frac{A'_1}{A'_2} = \frac{\lambda_1 N_1}{\lambda_2 N_2} = \frac{A_1}{A_2} \qquad [14\text{-}18]$$

from which it is seen that the ratio of the measured activities is the same as the ratio of the actual activities. When such ratios are not being measured the detecting efficiency must be considered. For instance, the efficiency of a G-M tube is very low for gamma rays whereas the efficiency of a scintillation detector is relatively high.

14-10. Electroscopes and Ionization Chambers

Ionization of air by alpha, beta, or gamma rays may be readily demonstrated by observation of the increased rate of collapse of the leaves of a charged electroscope. Ions of opposite sign to the charge on the leaves are attracted to the leaves and gradually neutralize the charge

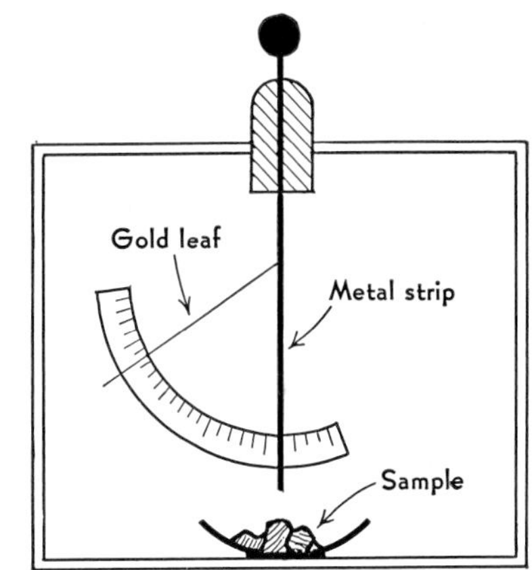

Fig. 14-8. Simple electroscope used in early measurements of intensity of radiation.

on them, allowing the diverging leaves to collapse. A single-leaf type of electroscope common in many earlier experiments is illustrated in Fig. 14-8. The rate of collapse of the leaf can be determined by making successive readings on the scale with the help of a short-range telescope. This rate of collapse is a measure of the activity of the sample.

An ionization chamber (Fig. 14-9) is somewhat similar in operation, but the ions formed in the chamber are attracted to opposite electrodes which are held at a difference of potential by means of a battery or other source of emf. One of the electrodes may be a metal lining of the chamber. A very sensitive electrometer tube or other device is used to determine the ion current, which is a measure of the activity of the source. Such ionization chambers serve many purposes in detecting

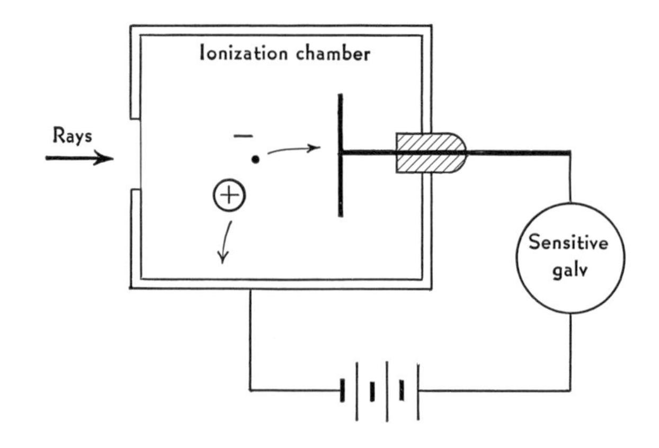

Fig. 14-9. Ionization chamber. When rays form ions in chamber, a current to the electrodes can be detected.

ionizing rays and are often used to measure cosmic-ray intensities (Chap. 20).

14-11. The Geiger-Müller Tube

One of the most useful instruments for detecting and subsequently counting the rays from a radioactive substance or cosmic rays is the Geiger-Müller or G-M tube. It responds to single particles, and thus by means of a suitable counting circuit the number of rays entering the tube in any given length of time may be determined. The Geiger-Müller tube in its simplest form consists of a metal cylinder, frequently enclosed in glass, with a fine tungsten wire stretched along the axis of the cylinder (Fig. 14-10). The tube contains a little gas at a few cm

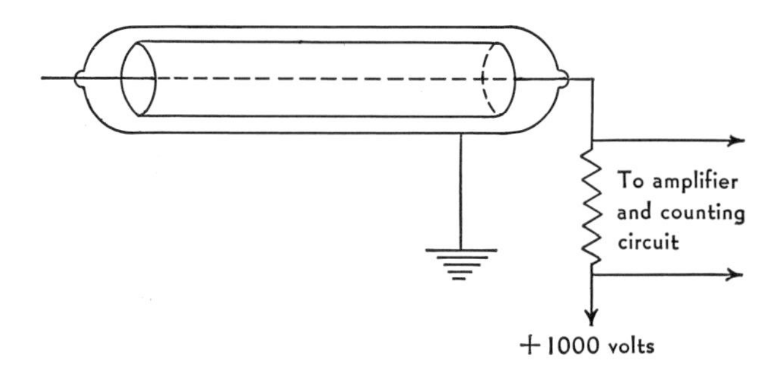

Fig. 14-10. Geiger-Müller (G-M) tube, for detecting and counting rays capable of penetrating to region between cylinder and central wire.

of mercury pressure. A potential difference of several hundred to a thousand volts is applied between the wire and the cylinder with the wire made positive. When a single ionizing ray passes through the glass or metal wall into the inside of the cylinder it needs only to produce a few gas ions in order to start a momentary discharge between cylinder and wire. This produces an electric pulse in the external circuit which is led to an amplifier and from there to more or less complicated electronic counting and recording devices. Such counter tubes may count at rates as fast as a billion per day or better.

The operation of the tube is as follows: If a high-energy ray liberates one or more electrons from the molecules of the gas in the tube they will be accelerated toward the positively charged wire at the center of the cylinder. On the way they produce more ions and free electrons by collision, and the number of free electrons multiplies in the form of a small electron avalanche until they reach the wire. Positive ions, being much more massive, acquire a smaller velocity in the opposite direction and produce less effect. The electron avalanche constitutes a sudden tiny surge of electric current from the cylinder to the wire which results in a pulse in the external circuit.

To prevent the discharge in the G-M tube from spreading along the wire and forming a glow, some method of quenching the discharge is required. In the earlier type of air-filled tubes a high resistance in series with the tube produced a voltage drop, when the discharge occurred, sufficient to reduce the voltage on the tube below the critical value to sustain the discharge. However, the common type of G-M tube today is what is called a *self-quenching tube.* It is often filled with argon gas, to which 10 per cent of alcohol or of some other organic vapor is added. The molecules of vapor absorb the radiation which tends to spread the discharge, and they may become dissoci-

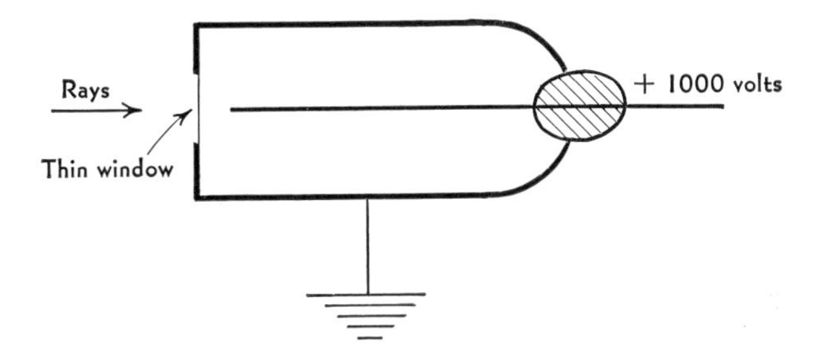

Fig. 14-11. End-on or end-window type of G-M tube with thin window useful for counting less penetrating rays such as beta and even alpha particles.

ated by it, but in the process the discharge is automatically quenched. Elaborate circuits have been devised for rapid quenching so that the counting rate of the tube can be increased, but quenching and deionization in conventional counter tubes usually require as much as 100 microseconds.

A useful type of G-M tube is the end-window counter (Fig. 14-11). Instead of the wire extending through the cylinder it terminates in a point, the end of the cylinder consisting of a thin diaphragm which acts as a window for the rays and may even be thin enough to let alpha particles enter.

14-12. Scintillation Counters

Since 1947 very efficient types of scintillation counters have been developed. For the scintillator a large crystal of one of several substances such as anthracene or naphthalene has been found to give scintillations. Not all scintillators are crystalline, and generally they are called phosphors. Even liquid scintillators are used.

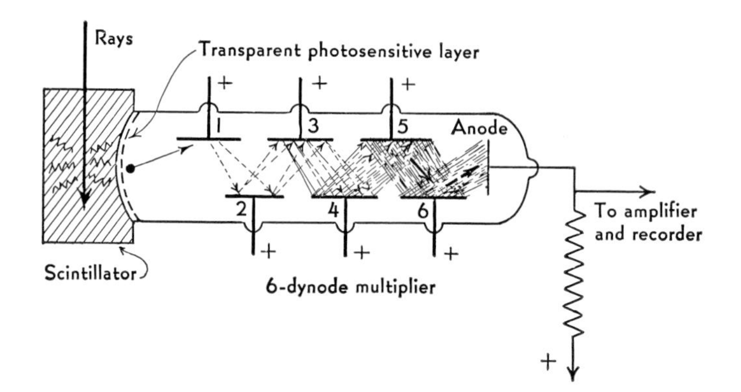

Fig. 14-12. Scintillation counter, consisting of scintillator or phosphor closely coupled to transparent photosensitive surface of photomultiplier tube.

One type of scintillation counter is illustrated in Fig. 14-12. A suitable crystal or other type of phosphor is fitted closely to the end of a photomultiplier tube. When an incident ray enters the phosphor and produces a tiny "flash" of light or scintillation some of the photons of this flash fall on the photosensitive coating on the inside surface at the end of the photomultiplier tube. They in turn eject one or more photoelectrons. The electrons are pulled by a potential of perhaps 100 volts to the first electrode (dynode) where secondaries are emitted; these in turn are pulled to the next dynode thereby increasing the magnitude of the pulse (§ 3-8). After this process is repeated at as many as 10 or 12 dynodes, each of which amplifies the pulse by secondary electron emission, the signal finally emerges at the anode where it may be further amplified and counted.

The entire process may take only a fraction of a microsecond, so that very high counting rates may be attained. Such a counter is of special value in counting gamma rays since its efficiency may be 20 per cent or even better as compared with 1 per cent or less for G-M tubes.

14-13. The Cloud Chamber

An explanation of the basic principle of the cloud chamber has been given in an earlier section (§ 2-4). Its power and the variety of purposes it serves have made it an indispensable tool in atomic and nuclear investigations, and the evidence that it furnishes is of a particularly direct nature. Here actual tracks of individual particles are seen, and direct hits with nuclei are sometimes observed. The decay of a nucleus or an artificial transmutation may be recorded. The energies and momenta of the individual particles can be measured or estimated, and the information is invaluable in the analysis of the observed event. To illustrate the great power and versatility of the cloud chamber a number of the leading types of phenomena observed by means of it and already encountered or to be encountered are listed:

Ranges of rays.
Absorption of rays by various substances.
Ionization densities of tracks.
Discovery of new particles.
Transmutations.
Pair production.
Fission products.
Decay processes.
Cosmic-ray particles.
Cosmic-ray showers.

The cloud chamber is often used in a magnetic field of known intensity to enable the direction of curvature of the path of a particle to be determined and consequently the sign of the charge. Measurement of the amount of curvature then enables the momentum to be calculated.

Cloud chambers are commonly combined with G-M tubes for many purposes. The tubes may be arranged to select rays to be observed under various conditions, or to detect the results of a particular type of nuclear event, or to control the time of expansion of the cloud chamber so that only desired events will be observed (§ 20-3).

14-14. Units of Radioactivity and Radiation Hazards

Intensities of radioactivity are commonly measured in terms of the number of particles emitted per second by a sample. This is the same as the number of disintegrations per second. The common unit, the **curie,** is defined as 3.7×10^{10} particles emitted per second. This is approximately what is given off by a gram of radium. The **millicurie** (mc) is then 37 million particles emitted per second. For weaker intensities a unit called the **rutherford** has been suggested. One rutherford is 10^6 particles emitted per second.

Since gamma rays are the most penetrating and the most dangerous, adequate protection from them must always be provided. This may be accomplished by means of shielding, or by the simple expedient of staying as far away as possible from radioactive material in any appreciable quantity.

The unit called the **roentgen,** defined in § 5-8, measures gamma radiation as well as x-radiation, and an exposure of 0.3 roentgen per week was for some time considered a safe limit for the prevention of any more or less immediate ill effects. According to an authoritative report by the National Academy of Sciences (1956) the limit of 0.3 roentgen per week should be sharply reduced for workers under 30 years of age, with some reduction for workers under 40. Even this may be too high. The best rule is to permit exposure to as little radiation as possible. Geneticists have advanced cogent reasons for the belief that even these small amounts over a long period of time may have serious results with regard to inheritance factors and what has been called the genetic "poisoning" of the human race. The cumulative effects of even occasional medical and dental x-rays over a long period of years may not be negligible.

SOME COMMON NUCLEAR TERMS

Nucleus. The central, positively charged "heart" of an atom.

Nucleons. Neutrons or protons in a nucleus.

Nuclide. A particular type of nucleus. Different nuclides have different numbers of protons or neutrons or both.

Isotope. One of a group of nuclides having the same number of protons but different numbers of neutrons.

Isobar. One of a group of nuclides having the same mass number.

Isomers. Nuclides having the same number of neutrons and protons but able to remain for an appreciable time in different energy states.

Mirror nuclides. Two nuclides for which the numbers of protons and neutrons of one are the reverse of the other.

PROBLEMS

1. The half-lives of radon and radium are 3.8 days and 1600 years, respectively. Find and compare their decay constants and their average lives.

Ans. λ(radon) $= 2.1 \times 10^{-6}$ sec^{-1},
av. life $= 4.7 \times 10^{5}$ sec;
λ(radium) $= 1.37 \times 10^{-11}$ sec^{-1},
av. life $= 7.3 \times 10^{10}$ sec.

2. If the decay constant of a radioactive substance is 2×10^{-6} sec^{-1}, what is the half-life and what is the average life?

Ans. Half-life $= 3.46 \times 10^{5}$ sec;
av. life $= 5 \times 10^{5}$ sec.

3. If a nucleus emits one or more alpha particles, by what further emission process can it become an isotope of itself? Give an actual example.

4. A nucleus emits successively 3 alpha particles and 2 electrons. By the rule of radioactive displacement, how far has it moved in the table of the elements?

5. If 3.7×10^{10} alpha particles are emitted per second per gram of radium ($_{88}R^{226}$), compute the half-life of radium in years.

Ans. 1570 years.

6. The decay constant for radium D is 1.00×10^{-9} sec^{-1}. How long will it take 2/3 of a given large number of atoms to disintegrate?

Ans. 35 years.

7. The half-life of radon is 3.8 days. After how many days will only 1/16 of the original radon remain? What fraction of a given large number of radon atoms will disintegrate in one day?

Ans. 15.2 days; 0.17.

8. Find the ratio of numbers of radon atoms to radium atoms when they are in equilibrium.

Ans. 6.5×10^{-6}.

9. If 0.338 microgram of radium is in equilibrium with 1 gram of UI, compute the half-life of UI.

Ans. 4.5×10^{9} years.

10. How long will it take for a sample of radium F (polonium) of half-life 140 days to decay to 1/10 its original strength?

Ans. 465 days.

11. If one-millionth of a gram-atomic weight of radium is found to be in equilibrium with its products radon and radium A, find the number of radon and radium A atoms present.

Ans. 3.9×10^{12} atoms of radon;
2.2×10^{9} atoms of radium A.

12. An alpha particle is ejected from a radon ($_{86}Rn^{222}$) atom with a velocity of 10^8 cm/sec. What is the velocity of recoil of the resultant atom?

Ans. 1.8×10^{6} cm/sec.

13. How much helium gas in cm^3 at 76 cm mercury pressure and 0° C could be produced by 1 gram of uranium ($_{92}U^{238}$) during a period equal to the "age of the earth," 3 billion years? (Since the half-lives of all daughter products are relatively short the alpha particles of all decay products may be counted.)

Ans. 35 cm^3.

14. What is the probability that 10 radon atoms would last 5.5 days without any one of them decaying? (Average or mean life is the time for which the probability of decay is 1/2 and equals half-life divided by 0.693.)

Ans. 1 in 1024.

SUGGESTED READING

G. E. M. Jauncey, "Early Years of Radioactivity," *American Journal of Physics, 14,* 226 (1946).

R. E. Lapp and H. L. Andrews, *Nuclear Radiation Physics,* 2nd ed. (New York, Prentice-Hall, 1954).

J. B. Hoag and S. A. Korff, *Electron and Nuclear Physics,* 3rd ed. (New York, Van Nostrand, 1948).

S. A. Korff, *Electron and Nuclear Counters,* 2nd ed. (Princeton, Van Nostrand, 1955).

E. Rutherford, J. Chadwick, and C. D. Ellis, *Radiations from Radioactive Substances* (New York, Macmillan, 1930).

R. D. Evans, *The Atomic Nucleus* (New York, McGraw-Hill, 1955).

CHAPTER 15

PARTICLES AND RAYS

15-1. Historical

Scientists have long tried to find the elementary particles of which all matter is composed. Early in this century it appeared that the nuclei of all atoms are composed of electrons and protons. No other elementary particles were known. In 1932 the picture was radically changed by the discovery of the positive electron (positron) and the neutron. After the success of the neutrino hypothesis and after the discovery of mesons in 1937, followed by the discovery of still other new particles, it became increasingly necessary to review the question of which particles, if any, are truly fundamental and which are not, and what their relations are to one another.

Evidently study of the many different kinds of so-called elementary particles has become much more complex than before 1932, and in some ways the problem of the nature of matter seems further from solution than at that time. Nevertheless, studies of the alpha, beta, and gamma rays from radioactive substances, together with the particles absorbed or ejected in other nuclear transformations, present the most powerful and direct means of attacking the problem of the nature of the atom, and to these we now turn for more details.

15-4. Nuclear Spins

One of the chief characteristics of nuclear particles is that they possess angular momentum which apparently results from spin about their own axes. Inside the nucleus a particle may also behave as if it has angular momentum, owing to revolution in an orbit or orbital "spin." Unfortunately both kinds of angular momentum are sometimes loosely referred to as spin. Axial spin is as much an intrinsic property of these particles as charge and mass. It was first ascribed to the electron in order to explain the doublet structure of the alkali metal spectra (§ 9-2), and the magnitude of spin of the electron was found to be represented by the quantum numbers $+\frac{1}{2}$ and $-\frac{1}{2}$ for units of $h/2\pi$. Later, with instruments of higher resolving power a new feature of the spectra of some elements was discovered and was called hyperfine structure. Pauli suggested that this might be explained by assuming that the atomic nuclei also possess angular momentum of spin. This suggestion proved to be correct. In the study of molecular spectra as well, the intensities of the lines can be explained by the assumption of nuclear spin. Study of these types of spectra, with the inclusion also of microwave spectroscopy, now furnishes methods of determining the amount of spin that a given type of nucleus possesses. The spin of a nucleus is the resultant of the spins of its component particles, and as it turns out, the spins of protons and neutrons, as well as of electrons, are all represented by the same quantum numbers $\pm\frac{1}{2}$.

One of the most serious objections to the proton-electron model of the nucleus arose over the matter of spins. On that model the total spin sometimes appears to be half-integral when it should actually come out zero or integral. This occurs with light nuclei of even mass number A and odd atomic number Z. On the proton-neutron model, however, the spin always comes out exactly as it should. For instance, let us consider the nucleus of beryllium ($_4Be^9$). Since it has a mass number $A = 9$ and a charge number $Z = 4$, on the proton-electron model it should be composed of 9 protons and 5 electrons. The total number of particles is $9 + 5 = 14$. This is an even number, and the resultant spin should be integral or zero, but the spin is found actually to be odd, $3/2$. On the proton-neutron model the nucleus is composed of 4 protons and 5 neutrons, the sum of which is odd, giving as it should half-integral spin or some odd multiple of it, if not all other nucleons are paired. The resolution of so many of the difficulties of the proton-electron model by means of the proton-neutron model not only is a source of satisfaction but firmly establishes the latter as a working model.

15-5. Alpha Rays and Range

A number of the first radioactive elements to be isolated are alpha-ray emitters. Among them are radium, radon, and polonium. One of the isotopes of polonium ($_{84}Po^{214}$), originally called radium C′, emits alpha rays of the highest energy (7.7 Mev) of any isotope in the uranium-radium series. In the three natural series the most energetic alpha rays of all (8.8 Mev) are emitted by thorium C′, another isotope of polonium ($_{84}PO^{212}$). The alpha emitters giving the highest energy rays have the shortest half-lives, measured in thousandths of a second or even millionths. Those alpha emitters with the longest half-lives, uranium 238 and thorium 232, emit the least energetic alpha rays, both of them close to 4 Mev.

The distance a particle travels in any substance is called its range in that substance. The alpha particles from any one isotope are all emitted with approximately the same energy and have a well-defined range characteristic of that isotope. Although most alpha particles may be stopped by a sheet or two of paper they may travel several centimeters in air at normal pressure. A cloud chamber is a convenient tool with which to study the ranges of alpha particles. It is found that for most alpha-particle emitters the ranges are between 2.7 and 8 cm in air. For instance, for alpha particles from uranium the range in air is 2.7 cm; for radium it is 3.3 cm. The substance with the shortest half-life (164 microseconds) in the uranium series, and the most intense activity, is radium C′. It emits alpha particles with energies of 7.7 Mev. Their range in air is 6.9 cm, and their speed is nearly 1/15 that of light.

The Geiger-Nuttall rule Early in this century a surprising empirical relation was found between the half-life of an alpha-ray emitter and the range of the alpha ray. In fact, a single formula was found to fit all the alpha emitters belonging to a particular decay series. This relation is known as the Geiger-Nuttall rule and is usually written in terms of the decay constant λ instead of the half-life, as follows:

$$\log \lambda = A \log R + B \qquad [15\text{-}2]$$

where R is the range in cm and A and B are constants for a given decay series. In terms of the variables $\log \lambda$ and $\log R$ this is seen to be the equation of a straight line with slope A and intercept B. When the experimental values are plotted they determine a separate straight line for each of the natural decay series (Fig. 15-1). However, the relation is an approximate and empirical one, and tells nothing of the reason why range and decay constant are so related. For a long time there could not be found any sound basis in theory for the unique relations involved in the rule, but recently considerable light has been thrown on the subject by the methods of quantum mechanics, and the analysis

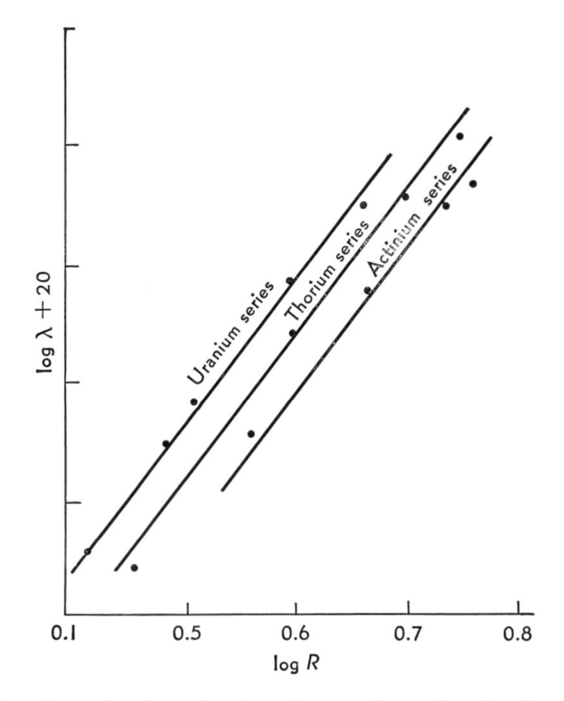

Fig. 15-1. The Geiger-Nuttal rule. The members of each of the natural radioactive decay series fall on or close to a straight line when the range *R* and decay constant λ for each element are plotted on a logarithmic graph as indicated.

makes it clear that this is no chance relationship but something deep-seated and fundamental. Because of the need for the concept of the nuclear potential barrier, an explanation of the theory of alpha decay and its relation to the Geiger-Nuttall rule will be delayed until the next chapter (§ 16-6).

Absorption and ionization losses Alpha particles are stopped in passing through a material medium such as air because of loss of energy by collisions with the atoms of the medium. In a gas the energy loss by collision is chiefly the result of the inelastic collisions that produce ionization of the atoms or molecules. At the start of its path 20 to 30 thousand ion pairs per cm of air may be formed by the passage of an alpha particle through it, and the probability of ionization rises as the speed of the alpha particle decreases, until a maximum is reached of as much as 70,000 ion pairs per centimeter. The variation of ionization with distance along the path is shown in Fig. 15-2, where the ionization is seen to rise to a maximum and fall sharply as the alpha particle comes near the end of its range. Beta rays, on the other hand, being less massive produce something like 1/100 as many ions per centimeter.

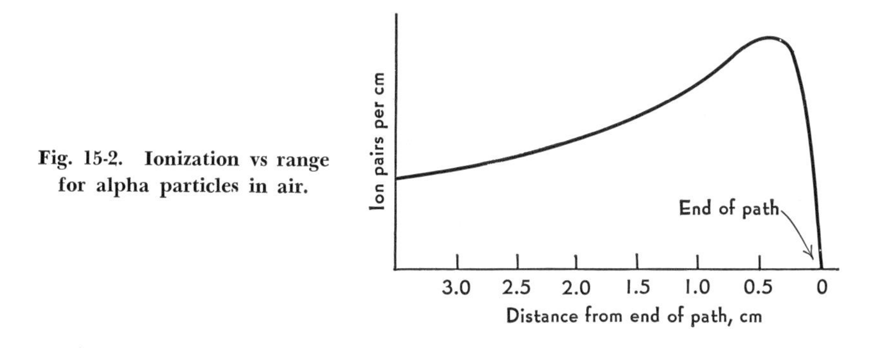

Fig. 15-2. Ionization vs range for alpha particles in air.

Different materials have different degrees of stopping power. The term *stopping power* is often used to express the comparative stopping power with respect to air at standard temperature and pressure. The stopping power of aluminum for alpha particles is said to be 1700 because 1 centimeter of air is equaled by 1/1700 centimeter of aluminum. A common method of expressing the thickness of an aluminum-absorbing layer is to give it in terms of the number of milligrams of material per square centimeter. For instance, 1.62 mg/cm^2 of aluminum has the same stopping power as 1 cm of standard air for alpha particles over a considerable range of speeds.

Energy spectrum and fine structure If observed in a cloud chamber, all the alpha particles from a given isotope seem to have the same range and consequently the same energy. However, closer study with more refined methods proved this not to be true, with a few exceptions. Rosenblum in 1929 found, by magnetic analysis, that alpha particles often fall into two or more groups which are close together in energy but have definite and fixed energy differences, as if different groups came from different energy levels within the nucleus. For instance, alpha rays from thorium C are found to be composed of five groups having a maximum energy difference between groups of less than 0.5 Mev. These sharply defined energy groups represent what is called the fine structure of the alpha-ray energy distribution.

Nuclear energy levels and decay schemes The discovery of the fine structure of alpha rays marks the real beginning of the analysis of nuclear structure. It furnished the clue that there may be different energy levels in the nucleus, that is, that the nucleus generally may exist in one or more higher energy states (excited states) above the lowest or ground state. The energy differences between groups do not, as was first thought, represent energy-level differences belonging to states of the parent atom; instead they belong to the daughter atom.

In Fig. 15-3 the decay of radium to radon is represented. Here, only two different energy groups of alpha particles are found, with energies, respectively, of 4.80 Mev and 4.61 Mev, but accompanying them gamma rays of 0.19 Mev are also detected. When an alpha ray (α_1), belonging to the higher energy group, is emitted from the parent nucleus it is believed that it is not accompanied by emission of a gamma ray. That is to say, the daughter element radon is formed at once in its lowest or ground state (Fig. 15-3). On this basis it is a simple matter to explain the origin of the observed gamma ray by assuming that the radon nucleus is not formed in the ground state by the emission of an alpha ray of the lower energy group, but that it is formed in an excited state, from which it passes to the ground state by emitting a gamma ray of

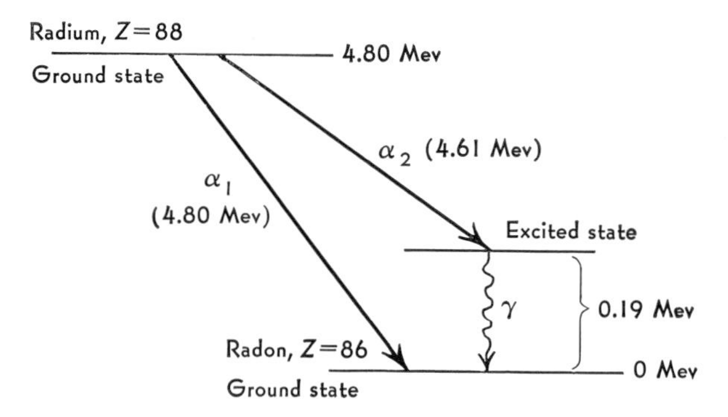

Fig. 15-3. Decay scheme for radium. Radium is transformed to radon by emission of an alpha particle. Two groups of slightly different energies are present. The less energetic alpha emission is followed by gamma emission.

energy 4.80 − 4.61 = 0.19 Mev. Figures such as 15-3 are known as decay schemes for alpha-ray emission. Similarly when thorium C decays to thorium C″ five groups of alpha particles are observed, and the existence of four excited states of thorium C″ above the ground state is inferred.

Long-range alpha rays A few alpha emitters, in particular thorium C′ and radium C′, are found to emit rays of unusually long range occasionally. These are ascribed to emission from the parent nucleus when it is in an excited state. Thus the alpha ray carries off not only its normal energy but the excess energy of excitation of the parent nucleus.

Alpha-ray spectrograph Magnetic analysis of alpha-ray energies may be accomplished by deflection in a magnetic field in a manner similar to that of the mass spectrograph (§ 2-6), except that all alpha particles have the same mass, and particles of different velocity are focused at different points (Fig. 15-4). Such a

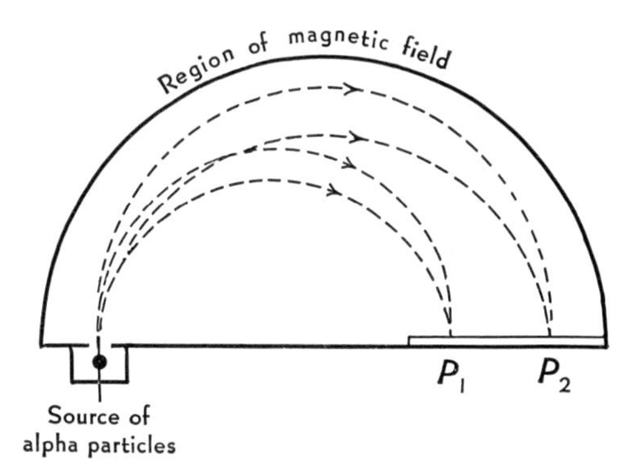

Fig. 15-4. Alpha-ray magnetic spectrometer with uniform magnetic field, showing focusing of rays of different energies at points P_1 and P_2.

device is called an alpha-ray magnetic spectrograph, and magnetic field intensities of the order of 10,000 gauss are required. Because the method requires quite intense sources of alpha rays less accurate methods must sometimes be resorted to.

15-6. Beta Rays

Among radioactive substances there are more beta-ray emitters of all kinds than there are alpha-ray emitters. In contrast with alpha-ray emission, beta rays from a beta emitter have a wide distribution of energies. The beta rays from most naturally radioactive substances

ray when the emission leaves the resultant nucleus with more than normal energy. With the emission of one or more gamma rays the nucleus then passes to the normal state. If it returns to the normal state in a single transition a single gamma-ray photon is emitted. If it returns by a series of transitions, "falling down the stair-steps" so to speak, a series of gamma-ray photons is emitted in what is called cascade emission (Fig. 15-9). Many measurements have been made of the energies of the gamma rays produced when a nucleus returns to the ground state, and these again serve to locate the energy levels for the various excited states of a nucleus.

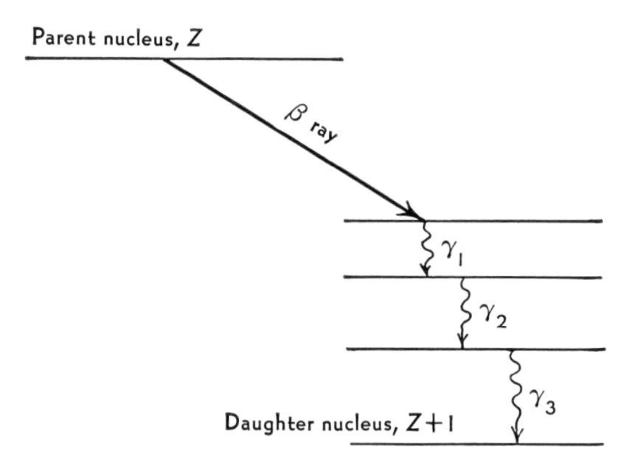

Fig. 15-9. Decay scheme, representing successive emission of a series of gamma rays (cascade emission).

Absorption of gamma rays The nature of the absorption process for gamma rays is essentially different from that of charged particles such as alpha and beta rays. When gamma rays pass through matter the intensity of the beam decreases in a manner similar to x-rays, and the intensity for a narrow beam of rays of the same energy is given by the same equation as for x-rays,

$$I = I_0 \epsilon^{-\mu x} \tag{15-3}$$

where μ, as before, is the absorption coefficient of the matter for the wavelengths in question and x is the thickness of the absorber. From this formula it is apparent that gamma rays have no definite range, as do alpha and beta rays. Absorption is said to result when any process deflects a gamma-ray photon from its path or uses up its energy. The decrease in intensity of a gamma-ray beam on passing through matter is chiefly due to three separate effects, photoelectric absorption, Compton scattering by electrons, and production of electron pairs (next section). When the beam is attenuated by any or all of these processes it is said to be "absorbed."

In photoelectric absorption all the energy of the gamma-ray photons is transferred to an electron, and the gamma-ray photon ceases to exist. The ejected electron may escape from the absorber, or its energy may be used up in collisions. In Compton scattering of gamma rays, just as with x-rays (§ 6-2), the photon loses energy at any collision with an electron and its frequency is thereby reduced. Its direction is also changed so that it may be scattered out of the main beam. Such scattering is increasingly probable with a substance composed of atoms of higher atomic number since there are more electrons per atom that may be hit. In electron-pair production the energy of the gamma-ray photon goes to form a positive and negative electron. At energies of 50 kev or less for aluminum, and 500 kev for lead, the loss of energy is chiefly the result of photoelectric absorption. At energies in the neighborhood of 1 Mev Compton scattering has become predominant. At higher energies pair production becomes increasingly important and finally becomes the principal factor in absorption.

15-10. Electron-Pair Production and Annihilation

According to the Einstein energy-mass relation it might be expected that a gamma-ray photon of sufficient energy might be transformed into matter. Since the photon has zero charge the production of a negative electron would also require the simultaneous production of a positive electron. Such a positive and negative electron constitutes an electron pair. This pair production has been observed (Fig. 15-10). The transformation must occur in such a way as to conserve momentum as well as energy, and it usually happens in the presence of matter

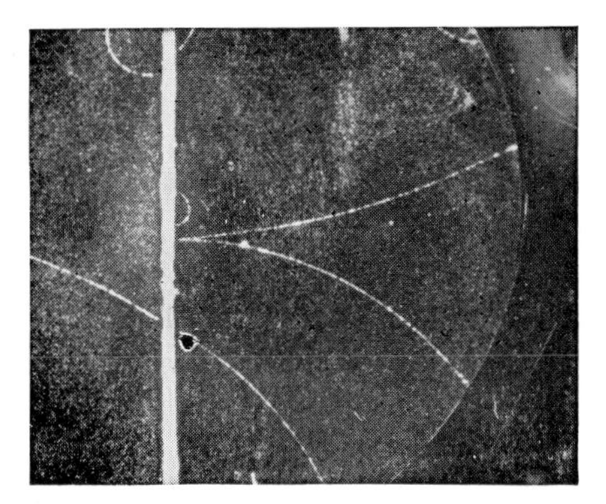

Fig. 15-10. Cloud-chamber photograph, showing production of an electron pair. Gamma-ray photon coming from left leaves no track but forms electron pair when it encounters metal plate. The paths of the positive and negative electrons are curved in opposite directions by a magnetic field perpendicular to plane of photo. (Courtesy, University of Illinois, Department of Physics.)

where some nucleus is available as a recoil mechanism to enter into the exchange.

Since the energy equivalent of the mass of each electron is 0.51 Mev the energy of an electron pair is 1.02 Mev. This is the minimum energy of the gamma-ray photon capable of forming a pair, the members of which would then have zero kinetic energy. The value of the photon energy fixes its frequency by the Planck quantum relation. However, the probability of pair formation with minimum energy is very low, and when an electron pair is formed by a higher-energy photon the excess energy goes into kinetic energy of motion of the two electrons of rest mass m_0 giving them velocities v_1 and v_2. For a gamma-ray photon of energy hf then

$$hf = 2m_0c^2 + \frac{1}{2}m_0v_1^2 + \frac{1}{2}m_0v_2^2 \qquad [15\text{-}4]$$

and the velocities of the electrons can be readily computed, assuming the excess energy is divided equally between them. If the excess energy is large, a more complete relativistic treatment must be given.

The opposite of pair production is pair "annihilation," though the word annihilation only applies to the disappearance of separate charged particles. If an electron and a positron come close together they should attract each other, their charges should cancel, and they could no longer exist as separate particles. Total energy along with total charge would be expected to be conserved, and the energy equivalent of the masses of the two electrons should appear in the form of radiation. The relatively large amount of energy involved indicates that the radiation would be in the form of gamma radiation. For momentum also to be conserved two gamma rays will be radiated in opposite directions. Since the rest mass of each electron has an energy equivalent of 0.51 Mev the minimum energy of each gamma-ray photon is 0.51 Mev, and the frequency of each photon may be computed by the Planck equation $E = hf$. This gives, for the maximum wavelength possible, 0.024 A.

The phenomenon of pair annihilation has been observed, and not only has the existence of two simultaneous photons traveling in opposite directions been experimentally verified by means of coincidence counters (§ 20-3), but the wavelengths of the photons have been found to agree closely with the computed values.

15-11. The Neutron

The discovery of the neutron was the culmination of a sequence of experiments by investigators in several countries and aptly illustrates the fact that science knows no national boundaries. In Germany in 1930, Bothe and Becker found that apparently a very penetrating radiation is emitted when high-speed alpha particles strike beryllium or boron. The high penetration of the radiation led them to assume that it was high-energy gamma radiation although it was more penetrating than any known gamma rays.

A little later Irene Curie, and her husband Frederic Joliot, in France investigated the new effect and tried to measure the absorbing power of various substances. Most substances such as copper or lead produced only a small decrease in the radiation, but when they put paraffin in the path of the beam they were surprised to find something quite different. The readings of the detector (an ionization chamber) actually increased, and rays instead of becoming weaker apparently became more intense. They finally concluded that the unknown rays from beryllium knocked protons out of the paraffin or out of any substance rich in hydrogen (Fig. 15-11) by a kind of Compton effect.

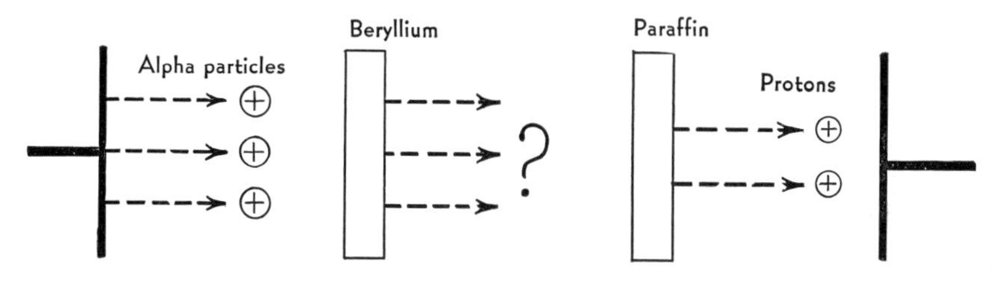

Fig. 15-11. The experiment of Curie and Joliot, showing protons dislodged by unknown rays from beryllium bombarded by alpha particles. Chadwick demonstrated that the rays were neutral particles (neutrons).

Applying the mathematics of the Compton effect they found that to give the protons the energies that they were found to have by recoil from gamma-ray collisions would require gamma rays from the beryllium of energies as high as 50 Mev.

Next, Chadwick in England took up the experiment and in 1932 pointed out two serious objections to the previous interpretation. First, thousands of times as many protons were produced as could be accounted for on the basis of the established theory of such occurrences. Second, there was no transformation of beryllium, when hit by an alpha particle, that could possibly release anywhere near the required energy of 50 Mev. Chadwick then arrived at the correct interpretation of the experiments and confirmed his hypothesis by ingenious and convincing experiments.

Chadwick not only measured recoil protons hit by the unknown rays, but he also found and measured the recoil of nitrogen nuclei. Though a 50-Mev gamma ray could give the measured recoil to a proton, it was easy to show that it could only give one-third the observed recoil energy to a nitrogen nucleus. Thus the gamma-ray hypothesis was untenable. Chadwick also demonstrated that if the rays were particles instead of gamma rays they must possess zero charge since they could not be deflected by electric or magnetic fields. He then showed that all contradictions vanish if the rays are assumed to consist of a new kind of particle possessing zero charge and a mass approximately that of a proton. To this particle the name **neutron** was given. The existence of such a particle had been suggested some years before, but all attempts to detect it had failed.

Cloud-chamber studies of the new particle were now made by Feather who confirmed Chadwick's work. Tracks observed in the cloud chamber were formed only when the newly discovered particles ejected protons from nuclei; the protons being charged particles left a trail of ions and a visible track in the chamber whereas the incident neutrons produced no appreciable ions directly and left no visible track.

Mass of neutron and magnetic moment The next problem was to determine the mass of the neutron. Knowing the momenta of the recoil protons and nitrogen nuclei, Chadwick applied the law of conservation of momentum and found that the mass of the particle must be slightly larger than that of a proton. After much more experimental work by many investigators the mass of the neutron m_n has now been more accurately determined and is seen to be slightly more than that of a proton m_p.

$$m_n = 1.008982 \text{ amu}$$

$$m_p = 1.007593 \text{ amu}$$

Although neutrons possess no detectable net electric charge, experiments by Dunning and others have shown that they possess a magnetic moment. Bloch and Alvarez found the magnetic moment of the neutron to be

$$\mu_n = -1.9135 \pm 0.02 \text{ nuclear magnetons}$$

In comparison it is interesting to note that the magnetic moment of the proton is

$$\mu_p = 2.79 \text{ nuclear magnetons}$$

The minus sign of the neutron magnetic moment is different from other particles and indicates that the spin vector and magnetic-moment vector are in the same direction. For other particles it is easy to conceive of the magnetic moment as due to a spinning charge, but where the net observed charge is zero the explanation seems to break down. However, with the discovery of mesons (Chap. 20) it has been assumed that there may be a net circulation of meson charge in the neutron even though the resultant charge is zero. Many such problems need further clarification.

15-12. Production and Detection of Neutrons

Chadwick assumed that when alpha particles bombard beryllium the neutrons are produced in the following manner. When a beryllium nucleus ${}_4\text{Be}^9$ is hit by an alpha particle ${}_2\text{He}^4$ the neutron carries away 1 unit of mass and zero charge, thus leaving a nucleus of charge $2 + 4 = 6$ and of mass $9 + 4 - 1 = 12$, identified as an isotope of carbon. The symbolic representation of the reaction is

$${}_2\text{He}^4 + {}_4\text{Be}^9 \rightarrow {}_6\text{C}^{12} + {}_0n^1$$

where ${}_0n^1$ is the symbol representing the neutron.

Neutrons may now be produced in great abundance in nuclear reactors, and intense streams of neutrons may be obtained from a suitable opening in the reactor shielding (Chap. 19). They may in theory be ejected from any atom possessing them, but particularly from the atoms rich in neutrons if such atoms are bombarded by sufficiently energetic particles. They are obtained especially by the bombardment of the lighter elements such as beryllium, boron, and lithium by alpha particles. They are produced in the upper atmosphere by cosmic-ray bombardment of air molecules.

The detection of neutrons, as distinct from other particles, was at first quite a problem. Since they possess no net electric charge they produce no appreciable ionization of a gas through which they pass and consequently leave no track in a cloud chamber, nor do they produce directly any ions in a G-M tube by which they may be detected. They may occasionally make head-on collisions with protons or other charged particles, imparting to them such speeds that they in turn produce ionization and are detected. This method has been adopted for fast neutrons, the counter being surrounded by a layer of paraffin or other material rich in protons.

A method more common for slow neutrons is that of lining the inside of a G-M tube or ionization chamber with a layer of something containing nuclei which may readily absorb neutrons, with the provision that the nucleus after absorption must be unstable and disintegrate by emitting an ionizing ray that can be detected (Fig. 15-12). A

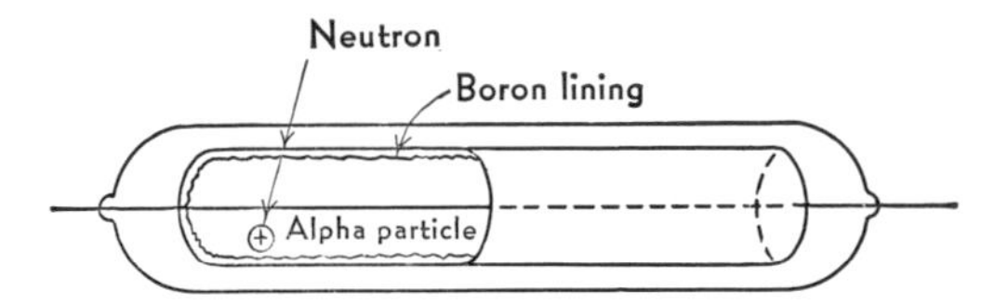

Fig. 15-12. Cut-away of G-M tube, showing boron lining for neutron detection.

commonly used substance is boron, containing B^{10}, which emits an alpha particle after capture of a neutron according to the following reaction:

$$ {}_0n^1 + {}_5B^{10} \rightarrow {}_2He^4 + {}_3Li^7 \qquad [15\text{-}5] $$

Since the alpha particle is strongly ionizing it is easily detected. The method is particularly successful when the neutrons have speeds for which the probability of capture is large.

15-13. Neutron Decay

Free neutrons, that is, those not inside atomic nuclei, are found to be unstable and to decay by beta emission. Theory indicates that, if conservation laws are considered, a neutrino should also be emitted, as is usual in beta-type decay. Early attempts to detect neutron decay were handicapped by the difficulty of procuring strong neutron beams and of controlling and detecting them. In 1948 it was estimated that the half-life was less than 30 minutes. In 1951 Robson, working with an intense beam of neutrons from the Chalk River (Canada) reactor, obtained a value of 12.8 minutes. Evidently in a stable nucleus a neutron is no longer a free particle and is unable to decay.

15-14. Fast and Slow Neutrons

Neutrons possessing energies of 1 Mev or more are known as fast neutrons. If neutrons are slowed down to speeds comparable to those of gas molecules at normal temperature and pressure they are spoken of as slow or thermal neutrons. Between these extremes is the indefinite region of neutrons of intermediate speed. Thermal neutrons have energies of approximately 0.03 ev, and sometimes neutrons with energies up to 10 ev are included in the term slow neutrons. Although there is no rigid classification the following is a convenient one:

Neutron Speeds and Energies

Fast	0.1 Mev up
Intermediate	10 ev to 0.1 Mev
Slow	0.03 ev to 10 ev
Thermal	0.03 ev (approx.)

The interaction of fast and slow neutrons with matter is a subject of much importance. Fast neutrons may sometimes pass right through the nucleus of an atom, whereas slow neutrons would much more readily be captured. The slowing down of neutrons then becomes a matter of importance, and at certain speeds the probability of capture may increase enormously (§ 16-17). On the other hand, fast neutrons may produce effects that slow neutrons cannot. Neutron capture at different speeds in uranium will be studied in more detail in Chap. 19.

15-15. Reduction of Neutron Speeds and Elastic Scattering

Neutrons do not ordinarily make ionizing collisions with atoms since they possess no electric fields, and if they do not enter into nuclei and lose energy the collisions are said to be elastic rather than inelastic. When an elastic object strikes a very much more massive object it rebounds with most of its energy, imparting only a small fraction to the massive object. However, if it rebounds from collision with an object more nearly its own mass, it may lose a considerable amount of its energy and in a head-on collision may lose nearly all or all of it. Since random collisions occur at different angles, a particle colliding at random with particles of equal mass loses on the average 63 per cent of its energy. Since protons possess nearly the same mass as neutrons, a neutron after two collisions with protons would retain on the average only 37 per cent of 37 per cent, or less than 14 per cent of its original energy. A 2-Mev neutron can be reduced to the thermal energy of a gas molecule in about 18 collisions in hydrogen. In collision with carbon nuclei, it would take 114 collisions on the average. Thus, to slow neutrons down they are passed through material rich either in protons or in nuclei of small mass. Water and paraffin are two of the most easily obtainable and common substances. Heavy water is effective because of its very low capture probability for neutrons.

The collisions just mentioned are elastic collisions, and neutrons undergoing such collisions are said to be elastically scattered. The scattering of neutrons has been studied considerably, and one of the results has been information concerning the sizes of nuclei. Heavier nuclei would be expected to be larger than light nuclei, and neutron scattering experiments agree with other experiments in indicating that the nuclear radius is proportional to the cube root of the mass number A. An average value from different methods may be taken to be

$$r = 1.5A^{1/3} \times 10^{-13} \text{ cm} \qquad [15\text{-}6]$$

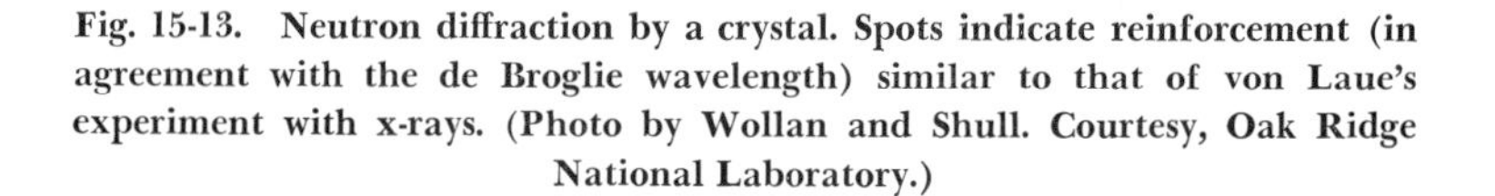

Fig. 15-13. Neutron diffraction by a crystal. Spots indicate reinforcement (in agreement with the de Broglie wavelength) similar to that of von Laue's experiment with x-rays. (Photo by Wollan and Shull. Courtesy, Oak Ridge National Laboratory.)

15-16. Neutron Diffraction

One of the tests of the de Broglie hypothesis that elementary particles have wavelengths given by the formula $\lambda = h/mv$ was made with neutrons. The equation predicts that neutrons having energies of the order of 1 ev would have wavelengths similar to ordinary x-rays and might show Bragg or von Laue diffraction by crystals, just as electrons do. The first experimental confirmation was obtained by Mitchell and Powers in 1936. With the development of intense neutron beams from nuclear reactors it was possible to obtain photographs of the reinforcement spot pattern by the method of von Laue (Fig. 15-13), as well as by the method of the Braggs.

In addition to confirming the validity of the de Broglie equation in its application to neutrons, the results are of much interest because neutron diffraction affords a new tool for the study of the structure of matter. Whereas the scattering ability of the lighter elements is relatively small for x-rays, it is relatively large for neutrons. Neutron diffraction is then a more powerful tool in locating hydrogen and other light elements in molecular groupings.

15-17. Neutron Velocity Selectors

For many experimental purposes it is desirable to have a "monochromatic" beam of neutrons, that is, a beam of neutrons all having the same speed. Since neutrons cannot be deflected by electric or magnetic fields, this presents quite an experimental problem. One method is that of making use of the wave properties of the neutron.

When a beam of neutrons of different speeds is reflected from the face of a crystal there will be one particular angle for which the de Broglie waves, representing the neutrons, will reinforce, just as in the Bragg method of x-ray diffraction. It will be the angle of maximum intensity for neutrons of just the right speed to have the proper de Broglie wavelength. This is one way of obtaining a beam of neutrons having the same or nearly the same speeds or velocities.

Another method of separating slow neutrons into velocity groups is by the time-of-flight or chopper method. Imagine two slits arranged at opposite extremities of the diameter of a wheel (Fig. 15-14). If the wheel is rotated a narrow beam of light would shine through the slits only when the slits are in line with the source of light. Substitute a neutron source for the source of light, and make the rim of the wheel out of a neutron absorber such as cadmium, with slits in it. The neu-

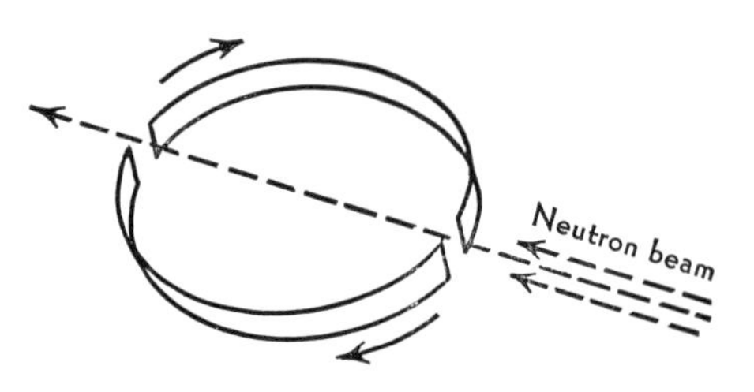

Fig. 15-14. Time-of-flight velocity selector for neutrons. Slits may be aluminum strips imbedded in cadmium absorber.

trons can only get through the slits when they are in line if the neutrons are moving with a certain minimum velocity, depending on the speed of rotation of the wheel. The slits need not be air gaps but may be slabs of aluminum or another substance through which neutrons pass readily. When a pulse of neutrons passes the slits, the detectors may be so timed as to make measurements on the last neutrons to pass through; these have the known minimum velocity.

15-18. The Proton and Antiproton

The proton Protons are not emitted by any naturally radioactive substance but may be ejected from a nucleus that has undergone bombardment by various types of rays. For instance, when nitrogen (${}_7N^{14}$) is bombarded by neutrons, protons are expelled, leaving carbon (${}_6C^{14}$), as follows:

$$ {}_7N^{14} + {}_0n^1 \rightarrow {}_6C^{14} + {}_1H^1 $$

and when aluminum (${}_{13}Al^{27}$) is bombarded by alpha particles protons are expelled, leaving silicon.

$$ {}_2He^4 + {}_{13}Al^{27} \rightarrow {}_{14}Si^{30} + {}_1H^1 $$

Although recognized historically soon after the discovery of the electron, the mystery still remains as to how the proton can have the same magnitude of charge as an electron but a mass 1836 times as large. In the nucleus at least it appears to behave as if it were composed of a neutron plus a positive electron. Like all elementary particles it possesses an intrinsic angular momentum or spin, and it has a spin quantum number of ½, just as an electron does. Owing to its spin, it would be expected also to possess a magnetic moment, and the value obtained by Rabi and his collaborators is $\mu_p = 2.785$ nuclear magnetons. A later value obtained by Gardner and Purcell is

$$ \mu_p = 2.793 \text{ nuclear magnetons} $$

The antiproton Following the same line of reasoning as in the production of electron pairs it might be expected to be possible to produce a proton pair, that is, a positive proton and a negative proton (antiproton) if gamma rays of sufficient energy could be used. In electron-pair formation gamma rays of sufficient energy were readily available, but the rest mass of a proton is 1836 times the rest mass of an electron. Consequently, by the Einstein energy-mass relation the equivalent energy is greater in the same ratio and for 1 proton is 931 Mev. To produce a proton pair would require a minimum gamma-ray energy of 2 times 931 Mev, or 1.86 billion electron volts (Bev). The probability of formation would be very low at such energies and would presumably be much greater at higher energies, so that actually gamma-ray energies of 2 or 3 Bev would be required.

Up until quite recently no particle accelerators were available to produce particles or gamma rays in the billion-volt energy region but now, with the Brookhaven cosmotron and the University of California bevatron, billion-volt particles are obtainable. Late in 1955, the group at the University of California headed by Segrè and Wheeler announced the discovery of the antiproton. Although it was not possible to find this particle free in nature, it is now possible to produce it in the laboratory, and another new particle has been added to those which we already have.

In a sense, with every new particle the situation becomes more complicated, but the symmetry of the Dirac theory, by which the "antielectron" or positron was predicted, was confirmed by the discovery of the positron, and now this symmetry must be extended to include both positive and negative protons. Measurements already indicate that the negative proton has exactly the characteristics that would be expected of it on a theoretical basis. It is a stable particle; it possesses the same quantity of charge as the proton; and it has the same mass. The interest in this new particle will lead to many new experiments and further measurements of its properties.

15-19. Positronium

The discovery of the positron led to the speculation that a positron might be captured by an electron, or vice versa, and would tend to rotate about it in a manner similar to that by which a proton captures an electron and forms a hydrogen atom. Since the two particles have the same mass they would actually rotate about each other or more accurately about the center of mass of the system. However, the positron and electron are capable of annihilating each other, and it would

consequently he suspected that such an "electronic atom," now called positronium, would be extremely unstable. Theory shows that if their spins are parallel (ortho-positronium), the "atom" is in what is called the singlet S state by analogy with optical spectra and should have a half-life of about 10^{-7} sec. This is long enough to make detection possible. Furthermore, when the two particles annihilate each other they should form two simultaneous gamma-ray photons. Deutsch looked for the formation of positronium in nitrogen gas, through which a beam of positrons was passed, and was successful in 1951 in obtaining evidence of the decay (and by inference the formation) of these tiny two-particle systems. Theoretical analysis further indicates that when the two spins are parallel (triplet state), the half-life should be much shorter, of the order of 10^{-9} or 10^{-10} sec, and that the system should decay into three simultaneous gamma-ray photons. Evidence for this was obtained in 1952 by De Benedetti and Siegel. Such experiments also appear to confirm in part the quantum theory for a two-particle system.

15-20. Dirac's Theory of Electrons

Ever since the discovery of electricity there have been theories about its ultimate nature. Dufay (1698-1739) proposed that there are two separate kinds of electricity, the two-fluid theory. Later Benjamin Franklin suggested the single-fluid theory in which he conceived of a negative charge as being the absence of a positive charge. Unfortunately the application of these theories to electrical phenomena does not enable as sharp a distinction to be drawn as might at first be thought. Although we may commonly think of positive and negative electricity as separate entities, the fact that one may cancel the other, as in pair annihilation, shows them to have a unique relationship.

The success of Schrödinger's equation in the atomic realm led Dirac to try to remedy what seemed to be a definite omission. The Schrödinger equation did not involve relativistic considerations. It was not invariant to the Lorentz transformations. Dirac searched until, in 1928, he found a satisfactory solution. The rewards for his efforts were ample. Whereas the spin of the electron had to be added gratuitously to earlier theory, it came naturally out of the interpretation of the Dirac equations. Instead of adding quantum numbers to previous theory as needed, all four quantum numbers n, l, s, m of atomic spectra appeared in the theory. Finally Dirac interpreted his equation to predict the existence of positive electrons, at that time unknown.

In his treatment of the electron there seemed no reason for ruling out the assignment of negative energy values to the electron. An electron in a positive energy state has a minimum energy $m_0c^2 = 0.51$ Mev. In a similar negative energy state it would have a value $-m_0c^2$. Dirac suggested that his equations could be interpreted to mean that the universe is an ocean of negative energy in which an electron can only be created by raising it from its negative energy state to a positive energy state. As no electron can exist in a positive energy state with less energy than 0.51 Mev, and its negative energy state must be not less than -0.51 Mev, to raise an electron from a negative to a positive energy state requires a minimum of 1.02 Mev (Fig. 15-15), but this leaves a

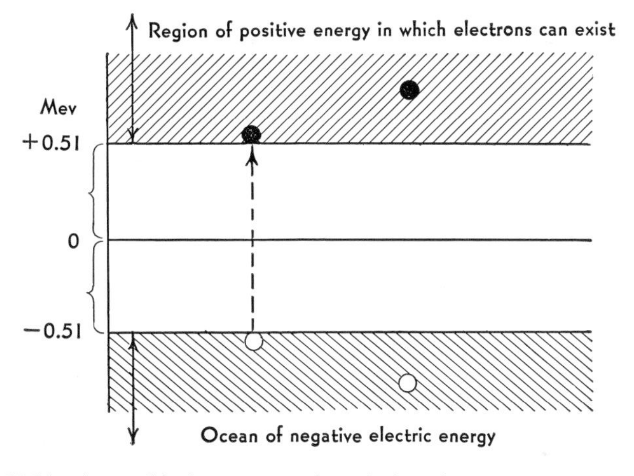

Fig. 15-15. A graphical representation of the Dirac theory of electrons.

"hole" in the ocean of negative energy. This "hole" has properties opposite to those of the electron created and would thus represent a positive electron or positron; to create such an electron pair would require 1.02-Mev energy. This is Dirac's theory of electrons, and in its broadest sense it describes pair formation and annihilation, along with implying the existence of positive electrons.

PROBLEMS

1. The range of alpha particles from radium is 3.2 cm in air at 76 cm of mercury pressure and 0° C. What would be the range in air at 38 cm and 20°?

Ans. 6.85 cm.

2. A positron and an electron moving in opposite directions combine (annihilation) to form a pair of similar gamma-ray photons. What will be the energy and wavelength of each gamma-ray photon if the kinetic energy of each member of the electron pair was 0.5 Mev before collision?

Ans. 1.01 Mev; 12.2×10^{-11} cm.

3. What must the wavelength and the energy in Mev be for a gamma ray to produce an electron pair, each electron having a kinetic energy of 1 Mev?

Ans. 4.1×10^{-11} cm; 3.02 Mev.

4. Find the wavelength of a gamma-ray photon and its energy in Mev if it can produce a proton pair (proton plus antiproton) each member of which has a kinetic energy of 1 Mev.

Ans. 6.6×10^{-14} cm; 1.88×10^{3} Mev.

5. How much thickness of lead is required to reduce the intensity of gamma rays from thorium C to 1/10 if the linear absorption coefficient is $\mu = 0.46\ \text{cm}^{-1}$?

Ans. 5 cm.

6. Gamma rays from RaB are passed through lead. If the linear absorption coefficient for these rays is $1.5\ \text{cm}^{-1}$, how much will the intensity be reduced by a thickness of 1 cm?

Ans. 77.7 per cent.

7. A radioactive compound emits beta and gamma rays. It is desired to count gamma-ray photons. What thickness of aluminum of linear absorption coefficient $12\ \text{cm}^{-1}$ for beta rays will reduce the beta-ray count to 1 in 100?

Ans. 0.384 cm.

8. If neutrons and protons in equal numbers could be packed as close together to fill a centimeter cube as they are packed in a nucleus, what would be the mass in metric tons of 1 cm^3? (Assume spacing of particles between centers is 10^{-12} cm, and use approximate proton mass for the particles.)

Ans. 1.67×10^{6} metric tons.

9. If the mass of a radium atom is 226.1031 amu, what is the kinetic energy of the alpha ray emitted if the mass of the product atom of radon (emanation) is 222.0940 amu and the mass of a helium atom is 4.003873?

Ans. 4.84 Mev.

10. Compute the energy equivalent in Mev of a proton pair (proton and antiproton) assuming that the antiproton has the same mass as the proton.

Ans. 1876 Mev.

11. An alpha particle travels 5 cm in an ionization chamber and forms on the average 30,000 ion pairs per cm. If all the ions of one sign are collected at an electrode of 5 micromicrofarads ($\mu\mu$f) capacitance, what is the charge in coulombs and what is the change of potential of the electrode?

Ans. 2.4×10^{-14} coulomb; 4.8×10^{-3} volt.

SUGGESTED READING

J. D. STRANATHAN, *The "Particles" of Modern Physics* (Philadelphia, Blakiston, 1942).

R. A. MILLIKAN, *Electrons, Protons, Photons, Neutrons and Cosmic Rays,* 2nd ed. (Chicago, Univ. of Chicago Press, 1947).

I. KAPLAN, *Nuclear Physics* (Cambridge, Addison-Wesley, 1955).

E. RUTHERFORD, J. CHADWICK, and C. D. ELLIS, *Radiations from Radioactive Substances* (New York, Macmillan, 1930).

G. GAMOW and C. L. CRITCHFIELD, *Theory of Atomic Nucleus and Nuclear Energy Sources* (Oxford, Clarendon Press, 1949).

CHAPTER 16

TRANSMUTATION, INDUCED RADIOACTIVITY, AND NUCLEAR PROCESSES

16-1. The First Transmutation of Atoms

In 1919 Rutherford produced the first nuclear transmutation by artificial means when he bombarded ordinary nitrogen with high-speed alpha particles emitted by RaC′. He knew that such alpha particles had a range in nitrogen of about 7 cm after passing through a silver-foil window, hence that they could not travel further than this in the nitrogen gas. Nevertheless, by means of a fluorescent screen he ob-

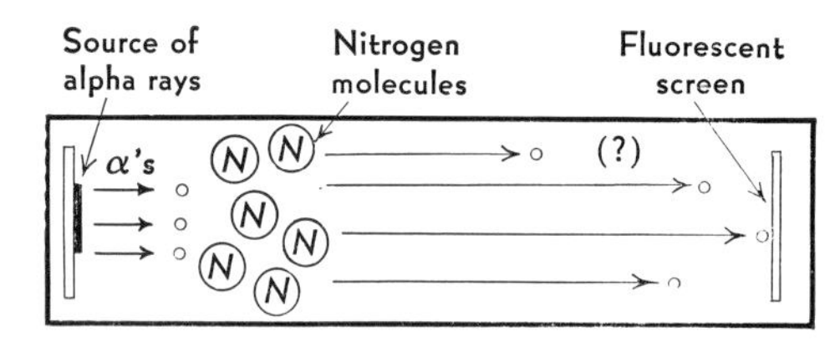

Fig. 16-1. Schematic diagram of Rutherford's first atomic disintegration experiment (1919).

served particles which traveled as far as 40 cm from the source (Fig. 16-1). Since the nitrogen atom itself was considerably more massive than an alpha particle, it could in no way be knocked so far by an ordinary collision. Rutherford then concluded that some less massive particle must have been ejected from the nitrogen nucleus, and by applying the ordinary laws of impact he found it to be most probable that the ejected particle was a proton. This conclusion was later confirmed. Such a transformation may be described in terms of the incident and emitted particles and is now called an alpha-proton (α, p) reaction.

Here was the first experiment in which an atomic nucleus had been knowingly disrupted by a man-made experiment, and the transformation was soon represented symbolically in the following manner:

$$_2He^4 + {}_7N^{14} \rightarrow ({}_9F^{18}) \rightarrow {}_8O^{17} + {}_1H^1 \qquad [16\text{-}1]$$

The assumption is made here that the nitrogen atom first captures the alpha particle to form momentarily a nucleus, called the **compound nucleus** of mass number $14 + 4 = 18$ and charge $7 + 2 = 9$, which shows it to be an isotope of fluorine. The ejection of the proton then leaves the nucleus with a mass number 17 and a nuclear charge 8, equal to the sum of the charges of the nitrogen nucleus plus the helium nucleus, diminished by the charge carried away by the proton. The nuclear charge of 8 identifies the product nucleus as an isotope of oxygen.

By this experiment Rutherford transmuted ordinary nitrogen into a rare isotope of oxygen. Similar experiments were performed on other light elements, and it was found that protons could be knocked out of all the light elements from boron to potassium, with the exception of carbon and oxygen which at first resisted attempts to disrupt them. A considerable number of light elements was thus studied by Rutherford himself, and this work was later extended by others who confirmed nearly all his work. The results were further confirmation of previous theories that protons are present in all atomic nuclei and that consequently the proton must be one of the fundamental "building blocks" of all matter.

16-2. Transmutation by Accelerated Particles

In 1930 Cockroft and Walton in Cambridge, England, first produced nuclear disintegrations by electrically accelerated, charged particles (§ 18-2). They used protons accelerated first by 100,000 volts and later by 700,000 volts, and bombarded lithium 7. The product nucleus was believed to disintegrate into 2 alpha particles, as follows,

$$_3Li^7 + {}_1H^1 \rightarrow ({}_4Be^8) \rightarrow {}_2He^4 + {}_2He^4 \qquad [16\text{-}2]$$

The assumption was beautifully confirmed by observations in a cloud chamber, which clearly indicated the tracks of two alpha particles diverging from the disintegrating nucleus.

The highest energies they applied are considerably below those of the top of the potential barrier of even the lightest elements, but they hoped to prove the new wave-mechanical hypothesis that the barrier of the nucleus might be penetrated by particles of energy too low to surmount it. Success attended their efforts, and they not only obtained a (p, α) reaction in lithium but similar reactions with several other light elements, thus proving barrier penetration. They even obtained occasional transmutations of lithium with proton energies of 100,000 ev and lower.

These experiments with electrically accelerated particles aroused intense interest and stimulated the demand for means of accelerating charged particles to higher and higher energies. In 1931 Lawrence, who had recently invented the cyclotron (§ 18-4), built one to give protons of 1.2-Mev energy. By the end of World War II an improved cyclotron had produced protons of nearly 300 Mev and alpha particles of 384 Mev. Van de Graaff meanwhile was developing his electrostatic generator with which he obtained several million volts constant potential difference and more intense beams of particles than could be obtained with the cyclotron. With the cyclotron and still other particle accelerators (Chap. 18), it was hoped to disrupt the nuclei of heavy atoms, which had resisted even the most energetic alpha particles. With such transmutations it was hoped to learn more of the secrets of the nucleus. In the years since World War II accelerators have gone from the million- to the billion-volt class, and particles having billions of electron-volts energy are now available. With such high-energy particles many new and surprising discoveries have been made, and the end is not in sight.

16-3. Symbolic Representation of Reactions, Energy Balance, and *Q*

With these powerful tools of investigation many types of reactions have been added to the alpha-proton (α, p) reaction of Rutherford's first experiment and to the first $(p, 2\alpha)$ reaction of Cockroft and Walton. Not only alpha particles and protons, but deuterons, neutrons, and high-energy gamma rays have also been used to bombard nuclei. Some of the most common reactions and their symbols are listed below.

Alpha-proton (α, p)
Alpha-neutron (α, n)
Proton-neutron (p, n)

Neutron-proton (n, p)
Gamma-proton (γ, p)
Proton-gamma (p, γ)

To represent a particular reaction, such as a deuteron bombarding nitrogen (N^{14}) producing N^{15} and a proton, the following symbols are used:

$$_7N^{14}(d, p)_7N^{15}$$

and

$$_9F^{19}(p, \alpha)_8O^{16}$$

represents the effect of proton bombardment on fluorine 19, with ejection of an alpha particle and the formation of oxygen 16.

Although reactions 16-1 and 16-2 are written in such a way that mass numbers balance before and after, and total electric charge balances before and after, the energies involved do not balance as the reactions are thus written. According to the law of conservation of energy, the total energy after the reaction, including any which is released or absorbed, should be equal to the total before the reaction. This, of course, includes the relativistic energy equivalent of the masses involved, and not the mass numbers but the actual masses. If there is a net decrease in mass after the reaction, the energy equivalent of that loss of mass is released and goes into kinetic energy of the products, including the energy of possible gamma radiation. Such a reaction is said to be **exothermic** (or *exoergic*), and if the mass is increased with attendant absorption of energy the reaction is said to be **endothermic** (or *endoergic*).

The amount of energy required to balance any reaction is designated by Q and is frequently spoken of as the **Q value.** When the Q value of a reaction is positive the amount of energy represented by Q has been released and is divided between the products of the reaction in the form of kinetic energy of motion. The complete symbolic representation for any reaction, including conservation of energy and mass, must include the symbol Q or its actual value in amu or Mev. For instance, to indicate energy-balance, reaction 16-1 should now be written

$$_2He^4 + {}_7N^{14} \rightarrow {}_8O^{17} + {}_1H^1 + Q \qquad [16\text{-}3]$$

16-4. Isotopic Masses from Nuclear Reactions

The precise measurement of Q values has made it possible to determine isotopic masses of many of the lighter elements with much precision from a knowledge of the energies and masses involved in various nuclear reactions. This serves as a valuable check on mass spectrographic measurements such as those given in Table 2-1.

The Q value of a reaction may be determined best from measurements of the energies of incident and emerging particles by magnetic or electrostatic deflection. Beginning with the known Q value of a reaction involving oxygen 16, if the masses of the incident and emergent particles are known, the mass of the product nucleus may easily be determined. However, if a complete evaluation is to be made by nuclear processes the masses of incident and emergent particles will not be known. It is then necessary to find enough independent reactions so as to set up as many energy-mass equations as there are unknown quantities. The equations may then be solved for the unknowns. In the determination of the mass of the proton by this method Li, Whaling, Fowler, and Lauritsen in 1951 made use of the Q values of 14 reactions. One of the most important results of this method is that masses may be determined for nuclei that do not lend themselves to the methods of the mass spectroscope. A few examples of the results of such measurements are given in Table 16-1. The agreement with mass spectroscopic measurements is particularly good for the lighter nuclei.

TABLE 16-1. SOME ISOTOPIC MASSES DETERMINED BY NUCLEAR REACTIONS

(compared with measurements by mass spectrograph)

Isotope	By Nuclear Reactions	By Mass Spectrograph
Helium 4	4.003873 (±15)	4.003860 (±12)
Oxygen 16	16.0000000 (standard)	16.0000000 (standard)
Lithium 7	7.018223 (±26)	7.018180 (±12)
Carbon 12	12.003804 (±17)	12.0038167 (±8)
Neon 20	19.998777 (±21)	19.997771 (±12)

16-5. The Potential Barrier of the Nucleus

When positively charged atomic projectiles are "shot" at atomic nuclei a positively charged projectile particle is repelled by the positive charge of the nucleus being approached. The nucleus of the atom is very similar to a walled fortress which resists attack, but the wall is not a material one. It is the electric field surrounding the positively charged nucleus. The closer the bombarding particle comes, the greater is the repelling force acting upon it, according to Coulomb's inverse square law. This law has been found to hold true up to an extremely small distance from the center of the nucleus being bombarded. Indeed, the early experiments of Rutherford on scattering of alpha particles (§ 8-3) indicated that the inverse square law was obeyed up to something like 10^{-12} cm. The nearest approach that a positively charged atomic projectile can make to the center of the nucleus of an atom, before repulsion turns to attraction and the particle is captured, defines the radius of the nucleus. If the particle passes this point it enters a region of attraction instead of repulsion. It is then "inside the nucleus."

It was suggested by Gamow that, instead of plotting the electric field, the curve representing the varying potentials about the nucleus could be drawn, and this is now called the **potential barrier.** The potential drops very rapidly inside the nucleus and forms a kind of potential well into which particles may fall if they succeed in passing the barrier. Since barriers are lower for light nuclei those were the first to be surmounted by positively charged "projectiles."

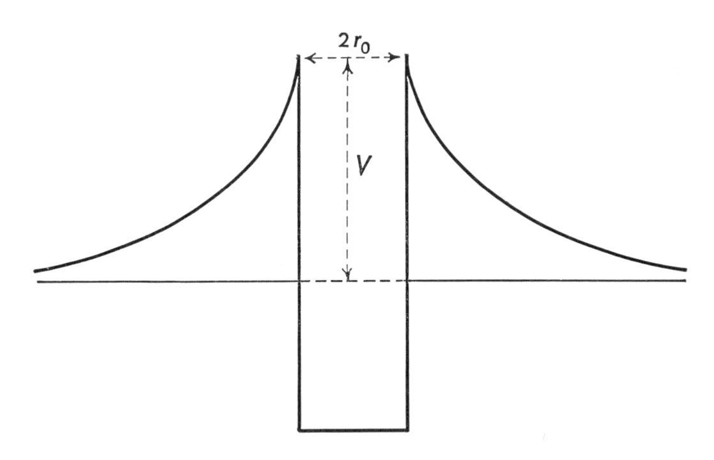

Fig. 16-2. Potential barrier with idealized rectangular well. Diameter of nucleus is $2r_0$ and height of barrier is V volts.

An idealized form of potential well, called the **rectangular potential well,** is shown in Fig. 16-2. The curved line outside the well is the potential barrier representing Coulomb repulsion. Distance $2r_0$ represents the diameter of the nucleus. The height V is the height of the barrier that must be passed by an incident particle if it is to enter the nucleus. The depth of the potential well is not uniquely determined. For most atoms the height of the barrier V is several million volts.

The type of potential well shown is an idealized form useful for mathematical purposes. The actual form of the barrier may be more like Fig. 16-3, with sloping sides and a round top. As a positively charged particle approaches the nucleus it finally reaches a point where a force of attraction becomes appreciable. At some critical point attraction balances repulsion, and no resultant force acts. This is the boundary of the nucleus. At less than this distance the attraction predominates, and the particle is inside the nucleus. The diameter of the nucleus is now not so sharply defined as in the more idealized diagram. The sloping sides of the well indicate a more continuous rather than discontinuous transition from outside to inside.

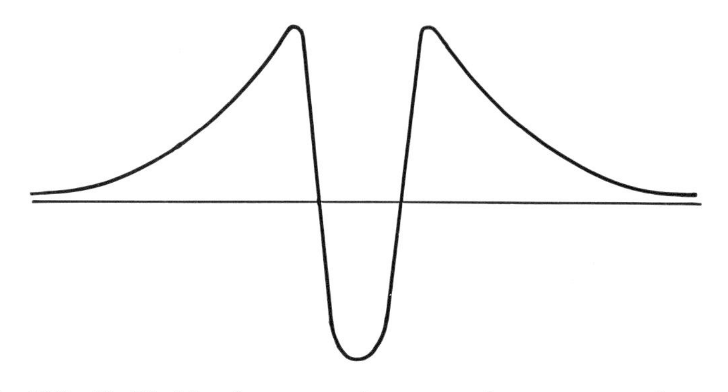

Fig. 16-3. Modified barrier presumed more nearly to represent the actual barrier.

According to classical theory an incident positive particle must have sufficient kinetic energy to surmount the top of the barrier. If it does not possess the required energy it is slowed down to zero speed, and its motion is then reversed. The analogy is sometimes made to a peculiar type of cup on a golf green where the green slopes upward sharply to the cup. A ball lacking sufficient kinetic energy could not go over the top. The application of simple classical theory to the problem of the atomic nucleus presented a dilemma, however.

For example, consider the heaviest natural atom, uranium 238 (U^{238}). Experiments indicate that the height of the potential barrier is more than 8.50 Mev, since alpha particles of this energy from thorium C′ are unable to pass over the barrier and are consequently reflected and scattered by the opposing Coulomb field, although they approach to within 3×10^{-12} cm of the center of the uranium nucleus. Rutherford showed this to be true in 1927. The difficulty comes when the energies of alpha particles emitted by the uranium are measured. To be emitted according to classical theory an alpha particle inside the nucleus must somehow reach the top of the barrier. Then like a ball rolling down a hill it should gain energy equal to the height of the barrier. But the emitted alpha particles only have energies of 4.2

Mev. Classical physics was unable to solve the dilemma, and wave mechanics was called upon for the explanation.

16-6. Theory of Alpha Emission

An explanation was given in Chap. 10 of how, according to wave mechanics, a particle within a barrier may sometimes pass that barrier. If the distance across the barrier is not too large an appreciable probability always exists that a particle may penetrate the barrier and escape. Where classical theory is helpless quantum mechanics enables us to formulate why U^{238} decays by alpha emission so slowly that its half-life is 4.5 billion years. Apparently the barrier is very high compared to the average energy that an alpha particle on the inside of the nucleus can have. Since the barrier is high, perhaps as much as 28 Mev, the alpha particle must penetrate the barrier where it is quite wide in order to gain energy of only 4.2 Mev when it escapes. The probability of passing through this barrier is extremely small, and consequently the half-life is very long. In a very intensely radioactive substance with a short half-life the barrier is either lower or is crossed nearer the top, or both.

With the aid of the idealized rectangular well Gamow determined theoretically the probability of escape of alpha particles, based on the idea that the particles in the nucleus possess random motion and collide incessantly with the barrier. It is assumed that the minimum possible velocity of a particle in the nucleus is such that its de Broglie wavelength h/mv is of the order of magnitude of the radius r of the nucleus. The number of collisions per second is then roughly

$$f = \frac{v}{2r} = \frac{h}{2mr^2} \qquad [16\text{-}4]$$

Since the decay constant is the probability of escape per second, it must therefore be equal to the probability P of escape each time the alpha particle hits the barrier, multiplied by the number of hits per second, or λ, the decay constant, is

$$\lambda = \frac{h}{2mr^2} P \qquad [16\text{-}5]$$

where P can be computed by wave-mechanical methods and depends on the energy of the particle. All this assumes that an alpha particle before emission has some sort of individual existence in the nucleus, at least for a brief time. What Gamow achieved, after assuming reasonable values for r, was a complicated equation which reduces to the same form as the Geiger-Nuttall rule (Eq. 15-2). Thus the Geiger-Nuttall rule, applying to all the natural alpha emitters, is no longer purely empirical but represents fundamental relations based on wave-mechanical analysis.

Nuclear energy levels In the discussion of alpha-ray fine structure (§ 15-5) it was pointed out that the various energy groups were believed to represent various energy states of the nucleus. To more nearly complete the representation of the nucleus in terms of a potential well, we must now add energy levels to the well, representing energy levels in the nucleus (Fig. 16-4). The energy of

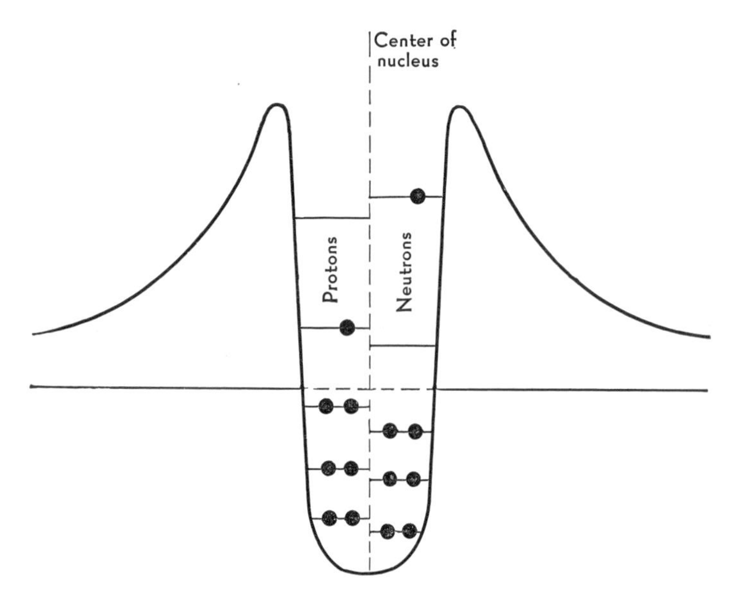

Fig. 16-4. Potential well of nucleus showing energy levels; neutrons in pairs and protons in pairs in lower levels, and one neutron in a higher or excitation level.

the escaping alpha particle then depends upon the energy level from which it comes in the nucleus. Since alpha rays have sharply defined energies, the indicated energy levels must also be unique and represent sharply defined energy states of the nucleus. Presumably, in a nucleus in the lowest energy state (ground state), the lower energy levels are mostly filled. When a nuclear particle (nucleon) is raised to a higher energy level the nucleus is then in an excited state.

16-7. The Compound Nucleus

Bohr put forth the idea of the compound nucleus in 1936. He described how an atomic projectile entering a nucleus may be thought to remain in the nucleus long enough to put the nucleus into an excited state, after which emission of one or more particles (or a gamma ray) occurs, and a resultant nucleus is formed. When an incident particle enters the nucleus, its excess energy is assumed to be temporarily distributed among the other nucleons, and thus the compound nucleus is in a transitional state between the initial state before bombardment and the final state. If the emitted particle (or particles) carries away sufficient energy the residual nucleus will be in its lowest energy state or ground state. If it does not carry away sufficient energy, the product nucleus will be in an excited state and will return to its ground state by gamma-ray emission.

The compound nucleus is believed to last a length of time which is very short by laboratory standards but may be very long in terms of nuclear processes. If the nucleons are assumed to be moving about inside the nucleus, then, after having been put into a state of greater agitation by capture of an energetic particle, they will move faster. A simple computation shows that the time for a nucleon to move from one side of the nucleus to another may easily be as little as 10^{-20} sec. The compound nucleus might last a thousand or even a million times longer than that and still break up very quickly by ordinary standards. If it only lasts that long it can have no "memory" of how it was formed, and consequently the manner of decay will be independent of the way in which the compound nucleus was formed.

The manner of decay of the compound nucleus is then presumed to depend on various possibilities called exit processes, which are in competition with one another, and also to depend on the energy brought to the nucleus by the incident particle. The energy contributed to the nucleus is made up of two parts, the kinetic energy of the incident particle and the energy equivalent of the mass that it loses in becoming part of the compound nucleus. If there is a small decrease in mass as the particle enters the nucleus the energy equivalent that is released is given by the Einstein energy-mass relation and is called the binding energy (§ 17-3) of the particle. This represents the energy that must be supplied to the nucleus to remove the particle from it and is usually of the order of several Mev. When the incident particle enters the target nucleus it is assumed that this energy is quickly shared by the other nucleons. If the energy becomes concentrated again on one (or more nucleons) it will have a chance to escape from the nucleus if its energy is sufficient.

This is the essence of Bohr's concept of the compound nucleus. It has been found useful in correlating some of the observed phenomena connected with nuclear transmutations, but it is far from a complete description of the nature of transmutation processes, and much remains to be done.

16-8. Induced Radioactivity

Induced radioactivity, sometimes called artificial radioactivity, was discovered in 1933 by Irene Curie and her husband Frederic Joliot. For this discovery they were awarded the Nobel Prize in 1935, which they shared with Chadwick for his discovery of the neutron. At the time of this discovery there were only some forty naturally radioactive elements known. Since that time it has been found possible to induce radioactivity in every known element not already radioactive, including even hydrogen.

The Curie-Joliots were studying the emission of positrons from light elements bombarded with high-speed alpha particles. They observed that sometimes the bombarded atoms continued to emit positrons after the alpha-ray bombardment had ceased. This emission of positrons was observed to decrease in time after the manner of natural radioactive decay. However, no naturally radioactive substance had been observed to emit any other than alpha, beta, and gamma rays. Half-life periods were measured for boron, aluminum, and magnesium, for which the values of 14 min, 3.25 min, and 2.5 min, respectively, were obtained. They then suggested that the effect of the bombardment of boron was to dislodge a neutron, leaving the nucleus of nitrogen 13 according to the following scheme:

$$ {}_{5}B^{10} + {}_{2}He^{4} \rightarrow {}_{7}N^{13} + {}_{0}n^{1} \qquad [16\text{-}6] $$

where ${}_{0}n^{1}$ represents the dislodged neutron. The nitrogen nucleus produced by this reaction they surmised to be unstable and suggested that it might decay from nitrogen 13 to carbon 13 by the emission of a positive electron, as follows:

$$ {}_{7}N^{13} \rightarrow {}_{6}C^{13} + {}_{1}e^{0} \qquad [16\text{-}7] $$

where ${}_{1}e^{0}$ represents the positron. This surmise was later confirmed although more accurate measurement of the half-life proved it to be slightly less than 10 minutes.

In a similar manner the bombardment of aluminum (Al^{27}) was found to produce by neutron emission an isotope of phosphorus, which was also unstable, giving rise to positron emission and the production of silicon (Si^{30}):

$$_{13}Al^{27} + {}_{2}He^{4} \rightarrow {}_{15}P^{30} + {}_{0}n^{1} \qquad [16\text{-}8]$$

$$_{15}P^{30} \rightarrow {}_{14}Si^{30} + {}_{1}e^{0} \qquad [16\text{-}9]$$

Later it was found that the atoms of some elements thus made artificially radioactive may decay by negative electron emission. The electron or positron emissions are sometimes accompanied by gamma rays.

K Capture Instead of emitting a positron the unstable nucleus may undergo another process with the same final result. The nucleus may capture an orbital electron; if it captures an electron from the *K* shell of the atom this is called *K* capture. Capture of a negative electron results in the same change of nuclear charge Z as the expulsion of a positive electron.

When the nucleus of an atom captures a *K* electron a vacancy is created in the *K* shell. If this vacancy is filled by an *L* electron the transition produces the first line of the *K* series of characteristic x-rays of the newly formed element. Filling of the *K* vacancy produces another vacancy to be filled and another line in the series of characteristic x-rays. Such characteristic x-rays have been detected and indicate the occurrence of *K* capture. *K*-electron capture in cadmium ($_{48}Cd^{107}$) to form silver ($_{47}Ag^{107}$) was confirmed when Pool, Edwards, and Blake in 1945 detected the *K* lines of silver emitted in the process. Although usually not so frequent a mode of radioactive decay as the direct-emission process, it is still an important mode of radioactive decay.

16-9. Radioisotopes and Their Applications

Shortly after the discovery of induced radioactivity, E. O. Lawrence in the United States produced a radioactive isotope of the common element sodium by bombarding it with high-speed particles produced in the cyclotron. Artificially radioactive elements may now be made in relatively large quantities by such methods and also by means of the radiations from a nuclear reactor (Chap. 19). The early experiments produced only comparatively short-lived isotopes, but in later experiments relatively long-lived ones have been produced. At present large-scale production is possible by application of the intense radiation from a nuclear reactor. This has become the answer to the scarcity of naturally radioactive elements and has put such substances within the reach of all who need them for experimental work or for the treatment of disease.

The production of radioactive isotopes (radioisotopes) of many common elements has made it possible to develop new experimental techniques in which a radioactive atom, such as carbon, may be substituted in a compound for an atom of the normal stable isotope. The behavior of the element in food or medicine can then be traced through various physiological processes of the body by means of a Geiger-Müller counter or other detector. The tracer technique is thus an extremely sensitive method of following a particular type of atom in a physiological process. It may also be used to follow a few atoms in a delicate chemical analysis, where the small number of atoms involved would be far too few to be detected by ordinary chemical processes.

By tracer techniques, radioactive calcium atoms in food have been traced to the teeth, and the rate at which they are taken up has been measured. By a similar method it has been found that 60 per cent or more of phosphorus absorbed by the body goes into the bones of the body within four or five days. It is possible to trace how quickly radioactive iodine is absorbed by the thyroid gland, and the rate at which the absorption and excretion take place may indicate the various abnormal conditions of that gland. Similar tracer measurements have been made on plant foods; the ensuing radiation is often intense enough to be detected on photographic film.

Short-lived radioactive substances may be taken into the body without the great harm that would be done by absorption of a long-lived substance. They are sometimes used for internal treatment of disease. Longer-lived radioactive elements may serve as a substitute for radium, and an amount of radioactive cobalt greater in intensity of radiation than all the radium in the world may readily be obtained.

16-10. Fermi and Transmutation by Neutron Capture

In 1934 particle accelerators were in their infancy and quite unable to produce particles of sufficient energy to disrupt the nuclei of the heavier atoms. In that year, Fermi in Italy tried to produce transmutations by neutron bombardment. The neutron has no detectable electric charge and consequently is not repelled by the charge on a nucleus. There is then for the neutron no appreciable potential barrier as there is for positively charged particles; a neutron may apparently enter a nucleus with ease. Whether or not it remains in the nucleus depends upon the nature of the nuclear forces, and if reasonable assumptions are made the probability may be computed by wave-mechanical methods.

Fermi studied the effects of neutron bombardment of the heavy elements, especially uranium. When U^{238} was subjected to neutron bombardment it was found that radioactivity was induced, and that the product was a beta-ray emitter, whereas U^{238} is an alpha-ray emitter. This was interpreted to mean that neutrons had penetrated uranium nuclei and had produced an unstable isotope of U^{238}, presumably U^{239}. It was this product nucleus that was apparently radioactive and decayed by electron emission. Such emission would change a nucleus of atomic number 92 to one of atomic number 93, and this would represent the production of an atom of higher atomic number than any known natural atom.

Fermi concluded that nuclei of a new element beyond uranium in the atomic number series had been produced. The element was called a transuranic element. Yet, since there were several observed rates of beta decay it seemed that there might be several different types of nuclei formed, and there was some confusion as to exactly what was happening. As a matter of fact, a quite different and most extraordinary phenomenon was also occurring, but this Fermi was unable to detect. Indeed, he did not suspect it. The new phenomenon was the splitting or fission of the uranium atom, a subject which will be discussed more fully in Chap. 19.

16-11. The Transuranic Elements

Fermi's belief that he had produced transuranic elements was amply confirmed after World War II and after the excitement of the discovery of fission had died down somewhat. Now it is possible to produce by bombardment, and by induced radioactivity, elements up to atomic number 100 and over, and the properties of several elements of still higher atomic number have been predicted. The production of

TABLE 16-2. TRANSURANIC ELEMENTS

Atomic Number	Element	Symbol
93	Neptunium	Np
94	Plutonium	Pu
95	Americium	Am
96	Curium	Cm
97	Berkelium	Bk
98	Californium	Cf
99	Einsteinium	E
100	Fermium	Fm
101	Mendelevium	Mv
102	Nobelium	No

two of these, neptunium and plutonium, will be described in more detail when the reactors are considered in which they are involved (§ 19-9). Table 16-2 presents a list of these new elements to 1958.

16-12. Neutron-Induced Transmutations

Since Fermi's first transmutations produced by neutrons, many studies of the effects have been made, and since World War II nuclear reactors have furnished intense neutron sources. The result is that more types of transmutations have been produced by means of neutrons than by any other means. Low-, intermediate-, and high-energy neutrons have been used to bombard all types of light and heavy nuclei, and many hundreds of different types of reactions have been observed.

The higher the energy of the incident neutron is, the more likely it is that a charged particle or a neutron will be emitted by the compound nucleus. When a slow neutron is captured by a nucleus, the kinetic energy of the neutron added to the nucleus is negligible, but the nucleus receives energy from a different source. The mass of the product nucleus is usually less than the sum of the masses of the original nucleus and the captured neutron. By the Einstein energy-mass relation this loss in mass is equivalent to a loss or release of energy, the binding energy (§ 17-3) of the product nucleus, and it is usually released in the form of gamma radiation. However, when a fast neutron is captured the kinetic energy of the neutron is also added to that of the nucleus, and the compound nucleus that is formed may be in a sufficiently high energy state to eject one or more charged particles. Usually an energy of something like 8 Mev is required to separate a nucleon from a nucleus. With increasing energies of the incident particle very much above this level, the probability increases that enough energy may be imparted to the compound nucleus to result in the ejection of two or more nucleons.

Two typical neutron-induced reactions, both with aluminum 27, are shown below. In the first, neutron capture results in gamma-ray emission (n, γ).

$$_{13}\mathrm{Al}^{27} + {}_0n^1 \rightarrow ({}_{13}\mathrm{Al}^{28}) \rightarrow {}_{13}\mathrm{Al}^{28} + \gamma \qquad [16\text{-}10]$$

In the second reaction (n, α), the capture of a higher energy neutron by the same nucleus results in alpha emission.

$$_{13}\mathrm{Al}^{27} + {}_0n^1 \rightarrow ({}_{13}\mathrm{Al}^{28}) \rightarrow {}_{11}\mathrm{Na}^{24} + {}_2\mathrm{He}^4 \qquad [16\text{-}11]$$

16-13. Proton-Induced Transmutations

Reactions induced by proton bombardment were the first to be produced by artificially accelerated particles (§ 16-2). A typical reaction occurs when aluminum 27 is bombarded with protons. It is a (p, α) reaction, in which an alpha particle is emitted.

$$ {}_{13}Al^{27} + {}_{1}H^{1} \rightarrow ({}_{14}Si^{28}) \rightarrow {}_{12}Mg^{24} + {}_{2}He^{4} \qquad [16\text{-}12]$$

An interesting reaction is the bombardment of boron 11, in which the compound nucleus breaks up into three alpha particles $(p, 3\alpha)$.

$$ {}_{5}B^{11} + {}_{1}H^{1} \rightarrow ({}_{6}C^{12}) \rightarrow {}_{2}He^{4} + {}_{2}He^{4} + {}_{2}He^{4} \qquad [16\text{-}13]$$

Many other reactions are observed in which neutrons (p, n), gamma rays (p, γ), and deuterons (p, d) are produced.

16-14. Deuteron-Induced Transmutations

Deuterons speeded up by a particle accelerator have served to produce many types of transformation such as (d, α), (d, p), (d, n). As an example of the last type, consider the bombardment of carbon 12.

$$ {}_{6}C^{12} + {}_{1}H^{2} \rightarrow ({}_{7}N^{14}) \rightarrow {}_{7}N^{13} + {}_{0}n^{1} \qquad [16\text{-}14]$$

The proton part of the deuteron may in effect be turned back by the opposing field, leaving the neutron to be captured as

$$ {}_{6}C^{12} + {}_{1}H^{2} \rightarrow ({}_{7}N^{14}) \rightarrow {}_{6}C^{13} + {}_{1}H^{1} \qquad [16\text{-}15]$$

16-15. Photon-Induced Transmutations

The disintegration of an atomic nucleus by high-energy gamma-ray bombardment is called photodisintegration. Of the various ways in which photodisintegration of a nucleus may occur, a single example, that of aluminum 27 $(\gamma, 2p)$, is here given.

$$ {}_{13}Al^{27} + \gamma \rightarrow ({}_{13}Al^{27}) \rightarrow {}_{11}Na^{25} + {}_{1}H^{1} + {}_{1}H^{1} \qquad [16\text{-}16]$$

16-16. Cross Sections for Nuclear Processes

The term cross section is frequently used in describing the efficiency of a nuclear process or rather the probability of its occurrence. If the diameter d of a nucleus could be obtained by direct measurement the projected area of the nucleus would be called its geometrical cross section and would be given by the simple geometrical formula: area = $\frac{1}{4}\pi d^2 = \pi r^2$. If there is 1 nucleus per cm^3 in a volume, the projected area of which facing the bombarding particles is 1 cm^2, the probability that a bombarding particle crossing the region will hit the single nucleus is merely the ratio of the projected area πr^2 of that nucleus to the projected area 1 cm^2 of the entire region. If n nuclei are exposed to bombardment per cm^2 the probability of a hit is n times larger, assuming that there are not enough particles for their projected areas to overlap appreciably. The probability of a hit on some nucleus, when a particle strikes a given area, is then simply the ratio of the total projected areas of the nuclei to the total area (Fig. 16-5). On account of

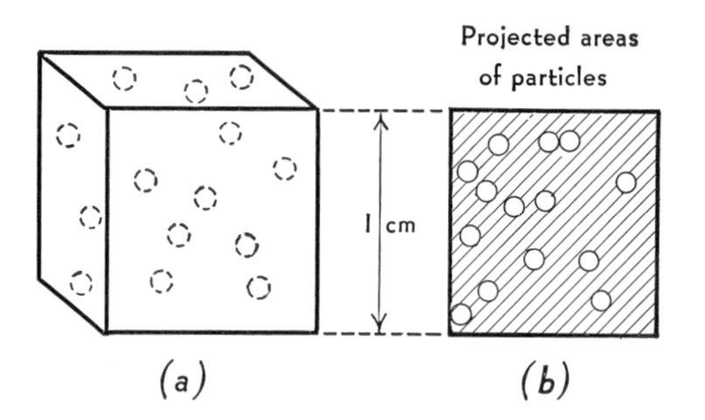

Fig. 16-5. Probability that a particle entering an area of 1 cm^2 will hit a particle in the volume indicated at *a* is the ratio of total projected cross-sectional area of the particles shown at *b* to the total target area of 1 cm^2.

the small area of cross section of a nucleus, the probability of a hit is extremely small unless very large numbers of nuclei are present, and to assure many hits it is necessary to have intense beams of bombarding particles. Even under favorable conditions only one hit in a hundred thousand may be successful.

The bombardment of nuclei may result in many different effects such as elastic or inelastic scattering, transmutations of various kinds, or the splitting of a nucleus (fission). Instead of speaking of the relative probabilities of such events, it is customary to speak of the relative cross sections of a given nucleus for such events. The cross sections are computed from observed probabilities. For a type of event that occurs readily the computed cross section is relatively large, and for rare events it may be very small. Since the square centimeter is an awkwardly large unit with which to measure anything so small as the cross section of a nucleus, a more appropriate unit has been chosen. It is 10^{-24} cm^2 and is called the barn. The story is that for certain processes this area was humorously referred to as being "as big as a barn," and the name persisted, an interesting commentary on scientific jargon and the growth of language.

For a type of event that occurs readily the computed cross section is relatively large and may be as much as a thousand barns or more. For a rarer type of event the cross section is small and may be much less than a thousandth of a barn. In ordinary elastic collision of gas molecules the cross sections are referred to as "geometrical," since they depend essentially on ordinary geometrical cross sections. The **cross section** of a particle for other types of events is defined as the effective projected area which would account for the frequency of the event if it depended only on the geometrical dimensions. But when the probability of occurrence is much larger or much smaller the cross sections are hardly geometrical in the ordinary sense and may involve electric and magnetic fields and other factors.

16-17. Resonance Capture of Neutrons

Low-energy neutrons are generally more likely to be scattered by elastic collisions after the manner of billiard balls than to be captured by a nucleus, but for certain quite sharply defined energies of the incident neutron the probability of capture is greatly increased, sometimes a thousandfold or more. This is called resonance capture, and has been explained by Breit and Wigner as being due to the neutron having exactly the right amount of energy corresponding to an excited state of the nucleus. At this energy the neutron is much more likely to produce excitation and remain in the nucleus than to pass through it. The cross section (§ 16-16) for such resonance capture is then said to be relatively large and may be hundreds or even many thousands of barns.

When low-energy neutrons are captured by light nuclei the most likely way for the compound nucleus to return to the normal state is by emission of a gamma ray. When low-energy neutrons are incident upon heavy nuclei the probability of capture is generally much larger, but either elastic scattering or capture with consequent gamma radiation may occur. Nuclei, however, do not all fall into simple classifications. There are frequent exceptions, and some nuclei are found to have few resonances and occasionally none at all for low-energy neutrons. For higher-energy neutrons there may be many resonances, or these may overlap so as not to be separately distinguishable.

16-18. Basic Relations Involved in Nuclear Transformations

It is now desirable to mention certain fundamental "rules of the game," as we know them, by which we can describe and analyze nuclear interactions. First and foremost is the law of conservation of energy. Although occasionally it has been suggested that the law of conservation of energy might not always apply, there seems to be no valid reason for believing that it does not apply in the atomic realm just as it does in the realm of everyday phenomena, and this law is the basis of all scientific thought. Closely related are the laws of conservation of linear momentum and angular momentum, the latter being particularly important since it has to do with the spin and also the orbital motion of nuclear particles. Since there seems to be no reason why electric charge should not be conserved in the atomic realm, as it is in the everyday world, this is also accepted as a basic rule.

We may therefore tabulate the foregoing conservation laws for nuclei, with one addition, as follows:

1. Conservation of energy (including equivalent mass).
2. Conservation of linear momentum.
3. Conservation of angular momentum (spin and orbital).
4. Conservation of charge.
5. Conservation of statistics.

The last condition of conservation belongs distinctly to the atomic realm. The conservation of statistics is one of the important rules "obeyed" in any nuclear transformation. The correlation of statistics with the wave functions of nuclear particles was mentioned at the end of § 13-2; it was stated there that Fermi statistics apply to single particles or to groups in the nucleus when the number is odd. Bose statistics (§ 12-8) apply when the number of nucleons is even.

If Fermi and Bose statistics are represented symbolically by -1 and $+1$, respectively, the statistics of a group of quantities are determined by the product of the symbols for each. For instance, if an electron and positron annihilate each other, before annihilation the statistics of the system are $-1 \times -1 = +1$. After annihilation the statistics of the system, according to conservation of statistics, should still be $+1$. Since we have agreed to represent the statistics of photons (Bose statistics) by the symbol $+1$, and since two photons are formed by pair annihilation, the two photons have statistics represented by $+1 \times +1 = +1$, and the law of conservation of statistics is obeyed.

With these rules of conservation, **allowed** and **forbidden reactions** may be predicted, and by application of one or more or all of these principles the character of the reaction may be more completely described.

Parity Another quantity which has been applied to the interpretation of subatomic phenomena is called parity. Until 1957 it was believed that parity was conserved in all nuclear transformations, and it was usually listed with the foregoing conservation laws. However, following the theoretical work of Lee and Yang, direct experimental evidence was obtained by Wu and Ambler showing that parity is not always conserved (§ 20-15). The overthrow of such an apparently well-established conservation law is an unusual occurrence and created much excitement in the scientific world. It all came about when a lack of symmetry was found in certain nuclear events. Since the experimental evidence will be described in § 20-15, it is pertinent to explain briefly what is meant by parity.

Parity is a mathematical concept which refers to one kind of space symmetry of physical phenomena. The test of this symmetry is to "reflect" the mathematical wave function in its space coordinates. This merely means changing the signs of the x, y, and z coordinates from plus to minus (excluding coordinates representing spin). If the sign of the wave function as a whole does not change when the signs of the coordinates are changed, it is said to represent *even parity.* If the sign of the function does change, it is said to represent *odd parity.* The parity of a system of particles is determined by the product of the parities of the separate particles.

If parity is conserved the new equations after reflection will be equally valid wave functions for the physical phenomenon that they describe. Since a glove for the left hand is a similar reflection of a glove for the right hand, it can be said that if parity is conserved "Nature does not know her right hand from her left." If parity is not conserved she does. One suggested explanation, when parity is not conserved, is that the phenomenon involves a kind of spirality that distinguishes right from left.

PROBLEMS

1. Write the possible reactions indicated by the following symbols: (α, n), (α, p), (α, γ), $(\alpha, 2p)$ for sodium 23 bombarded by alpha particles.

2. Write the possible reactions indicated by the following symbols: (p, n), (p, d), (p, γ), $(p, 2n)$ for chlorine 35 bombarded by protons.

3. Write four possible reactions for phosphorus 31 bombarded by neutrons.

4. Write four possible reactions for mercury 200 bombarded by deuterons.

5. Give one or more possible reactions for changing one of the "baser metals" into gold, and tell whether it is practical.

6. Write the symbols for the reaction by which carbon 14 is formed in the earth's atmosphere, assuming that it is an (n, p) reaction.

7. If a neutron is captured by a heavy nucleus the following reactions are possible: (n, γ), (n, p), (n, α). What are their relative probabilities of occurrence, based on ease of escape from a potential barrier?

SUGGESTED READING

I. Kaplan, *Nuclear Physics* (Cambridge, Addison-Wesley, 1955).
E. Pollard and W. L. Davidson, *Applied Nuclear Physics*, 2nd ed. (New York, Wiley, 1951).
D. Halliday, *Introductory Nuclear Physics*, 2nd ed. (New York, Wiley, 1955).
N. Feather, *Nuclear Physics* (London, Cambridge Univ. Press, 1936).
Nuclear Data, compiled by K. Way, L. Fano, M. Scott, and K. Thew (Washington, D. C., National Bureau of Standards, Circular 499, 1950) (and supplements).

CHAPTER 17

NUCLEAR STRUCTURE AND NUCLEAR FORCES

17-1. The Problem of the Nucleus

The fundamental problem in nuclear physics is that of investigating the structure of the nucleus and the nature of the forces that hold nuclear particles together. The protons and neutrons of which a nucleus is composed are called nucleons, and a particular type of nucleus is called a nuclide. Since protons are positively charged and neutrons possess zero net charge, the protons must experience forces of mutual repulsion according to Coulomb's law. Other forces must then be sought which bind the nucleons together to form a nucleus. Experimental observations indicate that these forces must be appreciable only over the very short distances that are comparable to the size of the nucleus. Some information about them can be obtained from a study of binding energies of the nucleus and from experiments on the interaction of beams of particles, as, for instance, the particles of a proton beam colliding with the particles of another proton beam or colliding with the particles of a neutron beam.

17-2. Nuclear Structure

The lightest nuclide with more than one nucleon is that of heavy hydrogen H^2 (deuterium). The nucleus is composed of 1 proton and 1 neutron, indicating that there is some force acting between a proton and a neutron to bind them together. There is no nuclide consisting of 2 protons. The next stable nucleus is that of the extremely rare helium 3, consisting of 2 protons and 1 neutron. Next comes the ordinary helium nucleus which has 2 protons; it also has 2 neutrons, and it is a very stable combination. If the stability and abundance of ordinary helium were taken to indicate a tendency for the nucleons in a nucleus to form such groups it might be expected that stable nuclei would be composed of equal or fairly equal numbers of protons and neutrons, and perhaps even numbers of each. For the lighter elements up to about $Z = 30$, it turns out that few common stable nuclides have more neutrons than protons, and some of the most common nuclides such as helium 4, carbon 12, oxygen 16, and neon 20 are composed of even numbers of each and the same numbers of each. On the other hand, the common nitrogen nuclide has 7 of each, and beryllium 8 with 4 of each is violently unstable, breaking up to form 2 alpha particles (reaction 16-2).

Nearly six-tenths of all stable nuclides have even numbers of both neutrons and protons (Table 17-1, p. 380). The remainder are nearly equally divided between those having an even number of one or the other, with the exception of four only, which have odd numbers of both. These are all light nuclides, H^2, Li^6, B^{10}, N^{14}. With increasing mass, as will be seen from the chart (Fig. 17-1), the proportion of neutrons to protons increases considerably. This may be taken as evidence that more binding force is required for nuclei of higher nuclear charge to balance the forces of repulsion between protons and that the extra neutrons supply what is needed.

A lithium 7 nucleus has 3 protons and 4 neutrons; a beryllium 9 nucleus, the only stable beryllium nuclide, has 4 protons and 5 neutrons; carbon 12 has 6 of each, nitrogen 14 has 7 of each, and oxygen 16 has 8 of each. On the other hand, the heaviest natural element, uranium 92, has a mass number $A = 238$ and must then have $Z = 92$ protons, and $A - Z = 238 - 92 = 146$ neutrons, an excess of 54 neutrons over protons. Evidently stability requires an increasing ratio of mass to charge as the mass increases.

We are now in a position to state more satisfactorily the conditions of electron or positron emission in induced radioactivity. When the nucleus of an atom captures one or more neutrons, its ratio of mass to charge increases. If in any transformation it loses neutrons its ratio of mass to charge decreases. If such a resultant nucleus is unstable it is presumed to have too much charge for its mass or too much mass for its charge. If there is too much charge for the mass it can achieve

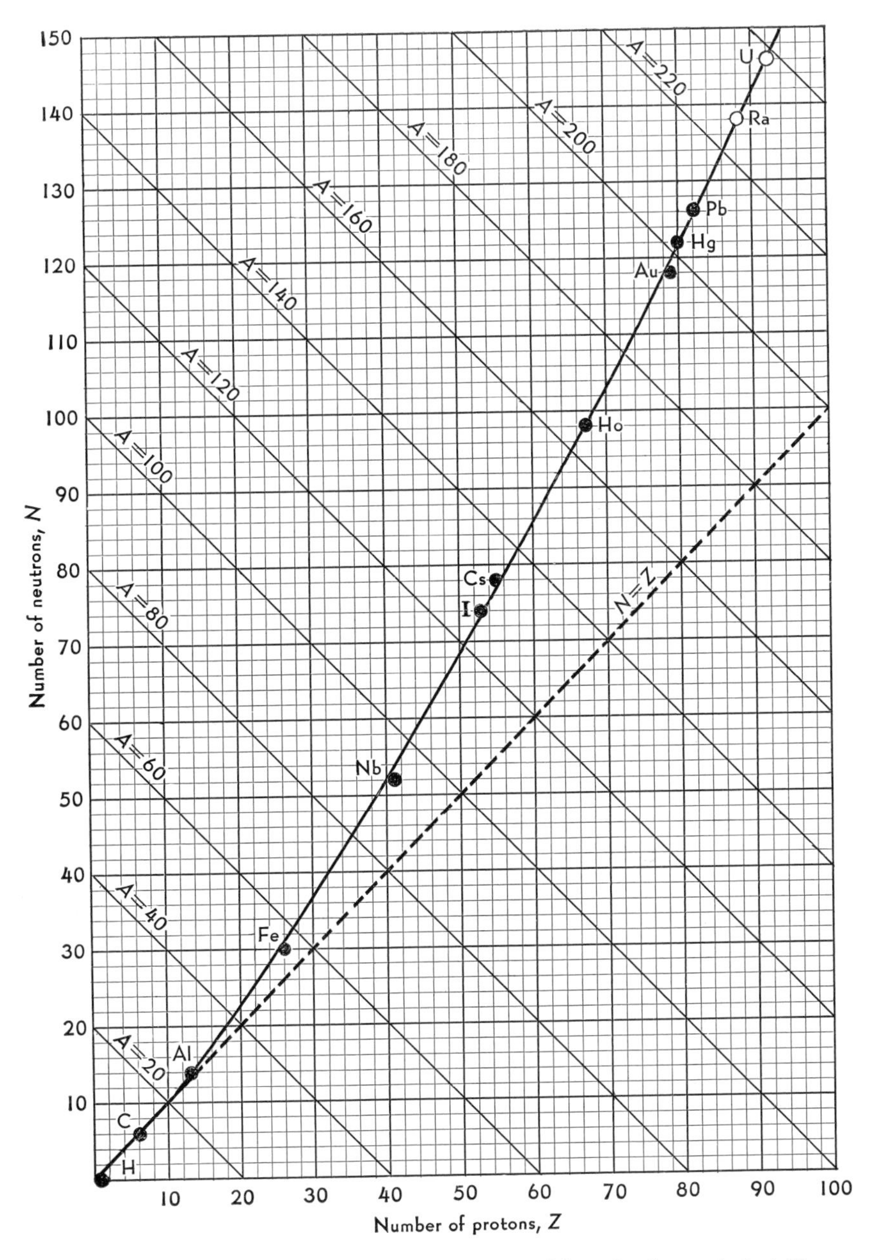

Fig. 17-1. Curve showing proton-neutron composition of a few typical stable nuclei (and two unstable ones). All stable nuclei would be located close to this curve, and all unstable nuclei cluster nearby. The increasing departure of the curve from the $N = Z$ line with increasing atomic number shows that the ratio of neutrons to protons also increases.

stability, or approach it, by emission of a positron, thus losing a unit of charge and increasing its ratio of mass to charge. If it has too much mass for its charge it can approach stability by emitting an electron, thus decreasing its ratio of mass to charge.

17-3. Stability of Nuclei and Binding Energies

Stable nuclei are formed when the mass of the nucleus is less than the sum of the masses of its component nucleons. The loss in mass is released in the form of equivalent energy, according to the Einstein energy-mass relation. The larger the energy-mass deficit is, the more stable the nucleus is.

The alpha particle is a particularly stable nuclide because it has a large mass deficit. For instance, the alpha particle is composed of two protons and two neutrons. The sum of the masses involved (Table 2-1) is as follows:

$$\begin{aligned} \text{Mass of 2 protons} &= 2 \times 1.007593 = 2.015186 \\ \text{Mass of 2 neutrons} &= 2 \times 1.008982 = 2.017964 \\ \hline \text{Total} &\qquad 4.033150 \text{ mass units} \end{aligned}$$

Subtracting from this sum the mass of the alpha particle, which is 4.002775 mass units, gives

$$4.033150 - 4.002775 = 0.030375 \text{ amu}$$

or approximately 0.03 atomic mass unit for the mass deficit. Reducing this to grams

$$0.03 \times 1.66 \times 10^{-24} = 4.98 \times 10^{-26} \text{ gm}$$

and then reducing to ergs by Eq. 7-17 and finally to Mev

$$\begin{aligned} 4.98 \times 10^{-26} \times (3 \times 10^{10})^2 &= 44.82 \times 10^{-6} \text{ erg} \\ &= 44.82 \times 10^{-6} \times (1.6)^{-1} \times 10^{12} \text{ ev} \\ &= 28 \text{ Mev} \end{aligned}$$

This is the amount of energy that would have to be supplied to an alpha particle to separate it into its component parts, and consequently it is called the binding energy of the nucleus. It is also the energy that a bombarding particle would need to have to disrupt the nucleus completely. This large energy-mass deficit explains why the alpha particle is such a stable particle.

The strong tendency of two neutrons and two protons to form an alpha particle may be taken to indicate that binding forces between nucleons are most effective when only a few nucleons are involved. There is evidence that in the nucleus any one nucleon does not act on an unlimited number of other nucleons but only on a relatively few nearest to it. As an example of the tendency of protons and neutrons sometimes, at least, to group themselves as alpha particles, it will be remembered that, when lithium is bombarded with protons to form beryllium 8, the beryllium is unstable and breaks up into two alpha particles (reaction 16-2). This does not mean that protons and neutrons in a nucleus are grouped to form alpha particles. There are reasons for thinking that this is not so and that when a radioactive nuclide emits an alpha particle the alpha particle is formed at or near the time of its ejection.

Nuclei of a given type are characterized as possessing a fixed amount of binding energy, meaning that the same amount of energy would always be required to take the nucleus completely apart, that is, to pull all the nucleons so far apart that there would be no appreciable force between them. This amount of energy divided by the number of nucleons in the nucleus is the average binding energy per nucleon. The amount of the energy is obtained from the mass deficit. If a nucleus contains Z protons their combined mass is Z(1.00813) atomic mass units. If it also contains $(A - Z)$ neutrons their combined mass is $(A - Z)(1.00894)$ amu. The total mass of the separate nucleons is the sum of these masses. Subtracting from this sum the actual mass m of the product nucleus gives the mass deficit Δm in amu.

$$\Delta m = Z(1.00813) + (A - Z)1.00894 - M$$

The energy equivalent mc^2 of the mass deficit is the binding energy of the nucleus. It is commonly expressed in ergs, joules, or electron volts. The binding energy of the nucleus divided by the number of nucleons A in the nucleus is the average binding energy E_B per nucleon

$$E_B = \frac{\Delta mc^2}{A} = \frac{[Z(1.00813) + (A - Z)1.00894 - M]}{A} kc^2 \qquad [17\text{-}1]$$

E_B is the average binding energy in ergs if k is the number of grams in 1 amu and c is the velocity of light, 3×10^{10} cm/sec. E_B may then readily be reduced to Mev.

The curve representing the average binding energy per nucleon in Mev is given in Fig. 17-2, with the location of a few of the more important elements indicated. From the figure it is seen that the binding energy per nucleon rises rapidly to a broad maximum for elements in the middle of the periodic table and that it then decreases only slowly for isotopes of increasing atomic mass up to the end of the series of elements. Consequently it is evident that elements in the middle of the periodic table are most stable since they have the largest average binding energy, a value in the neighborhood of 8.5 Mev.

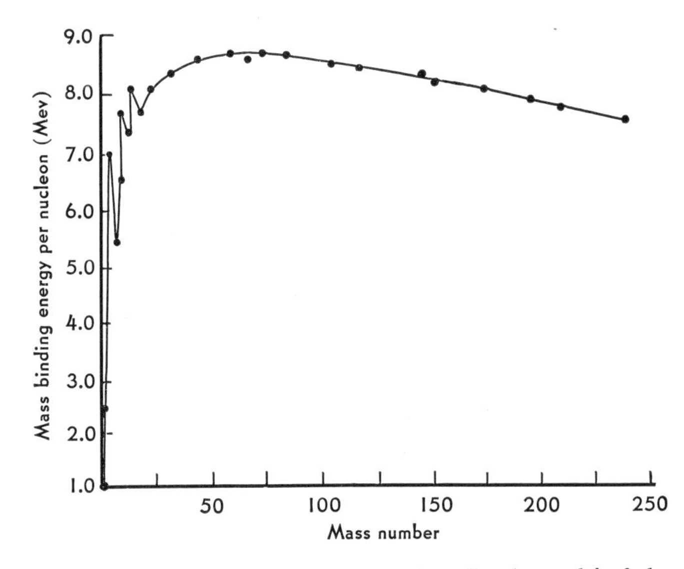

Fig. 17-2. Average binding energies per nucleon for the nuclei of the most stable elements.

From computations based on experimental data it is possible to find the energy required to remove a given type of particle from a given nucleus, and we now have considerable knowledge of the binding energies of individual nucleons. These vary considerably from the average values just mentioned. For instance, in a reaction in which a neutron is knocked out of a potassium 41 (K^{41}) nucleus the required energy is found to be 10.19 Mev although the average binding energy per nucleon is 8.56 Mev. However, to remove a neutron similarly from oxygen 17, for which the average binding energy per nucleon is 7.71 Mev, requires only 4.13 Mev. To remove a proton from magnesium 24 requires an energy of 11.00 Mev whereas to remove a proton from helium 3 requires 5.44 Mev. To remove a proton from lithium 5 the required energy is found to be negative, −1.5 Mev. This means that the nucleus is unstable and would spontaneously emit a proton with 1.5-Mev energy.

The average binding energy per nucleon (Fig. 17-2) reaches a maximum in the neighborhood of mass number 50, a little below iron in the atomic number series. Nuclei in this region are consequently the most stable of all the elements, and nuclei on either side of the maximum are less stable because they have not given up as much binding energy per nucleon, on the average. A study of the curve shows that, if the very light nuclei could be combined (fusion) to form heavier nuclei or nuclei nearer the maximum of the curve, energy must be released. On the other hand, if the very heavy nuclei could be split (fission) to form atoms nearer the top of the curve, energy must also be released. The importance of these processes of fission and fusion will be discussed in Chap. 19.

17-4. Nuclear Forces and the Meson Theory

No matter what particles we assume an atomic nucleus to be composed of, there must be strong forces of attraction binding them together. For a nucleus composed of neutrons and protons, the binding forces can hardly be electric in any ordinary sense and are said to be charged independent. Since a proton and a neutron combine to form a stable nucleus, the deuteron, there must be binding forces between protons and neutrons. Experiments indicate that, not only are there similar binding forces between protons and protons, and also between neutrons and neutrons, but also these forces represented as n-p, p-p, and n-n forces are all the same. Since they only operate over the extremely short distances inside the nucleus they are nothing like inverse-square-law forces, representing the Coulomb forces between electric charges, and they are distinguished by the name **short-range nuclear forces.**

As is seen from Fig. 17-2, the average binding energy per nucleon for a large number of nuclides only varies over a small range although the number of nucleons in each type of nucleus may vary over a large range. This points to the idea that nuclear forces are what is known as saturated. Saturation of nuclear forces means that the force of attraction due to 1 nucleon is nearly all taken up by 1 or 2 or at least a small number of other nucleons, probably not greater than 12, since 12 is the number of neighbors with which each nucleon is presumably surrounded if the nucleons are closely packed together. In other words, a single nucleon does not interact equally with all the nucleons in the nucleus. This characteristic is similar to that of the saturation forces noticed by chemists in the formation of molecules. It is difficult to explain on a classical basis but can be explained in part on the basis of quantum mechanics, in terms of what are called **exchange forces.**

The idea of an exchange force comes out of quantum-mechanical analysis, and represents an attempt to give a physical interpretation to certain terms in the mathematical equations. The interpretation is usually based on the concept of an actual exchange of some type of particle between nucleons. At first it seemed that the electron might be such a particle, but computation showed that the electron as an exchange particle is too small to come even close to accounting for the forces that must be present in the nucleus.

In 1935, Yukawa in Japan proposed that exchange forces could account for nuclear forces if the particles were considerably more massive than an electron but less massive than a proton. The general name now given to these particles of intermediate mass is **meson.** Yukawa's theory was interpreted as predicting the existence of such "heavy electrons" or mesons, and they were later discovered (§ 20-11). The difficulty was that after their discovery it was found that they had little interaction with nuclei. Still later, however, it was found that the first-discovered meson, the **mu meson,** was actually a decay product of a somewhat heavier meson, called the **pi meson,** which did interact strongly with nuclei.

The discovery of a pi meson appears to be direct fulfillment of Yukawa's prediction, but whether it is complete confirmation of his theory of nuclear exchange forces is not entirely settled. The theory that nuclear binding forces depend largely on exchange of mesons between nucleons is very attractive, and there is no rival theory. In the field of chemistry the exchange forces have proved useful in explaining the formation of molecules by atoms of the same kind, such as the combination of two hydrogen atoms to form a hydrogen molecule. Nevertheless, there have been many mathematical difficulties in working out the details of the theory of the nucleus, and further experimental and theoretical development is needed.

To summarize briefly, it is evident that Coulomb repulsion between protons in a nucleus must at least be balanced by attractions of another kind which are less well understood. These attracting forces are evidently short-range nuclear forces, and they are independent of electric charge. The idea that gravitational forces between nuclear particles play a part must be abandoned, since computation shows them to be far too small to be appreciable. Besides, gravitation is an inverse-square-law (long-range) force and does not show saturation characteristics. A complete theory of the forces involved in the nucleus must be able to cope with such phenomena as radioactive decay, nuclear energy levels, nuclear fission, and the effect described by "magic numbers," which seems to involve completed shells or groups of nuclear particles within the nucleus.

17-5. Liquid-Drop Model of Nucleus

The two basic theories of nuclear structure are the liquid-drop theory and the shell theory. Each is capable of giving only a partial explanation of nuclear phenomena. Where one theory is most applicable the other is least applicable, but each theory has its uses. Because the two theories involve apparently conflicting ideas, attempts have been made to develop other theories. One of these is based upon what is called the "collective model." With this model the attempt has been made with some success to take a middle position between the first two. Nevertheless, many difficulties are involved.

The formation of what Bohr called the compound nucleus (§ 16-7) gave a basis for explaining some of the phenomena of nuclear transformations. In support of this theory Bohr further proposed that the nucleus with its particles might be expected to behave very much like a droplet of some liquid in which the forces of attraction and repulsion between particles in the liquid are balanced. In such a "liquid droplet," the nucleons are presumed to be closely packed together and in a state of continual thermal agitation, moving in various directions with random motions. Emission of nucleons from such a nucleus is then considered similar to evaporation of molecules from a liquid droplet. Nucleons are continually gaining and losing speed in collision with other nucleons because of thermal agitation. If a high-energy particle has been captured by the nucleus, the nucleons in the newly formed compound nucleus quickly share the energy, and a particular nucleon may gain enough energy from its neighbors to escape from the nucleus.

Since the nucleons at the surface of a nucleus are in a different energy state from those on the inside, an effect similar to that of surface tension in liquids is presumed to occur and must be taken into consideration. Nucleons at the surface of a nucleus are not surrounded by neighbors on all sides, as are the nucleons beneath the surface. Like molecules at the surface of a liquid droplet these nucleons are in a higher energy state, and the effect of surface tension occurs. This may explain the smaller average binding energy per nucleon for nuclides of small mass number, as seen from the curve (Fig. 17-2), where for small mass number the curve drops rapidly. At the smaller mass numbers not only is the ratio of area to volume larger, but also when the numbers of nucleons are small each nucleon may not be surrounded by a sufficient number of nucleons with which it can interact.

On the basis of this model of the nucleus it has been possible to account fairly well for the binding energies of nucleons. As a first approximation we may write an equation for the binding energy E

$$E = k_1A - k_2Z^2A^{1/3} - k_3A^{2/3} \qquad [17\text{-}2]$$

where k's are proportionality constants. The first term k_1A is the part of the energy resulting from the attraction between nucleons. It is taken to be proportional to the number of nucleons A (the mass number) or, what amounts to the same thing, the volume of the nucleus. The effect of Coulomb repulsion of protons is negative and is proportional to Z^2, the square of the number of charges, and to the diameter of the nucleus which is known to vary approximately as $A^{1/3}$. The third term $k_3A^{2/3}$ represents the effect of "surface tension." It is proportional to the area of the nucleus or to $A^{2/3}$, and it is also negative. In a more complete equation other terms may be required to take account of the surplus of neutrons over protons and of the effect of an odd or unpaired nucleon. Because Eq. 17-2 is derived neither wholly from theory nor wholly from experiment it is called a semiempirical formula.

One of the most useful applications of the droplet model is to the phenomenon of nuclear fission, where a nucleus divides into two more or less equal parts in very much the same way as a droplet of water or other liquid, if set vibrating with sufficient energy, becomes unstable and breaks into two or more droplets (§ 19-2). However, for higher-energy nuclear reactions, of a few hundred Mev or more, the liquid-drop model, together with the idea of the compound nucleus, becomes less and less useful. A high-speed particle, for example, may pass through the nucleus and hit only one or two nucleons in the process, or none at all. Such a picture is radically different from what would be expected to happen at lower energies. Furthermore, the distinct evidence for the existence of sharply defined excited states and energy levels in the nucleus is difficult to explain by means of the liquid-drop model. These difficulties have led to the development of another nuclear model.

17-6. The Shell Model of the Nucleus

It is difficult if not impossible to give a satisfactory explanation of excited states of nuclei and of sharply defined energy levels in terms of nuclear particles which are assumed to be closely packed together and to have random energy distributions, as in the liquid-drop model. This has led to various attempts to picture the nucleus in terms of orbits or shells, just as was done with the electronic structure of the atom outside the nucleus. There are at least two lines of evidence in favor of some type of shell model. For one thing, it is certainly simpler to think of excited states of nuclei in terms of nucleons being raised from one energy level, represented by one shell, to a higher energy level represented by another shell, the idea being borrowed directly from the common picture of extranuclear electronic behavior.

There is another feature of the external electronic structure which has been borrowed from the atom. Evidence clearly indicates the existence of completed or filled shells, so that the addition of another nucleon means the beginning of a new shell on a different energy level. Now, it has been noticed that nuclei having 2, 8, 20, 82, or 126 nucleons of the same kind, either neutrons or protons, are especially stable, as if the numbers represented the completion of a first, second, third, fourth, or fifth shell. This is a strong reminder of one of the chief features of extranuclear electronic structure, and a considerable amount of evidence now seems to indicate the desirability of thinking of the nucleons as existing in such shells for which, at each of the numbers just given, a proton or a neutron shell becomes filled.

The small size of the nucleus would seem to deny the possibility of large-scale orbital motion, with nucleons widely separated in the nucleus as in the electronic structure of the atom. From this, along with the successes of the droplet model, the difficulty is how to account for nuclear energy levels and nuclear shells. Here the two theories are in conflict. Where the droplet theory assumed a cluster of particles with random motion, the shell model must assume something like a central potential field. On either model the nucleons must be close together, but even if they are not widely separated in space they must somehow be separated into definite energy groups.

Magic numbers Since there was no simple theory to determine how and when nuclear shells become filled, the numbers just given were originally called "magic numbers." The implication is somewhat unfortunate, since science aims to eliminate "magic" in favor of logical processes, and it can be said that these magic numbers can be predicted in a logical way by quantum-mechanical analysis provided that certain assumptions are made. The most successful analysis has been made on what is called the assumption of the one-body model and of the rectangular potential well.

A considerable amount of evidence has been brought forth by Maria G. Mayer and others for the shell structure of the nucleus and for the so-called individual-particle type of shell model. The individual-particle model assumes that similar nucleons in the nucleus tend to pair off so that for such pairs the net angular momentum is zero and the net magnetic moment is zero. The resultant angular momentum and magnetic moment, if there are any, are then due to any unpaired or odd nucleons present.

It is convenient to classify nuclei according to whether the total number of particles in a nucleus is even or odd and whether the numbers of protons and neutrons, respectively, are even or odd. An even-odd nucleus, for instance, usually means a nucleus with an even number of protons and an odd number of neutrons. The mass number is consequently odd. At present about 22 per cent of known nuclides are stable. They are classified in Table 17-1, and it is seen that nuclei having odd numbers of both protons and neutrons are especially unlikely to be stable.

TABLE 17-1. NUCLIDES CLASSIFIED BY ODD-EVEN NUMBERS OF PROTONS-NEUTRONS

Class	Mass Number, A	Proton Number, Z	Neutron Number, $N = Z - A$	Known Number of Stable Nuclides	Spins
I	Odd	Odd	Even	50	Half-integral
II	Odd	Even	Odd	51	Half-integral
III	Even	Odd	Odd	4	Integral
IV	Even	Even	Even	165	Zero

The individual-particle model accounts for the angular momenta of nuclei in a simple manner. In classes I or II, where there is an odd proton or odd neutron, the angular momentum is presumed to be the vector sum of orbital and spin momenta. Since the angular momentum of either proton or neutron is ½, the sum will be half-integral, 1/2, 3/2, 5/2, or 7/2, etc. In class III the angular momenta ½ of the two odd particles add to give 1 or 0, and the resultant of orbital and spin momenta is integral. When there are even numbers of both protons and neutrons (Class IV) the spin and orbital momenta cancel giving a resultant of zero.

Although the shell theory of nuclear structure and the liquid-drop theory appear in many ways incompatible, each has its sphere of usefulness. The liquid-drop theory assumes particles to be close together with strong interactions between nucleons. The shell theory assumes that the particles, though all within the walls of a common potential well and perhaps as closely packed, at least have a more definite organization and probably interact with each other only slightly (weak interaction theory). The two models, however, were proposed to describe different groups of phenomena. The droplet theory deals with the over-all aspects of the nucleus as a whole, whereas the shell theory emphasizes energy levels and individual relations of the nucleons. The attempt at harmonizing these conflicting elements has led to the newer **collective model** which tries to preserve the best of the previous two.

17-7. Proton-Neutron and Proton-Proton Interactions

In the attempt to investigate forces between protons and protons, and also forces between protons and neutrons, studies have been made of the most uncomplicated examples of these forces. The deuteron is the simplest nucleus of all which possesses more than one particle, since it is composed of only one proton and one neutron. In the deuteron only the proton-neutron binding force is present, entirely uncomplicated by other forces. Thus the deuteron becomes a particle of extraordinary interest in the study of nuclear forces.

Much of present information comes from a study of the angles of scattering of neutrons by protons. The theory of scattering indicates that the angles of scattering should depend on the spins of the particles involved and their relative orientation at the time of collision. When a neutron and proton combine to form a deuteron they might presumably combine with spins parallel or with spins antiparallel. The latter turns out to be an unstable state, and in the stable deuteron the neutron and proton combine in such a way that the spins are parallel and the magnetic moments are in effect antiparallel, since the neutron has a negative magnetic moment (§ 15-11). The parallel mechanical spin of the neutron and proton in the ground state is confirmed by observations which show the observed spin for the deuteron to be unity, the sum of $\frac{1}{2}$ for the neutron and $\frac{1}{2}$ for the proton. Experimental evidence shows also that the magnetic moment of the deuteron is very close to the difference between the magnetic moments of the proton and neutron.

The scattering experiments are performed by directing a beam of neutrons toward a target containing hydrogen atoms, as, for instance, a block of paraffin. The number of neutrons deflected through various angles is then measured for different neutron energies. The information obtained is of particular value since neutrons have no net electric charge and are not affected by the electric field about the proton. The angles of scattering consequently would appear to depend only upon the short-range nuclear forces, which act between a neutron and a proton, and upon relative spins.

The experimental results confirm the idea that proton-neutron forces are independent of the charge on the proton and that they do depend on relative spin. The theory of the scattering can be worked out by an application of the wave-mechanical theory, in which instead of thinking of the scattering in terms of particle-like collisions and rebound the results are in terms of the scattering of waves according to the wave theory. Some of the terminology is borrowed from the subject of optical spectra by analogy with that field. If the spins of the neutrons and proton are antiparallel (unstable state) the total angular momentum is zero; this is called the singlet S state ($^1S_0$). When the spins are parallel (stable state) the total angular momentum is 1; this is called the triplet S state ($^3S_1$). When the bombarding particles are of low energy, S states predominate, and the analysis is made in terms of what is called S-wave scattering. At higher energies, where more units of angular momentum are more probable, the *P* waves may make a contribution to the scattering. Classical physics is helpless to deal with such scattering, and wave mechanics must be relied upon.

Further analysis leads to information concerning excited states, and it is possible to apply the Schrödinger wave equation to obtain approximate solutions for the higher energy states of the deuteron. This may then be applied to the approximate solutions for heavier nuclei.

Proton-proton scattering experiments have been performed by many people, and these experiments furnish information concerning proton-proton forces. The scattering in this instance is due in part to Coulomb repulsion of like charges. To obtain the effects due to the short-range charge-independent forces of attraction, the effects of Coulomb repulsion must be subtracted as a correction. Such experiments lead to the idea that binding forces between protons, called *p-p* forces, are similar to those between protons and neutrons, called *p-n* forces.

Information about neutron-neutron (*n-n*) forces, obtained from neutron-neutron scattering experiments, would be of great interest, but the experimental difficulties that must be overcome are discouraging.

17-8. Nuclear Magnetic Resonance

Any adequate theory of nuclear forces must take into consideration the spins of the nucleons and the resultant spin of the nucleus. Consequently information about spins is of utmost importance. Although nuclear spins were first deduced from a study of molecular spectra, the most direct experimental methods for measuring nuclear angular momenta (§ 15-4), commonly called spins, are the methods of magnetic resonance and of nuclear resonance or absorption.

The first accurate measurements of nuclear spin by magnetic resonance were made by Rabi and his coworkers, who developed to a high degree of precision a method based on the Stern-Gerlach experiment (§ 9-5). This is also known as the method of molecular beams. A beam of molecules from a small furnace or oven enters the region of nonuniform magnetic field of magnet *A* and follows a curved path passing through a slit S_1 (Fig. 17-3). The field must be nonuniform, as a uniform magnetic field would exert zero net deflecting force. The magnet *C* then produces a nonuniform field which bends the paths of the mole-

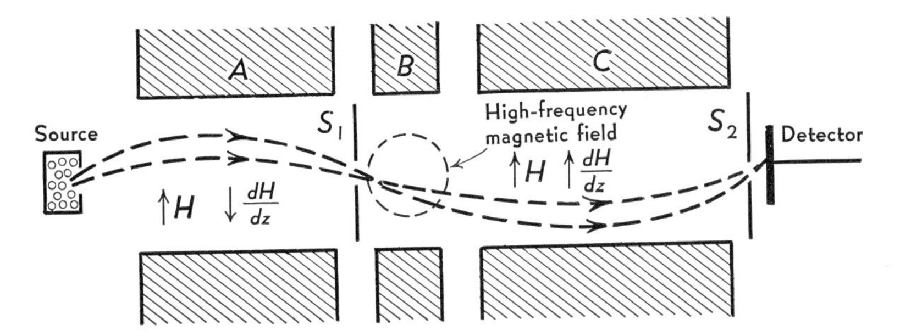

Fig. 17-3. Molecular-beam method of measuring nuclear magnetic moments. Magnets *A* and *C* give nonuniform magnetic fields in the same direction but with opposite gradients. Magnet *B* furnishes a constant field in the same direction, upon which a high-frequency field at right angles to that of *B* is superposed on that of *B*. The molecules are focused on the detector. When the frequency of the high-frequency field is adjusted to resonance with the precessional frequency of the nuclei, they will fail to focus, giving a dip in the curve of number recorded.

cules back again so that they pass through slit S_2 and are detected. Magnet *B* produces a uniform field which of itself has no effect, but in the region of the uniform field a high-frequency electric current produces a magnetic field at right angles to the uniform field.

The molecules passing through the uniform field have a definite quantized space orientation and precess like a spinning top about the direction of the field. When the frequency of the electric current is varied until it equals the frequency of precession, energy will be absorbed and the molecules take up a different quantized space orientation. They are then deflected by the field of magnet *C* either too little or too much to pass through slit S_2. The diminution in number of molecules passing through S_2 then marks the finding of the precessional frequency, which depends on the magnetic moment and the intensity of the uniform central field. By this method both the magnetic moment and the spin of the nucleus can be obtained.

In the method of **magnetic nuclear resonance absorption** of Purcell, Torrey, and Pound, and the closely related method of nuclear resonance induction of Bloch and his coworkers, no beams of molecules are used. A solid or liquid sample is placed in a uniform magnetic field, and upon this field a high-frequency alternating field is superposed at right angles. Protons or other simple nuclei precessing about the direction of the uniform field will have their quantized angles of space orientation suddenly changed by absorption of energy when the alternating field is tuned to resonance with the precession frequency. This absorption can be detected, and magnetic moments and angular momenta can be computed.

These and other experiments have verified the idea that the spins of single particles such as the proton, neutron, and electron are ½ times the quantum unit of angular momentum $h/2\pi$. However, spins of nuclei of odd mass numbers having a single unpaired nucleon may have half-integral values larger than ½, spins of as much as 9/2 having been determined. Similarly spins of even nuclei may have integral spins larger than 0 or 1. The simplest explanation is to assume that nucleons may have orbital as well as axial angular momenta, the word *spin* covering the sum of both of these. Just as was done in the case of external electrons, the resultant angular momentum I of a nucleon may be assumed to be the vector sum of the orbital angular momentum L and the spin angular momentum S such that by vector addition

$$I = L + S \qquad [17\text{-}3]$$

Although S is always +½ or −½ for nuclear particles the sum I, though half-integral, may be 3/2, 5/2, 7/2, etc., for odd nuclei. Similarly, for even nuclei, the total angular momentum (spin) may be 0, 1, 2, 3, etc.

SUGGESTED READING

F. K. Richtmyer, E. H. Kennard, and T. Lauritsen, *Introduction to Modern Physics,* 5th ed. (New York, McGraw-Hill, 1955).

I. Kaplan, *Nuclear Physics* (Cambridge, Addison-Wesley, 1955).

D. Halliday, *Introductory Nuclear Physics,* 2nd ed. (New York, Wiley, 1955).

H. Bethe and P. Morrison, *Elementary Nuclear Theory,* 2nd ed. (New York, Wiley, 1956).

F. Rassetti, *Elements of Nuclear Physics* (New York, Prentice-Hall, 1936).

M. G. Mayer and J. H. D. Jensen, *Elementary Theory of Shell Structure* (New York, Wiley, 1955).

CHAPTER 18

PARTICLE ACCELERATORS

18-1. Introduction

When Rutherford first disrupted atomic nuclei (§ 16-1) he bombarded them with alpha particles from naturally radioactive elements. The energies of such particles are between 4 and 9 Mev, depending upon the radioactive source. It then became desirable to produce high-speed particles by methods of direct acceleration in the laboratory for three chief reasons. First, it would allow experiments to be conducted with particles of a wider range of energies; second, it would be possible to use other than alpha particles as bombarding projectiles; third, it seemed entirely possible that particles of much higher energies than natural alpha particles could be obtained. The third reason was especially important since it had only been possible to transmute the lighter nuclei, even though the most energetic alpha particles known had bombarded them. Thus the need for particle accelerators became apparent, and experimenters soon began developing several kinds.

18-2. High-Voltage Generators

The first attempts at producing high-speed particles by direct acceleration were made with some form of high-voltage generator. Experiments were tried with step-up transformers, since theoretically it is possible to step up the voltage by one transformer and even to step it up again by another or several transformers. However, for voltages above a million, the difficulties of insulating the windings of a transformer became almost insuperable. Tesla coils were tried; these are two transformers in cascade, the second one being connected in a resonant circuit. They suffered from the same drawback as ordinary transformers.

Voltage multiplier By 1930 attention was being directed to other possible methods of obtaining high voltages or at least the effect of high voltages. Cockroft and Walton in England built a high-voltage generator, consisting of a number of capacitors arranged so that they could be charged in parallel and discharged in

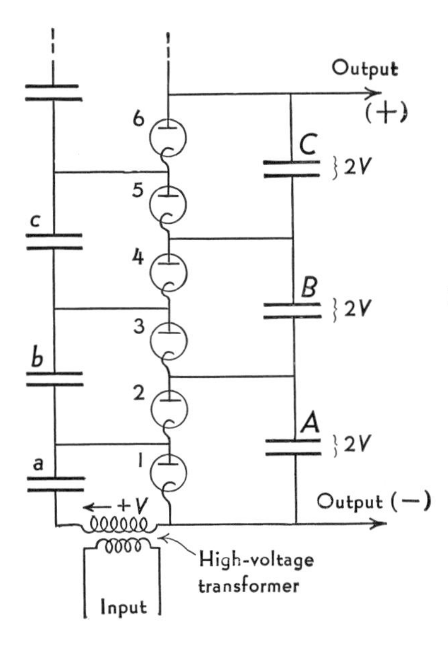

Fig. 18-1. Cockroft-Walton voltage multiplier for obtaining high voltages.

series. Between charge and discharge the connections had (in effect, at least) to be switched. Various schemes for doing this have been invented. An automatic method, known as voltage multiplying, was developed by Cockroft and Walton with vacuum-tube rectifiers. It will be described here since it represents a method still useful for high voltages in the million-volt range. Based on the same principle of charging capacitors in parallel and discharging them in series, a generator constructed by the General Electric Co. was the first to reach 10 million volts. This, however, was applied in studies not of nuclear disintegrations but of flash-over and simulated lightning-discharge tests on power lines.

In Fig. 18-1, two arrays of capacitors *a*, *b*, *c*, etc., and *A*, *B*, *C*, etc., are shown with high-voltage diode rectifiers 1, 2, 3, 4, etc., which are connected as indicated. A high-voltage transformer furnishes the charging current. During the first half-cycle, in which current flows as indicated in the transformer secondary coil, capacitor *a* charges through diode 1 to approximately *V* volts. During the second half-cycle the voltage of capacitor *a* adds to the reverse voltage from the transformer to charge capacitor *A* through diode 2. During the third half-cycle capacitor *a* charges through diode 1, and capacitor *A* partially discharges through diodes 1 and 3 into capacitor *b*. This process is repeated until capacitors *A*, *B*, *C*, etc., are charged to approximately $2V$ volts each. By extending the circuit to include a larger number of capacitors on each side an output voltage of approximately $2nV$ volts is obtained, where n is the number of capacitors on each side.

By this means Cockroft and Walton attained discharge voltages approaching a million volts with currents of as much as 5 or 10 microamperes. They then accelerated protons up to 0.7 Mev, and, as previously stated, they were the first to study reactions occurring when nuclei are bombarded with high-speed protons (§ 16-2). They were also the first to use electrically accelerated particles.

Van de Graaff generator In the early 1930's Van de Graaff in this country was working on the development of his glorified electrostatic generator, with which he was finally able to reach discharge potentials of several million volts. The Van de Graaff generator followed a very old and simple principle. More than a century earlier a primitive type of electrostatic machine for demonstrating production of visible electric sparks had consisted of a glass-insulating plate, on which electric charges were produced by rubbing. As the plate was made to rotate, the charges on the glass were carried to a metal electrode where continual deposit of charge built up the potential to an amount satisfactory for demonstrations.

In the Van de Graaff generator this principle is pushed to the limit. The moving carrier of charge is an endless belt of silk or other insulating material (Fig. 18-2). Electric charges are sprayed onto this belt by means of sharp-pointed discharge electrodes connected to an electronic generator of sufficient voltage to produce a discharge at the points. The moving belt continually carries electric charge to a more or less spherically shaped electrode, the potential of which continually rises until a limiting value is reached. The limiting value depends on the breakdown point of the insulation surrounding or supporting the large electrode on which the charge collects and also on the rate of leakage of the charge on the moving belt.

The electronic generator can be arranged to spray either positive or negative charges onto the belt and thus to charge the large electrode either positively or negatively. The potential reached can be controlled by adjusting the rate of charging the belt, and by controlling the speed of the belt in relation to breakdown voltage and belt leakage. In such

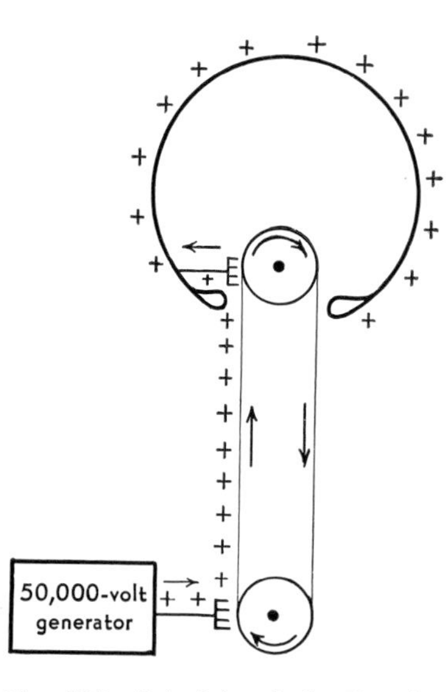

Fig. 18-2. Principle of the Van de Graaff generator. Electric charges are carried continuously to spherical electrode by moving belt.

Fig. 18-3. Discharge from early type of Van de Graaff generator, with two discharge spheres each 15 ft in diameter. (Courtesy, Robert J. Van de Graaff.)

a generator it is necessary to avoid sharp edges and corners except for the discharge and collector electrodes adjacent to the belt, since the corners or edges would allow the breakdown voltage to be reached too soon and a corona or spark discharge would develop.

A simple computation will illustrate the relationship of the quantities involved. The potential V to which any electrode is raised by a charge Q depends upon the capacitance of the electrode and is

$$V \text{ (volts)} = \frac{Q \text{ (coulombs)}}{C \text{ (farads)}} = \frac{300Q \text{ (esu)}}{C \text{ (esu)}} \qquad [18\text{-}1]$$

For the case of an ideal spherical electrode, the capacitance is equal to the radius in cm when esu are used and $V = Q/r$. If the maximum voltage obtainable is determined by the breakdown of the air insulation around the electrode the electric field intensity E at the surface of the sphere must be considered. This will be the same as if all the charge were concentrated at the center of the sphere, and therefore

$$E = \frac{Q}{r^2} \text{ (esu)} = \frac{E \text{ (volts/cm)}}{300} \qquad [18\text{-}2]$$

From these two relations

$$V \text{ (volts)} = r \text{ (cm) } E \text{ (volts/cm)} \qquad [18\text{-}3]$$

Assuming that the breakdown of field intensity is 30,000 volts per cm, the maximum attainable voltage V_{max} is

$$V_{\text{max}} = r \text{ } 30{,}000 \text{ (volts)} \qquad [18\text{-}4]$$

If the radius of the sphere is 150 cm, the maximum voltage before breakdown would be 4.5 million volts. Voltages of this amount have been approximated, but such large electrodes were a drawback (Fig. 18-3). In the modern design of a Van de Graaff generator the electrode size is often reduced, but to prevent proportionate reduction of output voltage the whole generator is enclosed in a gas-tight housing. The breakdown voltage is then considerably increased by filling the housing with compressed air or some gas such as freon, possessing good insulating properties. Voltages as high as 8 million have thus been attained. The attendant reduction in size has enabled portable units to be developed, and these are now commercially available.

The Van de Graaff generator was the first to reach output voltages of several million volts. Although other types of accelerators now far surpass it in ability to produce very-high-energy particles, it is still unsurpassed in its range for convenience, portability, and easy control of output voltage. Furthermore, it has the advantage of giving constant currents of considerable magnitude at high voltage, something that later types of particle accelerators do not do. It also has the advantage that all the particles in the beam have very nearly the same energies (monoenergetic), a favorable factor for many kinds of precision work. Because of these features it has had many applications not only in research work but in industry and in hospitals, where high voltages are needed for research or for the production of very penetrating x-rays.

18-3. Other Particle Accelerators

It is necessary to distinguish between particle accelerators that produce high-energy particles by the application of a single high-output voltage and those which operate on the principle of repeated accelerations at lower voltage. Devices like the cyclotron and the betatron may produce particles of 100 million-volts energy or more, but they do not produce differences of potential of anything like that much. Indeed, one of their advantages is that they produce high-energy particles without the requirement of insulation for the high voltages.

In the cyclotron particles revolve in expanding orbits, receiving two pushes per revolution, and after many revolutions attain very high energies. In the betatron particles circle about, receiving a certain amount of energy per revolution by a somewhat different method, but the principle, that of attaining high energies by repeated accelerations with a certain gain per revolution, remains. In what are called linear accelerators the particles to be accelerated travel in straight lines but receive successive impulses or a continuous sequence in one form or another until the end of the tube is reached.

18-4. The Lawrence Cyclotron

E. O. Lawrence began to develop his cyclotron at the University of California about 1930. The first successful machine was a small table model. It showed that the basic principle was all right, that such a machine could be made to work despite the unsuccessful efforts of others to make the same sort of machine and the dire predictions of some that the device could never be made to work. Following this first model, a succession of larger and larger models was built until about 1940, just before World War II, a great cyclotron was built weighing over 200 tons and costing several million dollars (Fig. 18-4). This was the first of many huge machines and the forerunner of improved and even larger accelerators to come. With the cyclotron the production of high-speed particles had become big business, with costs in the millions and machines so large that special laboratories had to be built to house them.

Lawrence's cyclotron soon produced, for the first time in history, particles of energies of 20 million electron volts. By the end of World War II, modifications had been made by which protons of nearly 300 Mev energy and alpha particles of 384 Mev were obtained. More recent developments in the production of high-speed particles have now left far behind the range of energies obtainable from naturally radioactive substances and have opened up many new possibilities for scientific research. For the part that Lawrence played in this development he received the Nobel prize.

The cyclotron has been described as a kind of merry-go-round, in which the particles spiral about in ever-larger (nearly circular) orbits

Fig. 18-4. View of the largest cyclotron before shielding wall was built around it. Central magnetic pole pieces are 184 inches in diameter. (Courtesy, Radiation Laboratory, University of California, Berkeley.)

receiving two impulses per revolution until they have acquired maximum energies. The particles are confined to these orbits by means of a magnetic field which continually bends the particle path for a given velocity into the arc of a circle.

To provide successive accelerations of the particles in a cyclotron they are made to spiral around the interior of two D-shaped electrodes, passing from one to the other twice per revolution (Fig. 18-5). These accelerating electrodes are called "dees" from their shape, and they may be visualized as something like the two halves of an empty double-crust pie. The path of a particle is illustrated by the spiral curve shown in the figure, and it is seen that twice per revolution the particle crosses the gap between the dee electrodes. Across this gap an alternating difference of potential of 50,000 to 100,000 volts is impressed; thus at each passage of the gap a particle is accelerated by this amount. After revolving through 180° a particle would enter a retarding field except that the potential difference between the dee electrodes has now been

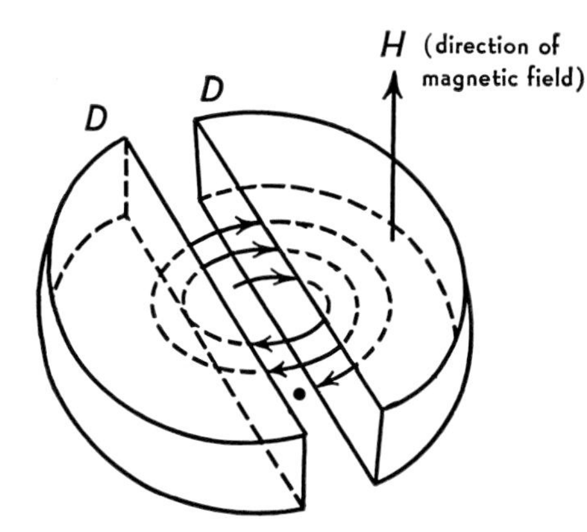

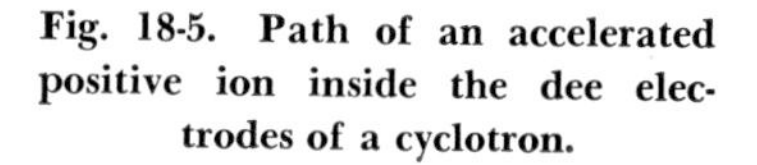

Fig. 18-5. Path of an accelerated positive ion inside the dee electrodes of a cyclotron.

reversed. This requires that the potential between the dees be reversed periodically in phase with the motion of the particle. The oscillating potential on the dees is obtained by coupling them to an electron-tube oscillator. The frequency of the oscillator is adjusted so that the potential reverses at just the right instant to produce successive accelerations in the same direction. Simple computation indicates that if the energy gained at each crossing of the gap is 100,000 ev the gain per revolution is 2 times that, and in 100 revolutions it would be 20 Mev.

The general plan of a cyclotron is shown in Fig. 18-6, where the

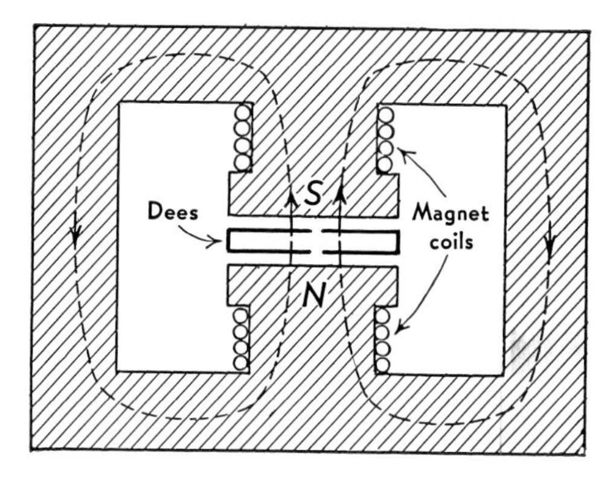

Fig. 18-6. Section plan of cyclotron magnet.

magnet is seen to consist of a large rectangular yoke with poles in the middle. The dee electrodes are located between the poles and are enclosed in an air-tight housing kept at a high vacuum. With an intense magnetic field the path of the particle is approximately a tight spiral of many turns, the change in radius occurring at each increase of velocity when the particle crosses the gap in the dees. The total energy gain of a particle depends on the number of revolutions that it can make before it reaches the outer edge of the dees and the field. This in turn depends upon the size of the magnet and the diameter of the pole pieces. The largest cyclotron, that at the University of California (Fig. 18-4), has poles 184 inches in diameter. The frequency of the dee oscillator is in the neighborhood of 12 megacycles/sec. The magnetic field intensity is 15,000 gauss, and a particle starting at the center spirals out to near the edge of the poles in little more than a thousandth of a second.

It might at first appear to be a difficult problem to adjust the oscillation frequency of the dee potential so as to be in step with the passage of the particles between the dees, especially when it is evident that the particle orbit is becoming larger at each revolution. However, a very simple analysis indicates that as long as the mass of the particle remains essentially constant, that is, as long as velocities are low enough so that the relativistic change in mass may be neglected, the period of revolution is independent of the radius of path. Thus the oscillator coupled to the dees can have a constant frequency. To show that this is true, let us consider the equation for the deflection of a particle of charge q in a uniform magnetic field of flux density B (Eq. 2-1), solved for the velocity of the particle.

$$v = \frac{Bqr}{m} \qquad [1\text{-}3]$$

However, the linear velocity of a particle in a circular orbit is also equal to the circumference divided by the period T of revolution, or

$$v = \frac{2\pi r}{T} \qquad [18\text{-}5]$$

Setting these equations equal to each other we find that the radius r cancels on both sides of the equation, and the period is

$$T = \frac{2\pi m}{Bq} \qquad [18\text{-}6]$$

Evidently for constants B, m, and q the time of the period of revolution is independent of the size of the orbit. It is this somewhat surprising result which makes the cyclotron possible in the first place. The reason why the cyclotron cannot successfully accelerate electrons also becomes quite evident from this equation. Long before electrons have reached the high energies desired, the relativistic increase in mass increases the period of revolution. This throws it out of step with the oscillating potential on the dees and makes further acceleration impossible.

In accelerating protons or alpha particles, velocities equivalent to energies of 25 Mev may be reached before relativistic change of mass becomes important enough to seriously affect the operation of the accelerator. To achieve higher energies of some hundreds of Mev, a modification of the operation of the cyclotron was found necessary, and in the modified form it became known as a frequency-modulated cyclotron or synchrocyclotron.

18-5. The Synchrocyclotron

The synchrocyclotron or frequency-modulated cyclotron is a cyclotron modified so that it will operate efficiently at higher energies than does an ordinary cyclotron. To remove the limitation resulting from relativistic increase in mass of the particles, the cyclotron is arranged so that when the frequency of revolution of the particle begins to slow down the frequency of oscillation of the accelerating potential between the dee electrodes is similarly slowed down. This permits the oscillation frequency on the dees to keep in step or in synchronism with the revolution of the particles, and this acceleration can be carried on to much higher energies. The process is repeated automatically for successive groups of particles, and the cyclotron is then said to be frequency-modulated.

One method of producing the frequency modulation is by having a rotating sector of a capacitor, which periodically adds to the capacitance in the oscillatory circuit of the electron-tube oscillator. At every revolution of the moving sector as it approaches a fixed sector, the capacitance rises to a maximum. When the capacitance is at a maximum the oscillation frequency is at a minimum. Without frequency modulation the high-speed particles would be produced in a steady stream, but with frequency modulation they only come in separate pulsations. Consequently the total current in the beam is reduced, but the gain in energy is often worth the sacrifice.

18-6. The Kerst Betatron

Although the cyclotron cannot be used to accelerate electrons, the chief function of the betatron is the acceleration of electrons. The first successful betatron or electron accelerator was built by Donald R. Kerst at the University of Illinois in 1941. In the betatron, electrons are continuously accelerated all the way around their circular path. In going around the path again, they are again accelerated, and in each successive revolution they receive added increments of acceleration until after having made 100,000 or more complete circuits they have gained energies of a hundred million electron volts or more. Since the acceleration around the circular path is continuous, any change of mass and slowing down of the rate of revolution have no harmful effect. There is no synchronism to be preserved, and the energy of each electron builds up continuously.

The fundamental principle of the betatron involves two separate factors which must act together to produce the desired effect. Consider the simple case of the north pole of a magnet which is moved toward a closed circular loop of conductor. As the magnet approaches the face of the loop the changing magnetic field through the loop generates an emf which acts around the loop in the direction of the arrow (Fig. 18-7*a*). The conduction electrons in the conductor would move in the direction opposite to the emf since they are negatively charged. An electron passing around the loop once would be acted upon by the emf generated in the loop, and in n round trips it would be acted upon

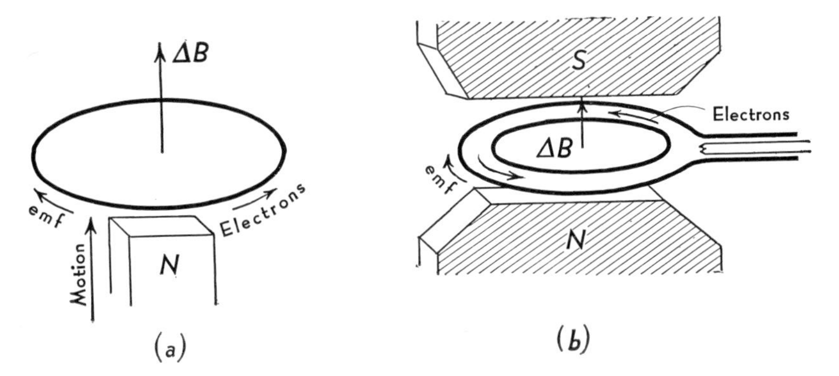

Fig. 18-7. Principle of betatron: *a*, emf induced in conducting ring by approaching magnetic pole; *b*, emf around ring-shaped tube induced by increasing flux density *B* between poles of magnet.

n times. But in the conductor, of course, it is not free to be accelerated indefinitely and because of collisions actually moves very slowly. Now, however, imagine the conducting loop replaced by a ring-shaped hollow tube with a high vacuum (Fig. 18-7*b*).

Every time an electron makes a complete circuit of the ring it gains energy in ev equal to the emf around its path. Substituting the ring-shaped orbital tube for the conductor, so that the electrons become free to move as fast as they can, there would now appear to be nothing to confine them to the circular path. However, since it is necessary to have a changing magnetic field at right angles to the ring-shaped orbital tube to produce the accelerating emf, the possibility arises of making this field of sufficient intensity at each moment to bend the paths of the electrons into the arc of a circle, so that they will remain near the axis of the orbital tube. As the electrons gain speed and move faster the magnetic field must become more intense; consequently it must be an increasing one.

Since it would be out of the question to move a magnet periodically toward the orbital tube, a fixed magnet is used with periodically increasing pulses of current which produce increasing magnetic fields. To operate the magnet a large alternating-current generator to furnish heavy current is required. The magnet is then tuned to resonance with the generator current by means of a large bank of capacitors. This in effect balances the inductive load and improves the power factor, thus

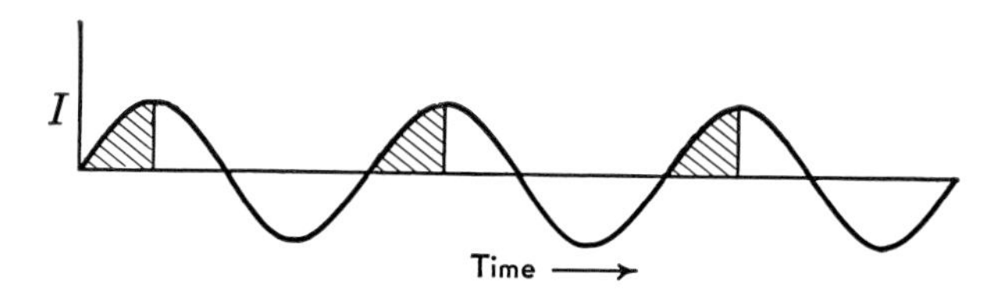

Fig. 18-8. Successive groups of electrons are accelerated in betatron during intervals in which current *I* is rising sharply.

reducing the volt-ampere capacity required of the generator. Because in alternating current the current increases to a maximum during one quarter-cycle the high-speed electrons are not produced continuously in the tube but are produced in pulses, one pulse for each cycle of the current (Fig. 18-8). The basic problem in building the betatron was to design the size and shape of the magnet, together with the necessary current-carrying coils, so that the magnetic field would fulfill its two functions. The rate of change of the magnetic field must give the electrons the requisite velocity, and the momentary intensity of the same field must bend their paths so as to repeatedly make them follow the same paths. The following analysis leads to the fundamental relation that must be satisfied.

The bending of the path of an electron moving in a circular orbit depends upon the magnetic field intensity B_r at the path itself, that is, at the distance r from the center of path, where r is the radius of path. Since in this application the speeds are in the extreme relativistic range, increase in momentum for the highest speeds is chiefly the result of relativistic increase in mass. The momentum mv from Eq. 1-3 for the bending of the path of an electron must now be replaced by the relativistic momentum p, and the equation becomes

$$p = B_r er \tag{18-7}$$

Now, tangential force is the rate of change of the tangential momentum, or

$$F_{\tan} = \frac{dp}{dt} = \frac{d}{dt}(B_r er) \tag{18-8}$$

Tangential force is also work eV done on the electron in one complete revolution, divided by the distance $2\pi r$,

$$F_{\tan} = \frac{eV}{2\pi r} = \frac{e}{2\pi r}\frac{d\varphi}{dt} \tag{18-9}$$

where the emf V is the rate of change of flux φ through the path. Then

$$F_{\tan} = \frac{e}{2\pi r}\frac{d(B_{\text{av}}\pi r^2)}{dt} \tag{18-10}$$

where φ, the flux, is the average magnetic flux density B_{av} times the area πr^2 enclosed by the path. Putting Eq. 18-8 equal to Eq. 18-10,

$$\frac{e}{2\pi r}\frac{d(B_{\text{av}}\pi r^2)}{dt} = \frac{d(B_r er)}{dt} \tag{18-11}$$

from which, by integrating both sides of the equation, assuming that $B = 0$ at $t = 0$, we obtain

$$\frac{B_{\text{av}} er}{2} = B_r er \tag{18-12}$$

and

$$B_{\text{av}} = 2B_r \tag{18-13}$$

From this we see that, for the magnetic field to perform its two functions of providing emf by its rate of change and of bending the electron by the proper amount for each instantaneous value, the average flux density through the loop must be twice the flux density at the orbit. To increase the average flux density of the field the gap at the central part of the field is narrowed by putting a slab of magnetic material there, as shown in Fig. 18-9*a*.

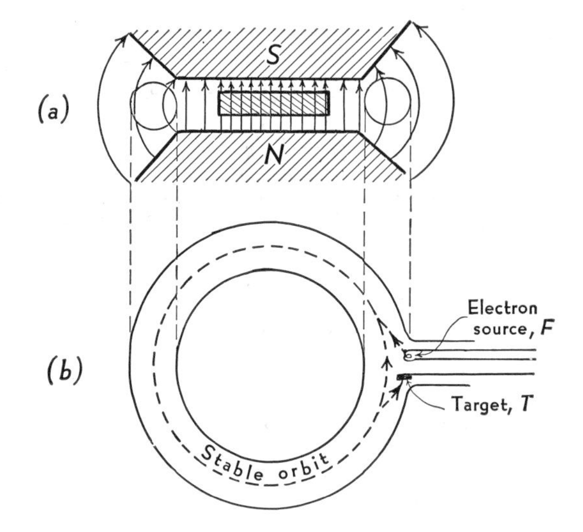

Fig. 18-9. ***a*, Tapered pole pieces and location of orbital tube in betatron. Central magnetic slab increases average field intensity to attain required emf; *b*, part of electron gun and target, together with the paths of electrons.**

The first betatron was designed to give energies of a mere 100,000 ev and was constructed with the technical aid of the General Electric Co. With increased efficiency of design and in response to the demand for higher and higher energies, a betatron with a 400-ton magnet was designed to give 340 million-volt electrons (Fig. 18-10). The circular tube in which the electrons revolve is 9 feet in diameter, and electrons travel 140,000 revolutions in 0.004 second, or more than 700 miles in this short time.

The importance of the betatron is that experiments may now be made with high-speed electrons as bombarding particles. Some limitation in the experimental uses of the betatron generator has been caused by the difficulty of removing the high-speed electron beam from the tube. One of the most important purposes that the betatron has served thus far is the generation of 100 million-volt (or more) x-rays,

Fig. 18-10. The 340-million-volt betatron at the University of Illinois. Electrons make 140,000 revolutions in a circular tube 9 ft in diameter in 0.004 sec, and thus travel more than 700 miles to gain this energy. The circular orbital tube is placed between the poles of the magnet at the middle of the 400-ton frame. (Courtesy, University of Illinois.)

the target being so placed inside the tube that electrons hit it when deflected after they make the required number of complete revolutions around the tube. In no other way can such high-energy and penetrating x-rays be produced. They are so short in wavelength and so penetrating in character as to surpass the gamma rays from radioactive substances and to be comparable with many of the gamma rays present in cosmic rays.

18-7. The Synchrotron

For electron energies much over 100 Mev the cost of a sufficiently large magnet for a betatron becomes prohibitive, and the efficiency of operation drops rapidly. The attempt to overcome these limitations led to the development of the synchrobetatron or synchrotron, which is a modified betatron. In the betatron the total energy that an electron acquires depends on the total number of revolutions that it makes before it departs too much from a stable orbit near the axis of the orbital ring-shaped tube. It was obvious that electrons could be made to attain higher energies if they could be kept rotating for a larger number of times. Since the electrons move almost with the velocity of light they do not move appreciably faster as they are accelerated, but they experience rapidly increasing relativistic change of mass. At an energy of 1 Mev an electron is traveling with more than 0.9 the speed of light, and its mass has increased to about 2½ times its rest mass. At 100-Mev energy it has a speed 0.9999 that of light, and its mass has increased to 200 times its rest mass. The increase in mass makes it more difficult for the magnetic field to bend the electrons into the same orbital path. For this purpose a magnetic field of greater intensity just at the orbit is needed. Indeed, if an accelerating emf is furnished by some method other than the change of magnetic flux through the orbit, the central part of the field could be omitted and only a bending field just at the orbit used. This bending field, however, has to be increased periodically to enable groups of electrons to be carried to higher energies. This is the principle of the synchrotron.

The accelerating emf for synchrotron operation is furnished by having the electron beam pass successively through two cylindrical metal electrodes which are built into the orbital tube (Fig. 18-11). At each revolution the electrons pass the gap between the two cylindrical elec-

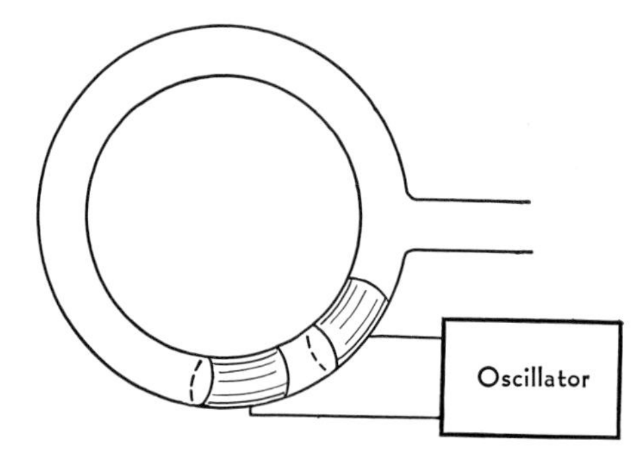

Fig. 18-11. How cylindrical accelerating electrodes are built into orbital tube of betatron for synchrotron operation.

trodes where an accelerating potential from an oscillator is applied. As the electron mass increases, the magnetic field which deflects them must similarly increase in synchronism with the accelerating potential. This is the principle of the synchrotron, as suggested by Oliphant in 1943, which has been used to obtain electron energies as high as 400

Mev. One limitation on the maximum attainable energies is that an accelerated charge radiates energy, and a limit would be reached when the rate of radiation of energy equals the rate at which energy is put into the particle. This radiation is appreciable at speeds achieved in the betatron but is not appreciable at the lower speeds attained by the more massive particles in a cyclotron. Although the electrons in a betatron soon reach a speed nearly that of light and further linear acceleration is slight, they are continually accelerated toward the center of path.

In operation, pulses of electrons are first accelerated by betatron action to speeds near that of light; then operation is automatically switched to synchrotron action. By contrast with the cyclotron, it is of interest to note that in the latter device relatively heavy positive particles move in ever-enlarging orbits with constant period of rotation up to some 25 Mev, when acceleration by frequency-modulated voltage pulses is made to take over. In the betatron the electrons move in the *same* orbit with ever-increasing speeds, until their speeds approach that of light, at which time synchronous increase of the magnetic field for each electron group takes over to keep it in its orbit.

18-8. Orbital Stability

In both cyclotron and betatron the problems of orbital stability loom large; attainment of stability must be assured by proper design. For an electron in the betatron to travel in a stable orbit of constant radius, there must be a restoring force acting inward to prevent the electron from moving to a larger orbit. There must also be a restoring force acting outward to prevent the electron from moving to a smaller orbit. In addition there must be restoring forces to produce vertical stability.

If the electron wanders into an orbit of larger radius, the required centripetal force mv^2/r for circular motion of that radius is reduced since it is inversely proportional to the radius. By Eq. 1-2 the magnetic flux density must then not decrease as fast as $1/r$ if there is to be a restoring force. This is the condition for horizontal stability. For vertical stability, a component of the magnetic field will act to restore the electron if the field is made to bulge outward. Indeed, both conditions of stability may be satisfied by properly tapering the pole pieces as shown in Fig. 18-12. Since the deflecting force of the magnetic field is at right angles to the field, the force vectors, marked F on the diagram, each have components inward and toward the median

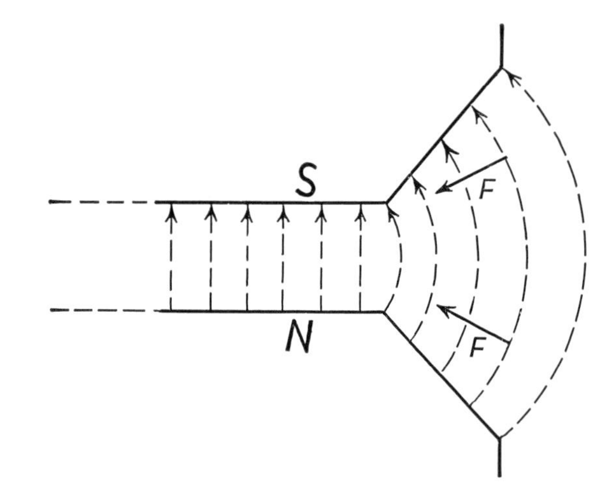

Fig. 18-12. Bulging field at edge of betatron magnet gives both vertical and horizontal stability to electron orbits.

plane of the orbit between the poles. Such a bulging field is also feasible for the cyclotron for vertical stability when the particles are near the edge of the field.

In the cyclotron the particles may be brought out in the form of a high-energy beam by means of deflecting electrodes. In the betatron it is so difficult to bring the beam out of the orbital tube that the target is usually put into the tube. The electrons to be accelerated are injected into the orbital tube at energies of 50 to 1,000 kev by means of an electron gun and are pulled by means of the bulging field into a stable orbit (Fig. 18-9*b*). At the end of each acceleration interval the orbit is expanded by means of an auxiliary field, and the beam is made to strike the target, as indicated in Fig. 18-9*b*.

18-9. Linear Accelerators

Linear accelerators have been developed at a number of institutions and have been successful in producing ion beams of considerable en-

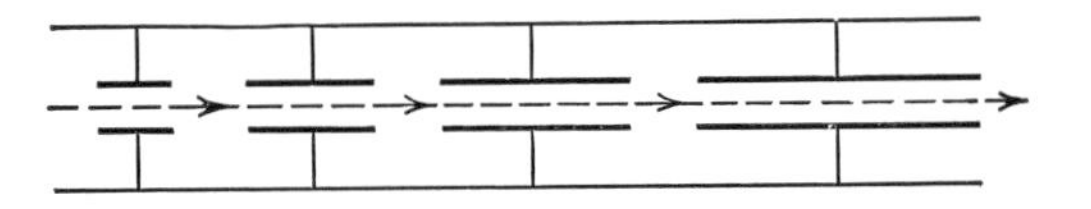

Fig. 18-13. Section of one type of linear accelerator. Voltages between cylindrical drift tubes accelerate the particles.

ergy. There are two closely related, general types of linear accelerators. In one, the voltage is switched from one pair of electrodes to the next pair of electrodes, so that the particle leaving the region between the first pair of electrodes enters the second region between electrodes just in time to be accelerated again (Fig. 18-13). Since the particles are now moving faster, the drift distance along each electrode must increase if the accelerating potential is switched at the same rate to successive electrodes. If the switching process is continued in step with the particles moving down the tube, there is no theoretical limit to the energies that might be reached, but there are practical limitations of length of tube and of available power.

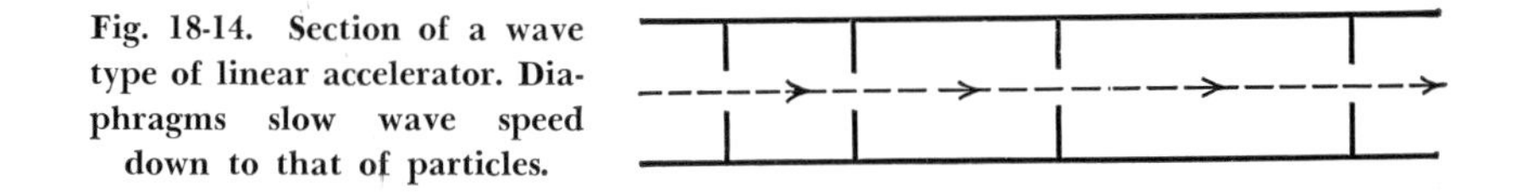

Fig. 18-14. Section of a wave type of linear accelerator. Diaphragms slow wave speed down to that of particles.

Another type of linear accelerator is called the wave accelerator. During World War II, methods were perfected of transmitting electromagnetic waves through hollow pipes of conducting material, called wave guides. In a wave guide it is possible to set up various modes of electromagnetic waves, and in one of these the electric field is parallel to the axis of the tube. Assume now that in the wave guide (Fig. 18-14) the waves move down the tube. If a stream of charged particles is injected into the tube in the direction of the axis at the right moment, the particles will be accelerated by the electric field of the wave parallel to the axis. For particles traveling near the velocity of light the wave in the wave guide may travel at the same speed. The electric field of the wave then exerts a constant force on the particle, continually accelerating it as it moves down the tube. With linear accelerators energies of several hundred Mev have already been attained.

18-10. Heavy-Ion Accelerators

Linear accelerators are now being developed to accelerate heavy ions (the ionized atoms of heavier elements). These are called heavy-ion accelerators. Although in the past the effects of atomic bombardment at high energies have been obtained chiefly by means of light particles, protons, deuterons, and alpha particles as projectiles, newer studies with heavy ions hold out the promise of securing important new information.

18-11. Billion-Volt Accelerators

Accelerators designed to give energies of billions of electron volts to particles have now been put into operation and have been given special names. All of them operate on essentially the same basic principle, although many improvements in design have been made, especially in the shaping of magnetic fields to reduce the size of the required magnets and also to produce greater orbital stability. The basic principle is that of synchrotron operation. The large energies given to the particles require that they travel in large orbits, their paths being curved by suitable magnetic fields. Acceleration of the particles is then accomplished periodically, in a manner similar to that of the synchrotron. The size and shape of the orbits have led to such accelerators sometimes being called race-track accelerators. Relatively small magnets are placed only at positions where the path is to be bent, thus averting entirely the need for any large central magnet. Accelerations are produced by the field between two cylinders, which form part of the orbital tube as in the synchrotron. The first large machine of this type

Fig. 18-15. The giant cosmotron ("race-track" accelerator) designed to give particles of several billion electron-volts energy. (Courtesy, Brookhaven National Laboratory, Upton, N. Y.)

was built at the Brookhaven National Laboratory, Long Island, and is called the cosmotron (Fig. 18-15). It was put into operation in 1952, and for the first time in history particles of energies greater than a billion electron volts were produced. After improvements in technique the energies of the particles were increased to 2.7 billion electron volts, and energies exceeding 3 Bev for protons and 5 Bev for alpha particles have been attained.

In the Brookhaven cosmotron the diameter of the particle orbit is 60 feet, and particles are injected into the system at more than 3 million electron-volts energy. Making approximately 3 million revolutions, they reached an energy of nearly 3 billion electron volts in something like 1 second of time. The cost of the cosmotron was $7,000,000.

Since completion of the cosmotron a larger accelerator, called the bevatron, has been constructed at the University of California. The bevatron has now produced proton energies of approximately 7 Bev. At Geneva, Switzerland, a still larger accelerator is in progress of construction at the newly developed laboratories of the Council for European Nuclear Research, known more commonly as CERN. Near Moscow, U.S.S.R., the world's largest proton accelerator (10 Bev) weighing 36,000 tons was put into operation in 1957. Recently a new method was found for keeping particles in a stable orbit by what is called strong focusing. This enables a considerable reduction in the size of the magnets. An accelerator of this type is now under construction at Brookhaven, and energies ultimately of 20 to 100 Bev are believed feasible. The race for higher energies is on, and no one can predict the outcome, but already very important scientific advances have been made. As high as these energies are, however, they are greatly surpassed by the higher energies of cosmic rays (Chap. 20), and, although man has progressed far, Nature is still ahead of him.

SUGGESTED READING

D. Halliday, *Introductory Nuclear Physics*, 2nd ed. (New York, Wiley, 1955).

E. Pollard and W. L. Davidson, *Applied Nuclear Physics*, 2nd ed. (New York, Wiley, 1951).

D. H. Sloane and E. O. Lawrence, "The Production of Heavy High-Speed Ions Without the Use of High Voltage," *Physical Review*, 38, 2021 (1931).

A. E. S. Green, *Nuclear Physics* (New York, McGraw-Hill, 1955).

D. W. Kerst, "The Betatron: Development and Applications," *American Scientist*, 35, 56 (1947).

CHAPTER 19

FISSION, ATOMIC ENERGY, AND NUCLEAR REACTORS

19-1. Fission

When other investigators repeated Fermi's experiments on the transmutation of uranium by neutron capture (§ 16-12), they were confronted with results that were puzzling. There seemed to be too many kinds of beta-ray emission and too many kinds of product atoms. In particular, Hahn and Strassmann in Germany worked with meticulous care, and finally succeeded in 1938 in separating by chemical means a tiny amount of an element only about half as heavy as uranium which they were sure had not existed before the experiments were started. Although there was scarcely enough to permit a chemical test, the tests that they did perform gave indications that the substance was barium. Later they concluded that krypton had been formed at the same time, along with the barium. This suggested that the uranium atom had been split into two nearly equal parts—the phenomenon that we now call fission.

The tremendous importance of this result was recognized by Lise Meitner, who had worked with Hahn and Strassmann, but who had been forced to flee from Germany. She perceived that if the uranium atom had actually been split into two parts there must have been, in the process, a release of energy of enormous proportions. Frisch in

Copenhagen and Joliot in Paris immediately looked for and found evidence of this large amount of released energy.

Early in 1939 word of these experiments was brought to the United States by Niels Bohr, and confirmation of the astonishing amount of energy release soon came from many laboratories. The newly discovered phenomenon now became the subject of investigation by many people. Very soon the importance of the discovery for military purposes was recognized, and at the instigation of Einstein, Sachs, and others our government became interested. By general agreement reports on further experiments were withheld because of the war clouds over Europe. Information as to what took place in the successful development of the nuclear bomb up to the end of World War II was finally summarized in the Smyth Report of 1945.

Early predictions were soon verified that the products of fission of uranium would be driven apart with total kinetic energies of as much as 200 million electron volts. To grasp the magnitude of this energy release we need only compare it with the most violent chemical explosives known to man, such as TNT, where the total energy released is not more than a few electron volts per molecule. Here, it was evident that the fission of uranium released nearly 100 million times as much energy per atom as any common explosives. Such a tremendous release of energy not only became at once a matter of great scientific importance but, through its military and peacetime possibilities, has now become a dominating factor in world politics and military policy.

19-2. The Nature of Fission

The nature of fission is best described in terms of the liquid-drop model of the nucleus. In an ordinary droplet of liquid, the total energy of the particles in the droplet is not usually adequate to overcome the forces holding the particles together in droplet form. However, if energy is added to the droplet in such a way as to set the droplet in vibration, it will alternately elongate and shorten until, if the amplitude of vibration is large enough, it may divide into two droplets. On the basis of the liquid-drop model, something like this is pictured as happening in the nucleus.

According to Eq. 17-2, the forces of repulsion between positive charges in the nucleus (Coulomb repulsion) are balanced by the binding forces between nucleons, but also there is a kind of surface effect similar to surface tension in the liquid droplet. Nuclear particles on the surface of the droplet do not have as many neighbors with which to interact as do particles inside the droplet. Since surface nucleons are in a higher energy state than interior nucleons they have less binding energy. This loss in energy acts along with Coulomb repulsion to reduce the total binding energy. For a first approximation then, the net binding energy of the nucleus is the volume binding energy diminished by the Coulomb energy of repulsion, and also diminished by the loss of binding energy from surface effects.

The net binding energy of a nucleus owing to these three factors, as given by Eq. 17-2, may be written:

$$E\ (\text{net}) = E\ (\text{volume}) - E\ (\text{coulomb}) - E\ (\text{surface})$$

In a complete formulation other terms may be needed, and in particular in the fission of uranium a term that depends on whether the mass number is even or odd turns out to be of importance. It need not, however, be considered in detail here. What is important here is to note that, if the nucleus is deformed, there will be a decrease in net binding energy owing to increase in the surface area, and if sufficient energy is added to the nucleus to produce such distortions or vibrations these may be sufficiently violent to disrupt the nucleus (Fig. 19-1).

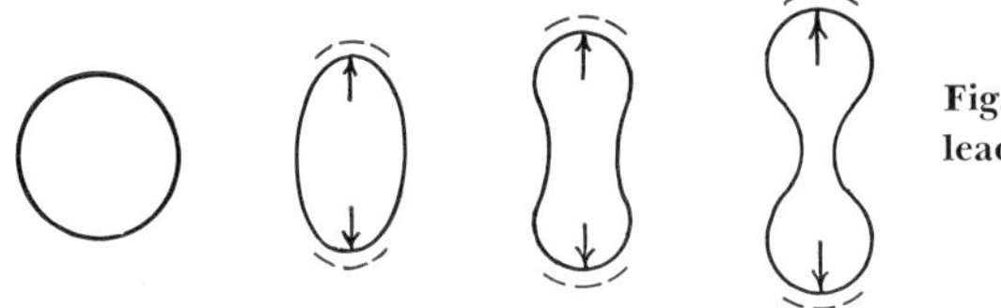

Fig. 19-1. Vibration of nucleus leading to fission, according to the droplet theory.

Bohr-Wheeler theory Bohr and Wheeler in 1939 made a detailed mathematical study of what can happen when energy is added to the drop causing oscillations of distortion. In a first approximation it appears that the volume energy remains unchanged when the drop is distorted and the energy of electrostatic repulsion decreases. The decrease is more than balanced by the effect of increased surface. In this connection it should be remembered that in all phenomena, where both surface and volume relations are involved, surface effects increase in proportion to volume effects for smaller and smaller spheres or droplets. The reason is that the ratio of the surface of a sphere to its volume is

$$\frac{4\pi r^2}{4/3\ \pi r^3} = \frac{3}{r} \qquad [19\text{-}1]$$

From this it is seen that, as a sphere is made smaller, the ratio of surface to volume increases in inverse proportion to the radius.

Bohr and Wheeler derived the following formula for the net gain in surface energy E_s for a small deformation of a droplet:

$$\text{Gain in energy} = \frac{2}{5} E_s \left(1 - 0.022 \times \frac{Z^2}{A}\right) \qquad [19\text{-}2]$$

where Z is the atomic number and A is the mass number. For nuclei of larger and larger Z, the second term in the parenthesis approaches unity, and would become unity if Z^2/A were to equal 45.4. The parenthesis would then become zero, and the result is taken to be the limit of stability. At this point the nucleus could presumably no longer exist as such and would perhaps undergo fission or break up into smaller pieces.

For U^{238} the value of Z^2/A is 35.5, and it times 0.22 is 0.78. A small increase in energy of vibration or deformation then might cause fission. Consequently, in any droplet, if large deformations occur the droplet should undergo fission when the energy of deformation is more than the limiting value known as the activation energy. In uranium the addition of a neutron to the nucleus may add more than this limit, and fission may then occur. Generally, it may be remembered that the average binding energy of a neutron in a heavy nucleus is in the neighborhood of 7.5 Mev. When an extra neutron is introduced into such a nucleus, especially if it is a high-energy neutron, the average binding energy may be so reduced that the nucleus becomes unstable and divides by fission. If in any nucleus the energy received is less than the limiting activation energy, the excess will most likely be removed by gamma-ray emission or other radioactive decay.

The liquid-drop theory, although describing some features of fission, is by no means all-inclusive. It does not explain why fission hardly ever produces two nuclei of equal masses. A considerable amount of study has been devoted to the products of nuclear fission, and the curve of Fig. 19-2 illustrates the percentage of products formed in many fissions. Note that at the two peaks of the curve in the largest percentage of cases fission occurs with one particle in the neighborhood of mass 94 and the other in the neighborhood of mass 140. The sharp drop at the middle of the curve indicates that uranium divides into equal nuclei in only about 1/100 of 1 per cent of the cases. Sometimes the fragment may be as small as mass number 72 or as large as mass number 158.

Some evidence in support of the types of fission observed comes from the shell model rather than from the droplet model of the nucleus.

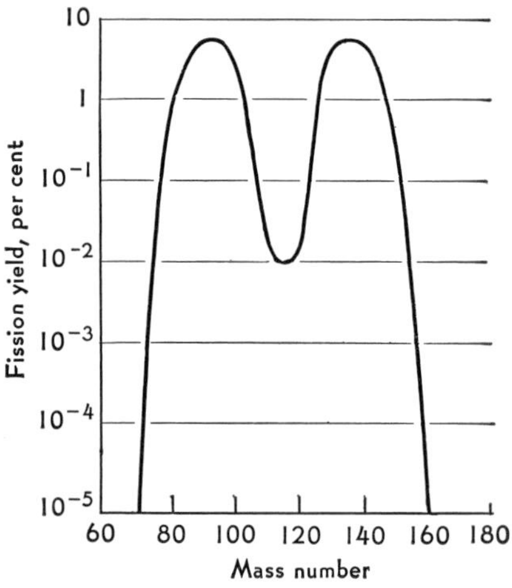

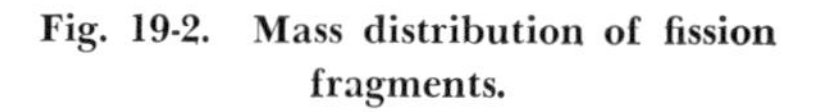

Fig. 19-2. Mass distribution of fission fragments.

The asymmetry of fission has been explained by the shell model on the assumption, for which there is other evidence, that certain numbers of neutrons or protons form closed shells within the nucleus (§ 17-6). Whereas the liquid-drop model has little to say about the internal structure of the nucleus, the shell model concerns itself with just that problem.

The phenomenon of fission is by no means confined to uranium. Most of the very heavy elements have been found to undergo fission under favorable conditions. Of special interest among these is thorium, since there is more thorium in the earth than there is uranium. Fission may also be induced by other methods than neutron capture. Indeed, any method by which the energy given to the nucleus is more than the activation energy can produce fission. Fission has now been obtained by high-energy alpha particles, deuterons, protons, and even by high-energy x-ray photons or gamma rays. In fact, occasional fission of uranium atoms may occur either spontaneously or by the action of cosmic rays.

19-3. Neutron Emission in Fission

It became apparent soon after the discovery of fission that neutrons would most likely be emitted in the fission process, and Fermi suggested that, if enough neutrons were emitted so that they themselves in turn produced fission of neighboring nuclei, a chain reaction might occur. From the curve of Fig. 17-1, showing relative numbers of protons and neutrons in stable nuclei, it is evident that for stability the heaviest nuclei require more neutrons in proportion than do lighter nuclei.

Therefore, when a heavy nucleus splits into lighter nuclei there would presumably be too many neutrons for the lighter nucleus, and some of them could be emitted in the process of fission. Evidence was soon obtained that neutron emission does occur, and that in the fission of uranium between two and three neutrons on the average are emitted per fission. Experimental values have been obtained of 2.46 neutrons per fission of U^{235} and 2.88 per fission of plutonium Pu^{239}.

Prompt and delayed neutrons About 99 per cent of the neutrons emitted in fission of uranium are ejected in a very short space of time, so short as to be almost instantaneous with the fission process. These are called prompt neutrons. Later it was found that a few other neutrons are emitted after an appreciable length of time (a matter of some seconds). These are known as delayed neutrons, and they originate from the unstable fission fragments that decay by neutron emission before reaching a stable state. The delayed neutrons are of great importance in the control of nuclear atomic reactors (§ 19-10).

19-4. Fission of Uranium

It has been known from the work of Dempster with the mass spectrograph that U^{238} possesses a rare isotope U^{235}. Ordinary uranium is composed of U^{238} for the most part, only 0.7 per cent of the atoms being U^{235}, or approximately 1 in every 143 atoms. There are also other possible isotopes of uranium. Early in the study of fission the question arose as to which of the isotopes of uranium underwent fission. The separation of very tiny samples of U^{238} and U^{235} by A. O. Nier made the first test possible, and later work proved that U^{238} nuclei would undergo fission only when subjected to bombardment by fast neutrons. U^{235} nuclei, on the other hand, would undergo fission by absorption of slow as well as of fast neutrons. Apparently the energy of a slow neutron is sufficient to give the U^{235} nucleus more than the activation energy, but it is not sufficient to give the U^{238} nucleus as much as its activation energy. Consequently slow neutrons would induce fission only in U^{235} nuclei, and fast neutrons would induce fission in U^{238} as well as in U^{235}.

According to Bohr and Wheeler, slow-neutron capture produces fission in U^{235} in the following way. They computed the energy required to produce fission in U^{235} and obtained a value of 5.2 Mev. The kinetic energy of a slow neutron is negligible, but the energy equivalent of the mass that it loses in the form of binding energy is large. The loss in mass when a neutron is captured by a U^{235} nucleus to form U^{236} is 0.0073 amu. This is equal to 6.8 Mev energy, and its release in the nucleus is therefore more than enough to produce fission. In U^{238} the binding energy is less, and not enough energy is released to produce fission unless the bombarding neutron has a minimum kinetic energy of 1.1 Mev.

19-5. Neutron Capture by Uranium

The method of describing the probabilities of nuclear events in terms of effective cross-sectional area for a collision producing that event has been described (§ 16-16). We shall now speak in particular of the cross-sectional areas of uranium for the capture of neutrons and for fission by neutron capture.

The cross-sectional area of U^{235} for fission is high enough for low-velocity neutrons whereas the effective fission cross-sectional area of U^{238} is approximately zero for low-velocity neutrons (Fig. 19-3). On the other hand, the fission cross section of U^{238} rises sharply when the neutron energy is large enough to produce fission. Both U^{235} and U^{238} have large capture cross sections for slow neutrons, but only capture of these by U^{235} is likely to result in fission. When the maximum rate of fission of U^{235} is desired, loss of neutrons by capture in U^{238} must be minimized. The nonfission capture of slow neutrons by U^{238}, however,

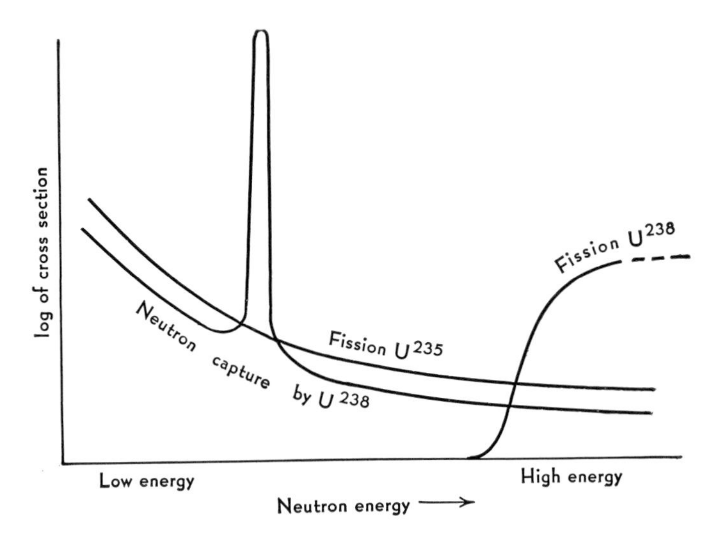

Fig. 19-3. An approximate curve representing the general trend of fission and capture cross sections for uranium.

is of great importance in the production of plutonium (§ 19-8). The curves of Fig. 19-3 show in a general way the variation of capture and fission cross sections of uranium for different neutron energies. The sharp peak of the capture cross-section curve for U^{238} represents the unusually efficient resonance capture (§ 16-17) for neutrons having energies in the neighborhood of 5 ev. The high probability of capture of slow neutrons by U^{235}, and the fact that fission is most likely to result from capture, is what made the slow-neutron nuclear reactor possible.

The capture cross sections of cadmium for neutrons is also of much importance, and it is often as high as many thousands of barns (Fig. 19-5). This means that cadmium can absorb neutrons to a very high degree, thus making it a most useful substance when it is desired to absorb neutrons.

19-6. Energy Release in Fission

Looking back at the curve (Fig. 17-2) for the average binding energy of nucleons in the nucleus, it is seen that the heaviest nuclei have less binding energy per nucleon than the nuclei of middle weight into which they would be split when fission occurs. Consequently the excess of energy over that required by these middle-weight atoms must be released when fission occurs. It was this energy release that Lise Meitner predicted if uranium atoms were found to be split. In U^{235} the actual kinetic energy of the separate particles released in fission has been measured by a delicate calorimetric method and has been found to be about 177 Mev. To this must be added the energy of the emitted gamma rays, amounting to something like 23 Mev. This brings the total close to 200 Mev, as predicted.

If the masses of all the particles before and after fission were known accurately, it would be a simple matter to compute the energy released by converting the loss in mass occurring during fission to energy. For instance, the total mass before fission of U^{238} is the mass of the U^{238} nuclide plus the mass of the neutron that produces the fission. The product nuclei might be krypton ($_{36}Kr^{94}$) and barium ($_{56}Ba^{141}$). Both of these are known to be produced by fission. If the number of neutrons emitted in any particular fission process is known, the total mass after fission would be known, and the energy release can be computed.

19-7. Separation of U^{235}

The scarcity of U^{235} and the great difficulty of separating it from U^{238} caused much concern among scientists, who foresaw the many uses of an atom such as U^{235} which could be split by the absorption of slow neutrons. Since U^{235} is an isotope of U^{238}, it is almost identical in chemical and physical properties. The difficulty of making a separation of the two becomes evident. The methods of separation that were attempted were based on the small difference in mass of U^{238} and U^{235}. This suggested two principal methods of separation. One of these was by some diffusion process in which the less massive atoms would diffuse slightly faster than the more massive ones.

In the process known as gaseous diffusion advantage was taken of the fact that root-mean-square velocities of molecules in a gas vary inversely as the square roots of the masses. Thus the more rapidly moving molecules will diffuse through a porous barrier faster than the less rapidly moving ones. Since the difference in velocities is small the quantity called the separation factor is also small, and an appreciable separation is only obtained by repeating the process over and over in what is called a cascade method.

A somewhat similar process, known as thermal diffusion, makes use of the difference in concentration found at a hot and a cold surface immersed in the gas. The diffusion processes are more complicated than would at first seem. If molecules acted as perfectly elastic spheres, having no forces of interaction other than at the moment of collision, the problem would reduce to a simple mechanical one. However, it is found that in the collision process the transfer of momentum from a light atom to a heavy one, or from a heavy atom to a light one, differs with various types of gases because of the complex nature of the interactions.

A second general method of separation was by magnetic fields. This was actually the method of the mass spectroscope on a large scale. Many units were used, each consisting of a very large magnet and means of accelerating the ions before entering the magnetic field. Since the separation process is a very slow one, amounting at best to only a few micrograms per day in any one machine, a large number of these magnetic separators was necessary.

The slowness of the separation processes, even with enormous batteries of separators, became the chief bottleneck in the production of U^{235} for military purposes during World War II. Also the enormous power requirements to operate these great batteries of separators put a limit on the results to be obtained. It was evident that few nations would have the available power to carry out such operations as the large-scale separation of U^{235} and that the grand scale on which this must be done would hardly make secrecy possible. Imagine then the revolution in viewpoint which occurred when a substitute for U^{235} was found that could be easily separated chemically. It was this which led to the somewhat exaggerated statement that now anyone could make an atom bomb in his own backyard.

19-8. Plutonium

In 1940, for the first time in history, an element was identified that had an atomic number greater than 92. This first transuranic isotope was identified by MacMillan and Abelson and was given the name neptunium, the symbol for which is ${}_{93}Np^{239}$. Fermi was right, after all, about the possibility of producing new elements beyond atomic number 92 by neutron capture; this was also the answer to what happened when a U^{238} atom absorbed a neutron with energy too small to produce fission.

A description of the process by which neptunium is produced follows. A U^{238} nucleus absorbs a neutron, thus increasing the mass number by 1, and becomes U^{239}, a heavier isotope of ordinary uranium. U^{239}, however, is unstable and decays, by beta emission with a half-life of 23 minutes, to the new element neptunium ${}_{93}Np^{239}$. Formation of U^{239} occurs with the emission of gamma rays according to the following reaction:

$${}_{92}U^{238} + {}_{0}n^{1} \longrightarrow {}_{92}U^{239} + \text{gamma rays} \qquad [19\text{-}3]$$

The short half-life of the U^{239} nucleus indicates that it is intensely radioactive. The decay process is

$${}_{92}U^{239} \longrightarrow {}_{93}Np^{239} + {}_{-1}e^{0} \qquad [19\text{-}4]$$

This is the story of the production through man-controlled processes of the new element neptunium, but it is only half the story since the neptunium itself is also strongly radioactive and decays, with a half-life of 2.3 days, to still another new element named plutonium (${}_{94}Pu^{239}$). The decay process here is

$${}_{93}Np^{239} \longrightarrow {}_{94}Pu^{239} + {}_{-1}e^{0} + \text{gamma rays} \qquad [19\text{-}5]$$

It now becomes evident that upon capture of a neutron by a U^{238} nucleus a series of decay processes begins by which plutonium is produced. The plutonium is also radioactive but with a much longer half-life of 25,000 years; consequently, it can be stored for long periods of time. Actually plutonium decays by emission of an alpha particle, thus becoming U^{235}. Most important of all from the practical viewpoint is the fact that plutonium is a different element from uranium and can be readily separated chemically from its parent neptunium and from its grandparent U^{238}. Plutonium, it was found, was in a sense a miracle element because it could be split by slow-neutron absorption, just as U^{235}, and when split it gave a similar, enormous release of energy. Furthermore, it could be produced by transformation of the common U^{238} nucleus. The problem now arose of how to accomplish this transformation on a large scale.

19-9. Nuclear Reactors

Early experiments with fission of uranium involved only harmless, isolated nuclear reactions. It was realized that if energy release were to be obtained on a large scale it would be necessary to search for a means of producing a chain reaction. The search would involve new techniques, and it was not even known whether or not a sustained chain reaction was possible. Worst of all, it might not be possible to control it.

In July, 1941, at Columbia University the first full-scale attempt to produce a chain reaction with fissionable uranium was made under the guidance of Fermi, who had recently moved from Italy to this country. The apparatus was called a **uranium-carbon pile.** It was built in the form of a cube eight feet on a side. The pile contained about 7 tons of uranium oxide in iron containers, and the space between the containers was filled with graphite as a moderator. A radon-beryllium source of neutrons was placed at the bottom of the pile, and arrangements were made to check the operation by measurements of the neutron density at different distances from the source.

The graphite, a very pure form of carbon, as a moderator was to reduce the speed from fast to slow of the neutrons emitted in the fission process. An extremely pure form of carbon was required to avoid absorption of neutrons by impurities, and since carbon nuclei are already in a very stable form, composed of pairs of neutrons and protons, it was expected that there would be little loss of neutrons by absorption in the graphite. Since the object of this atomic pile was to test the possibility of a chain reaction it was desired to slow the neutrons down sufficiently so that they would be absorbed more strongly by U^{235} than by the U^{238} atoms which might absorb them without undergoing fission.

When operation of the Columbia University pile was attempted it was found that a considerable amount of fission was obtained with a proportionate release of energy, but the pile would only operate so long as neutrons from the outside were injected into it to produce more fission. Instead of forming a self-sustaining chain reaction it behaved more like a fuse or explosive, which after being lighted fizzles out and has to be relighted. Apparently either not enough U^{235} was present to sustain the fission process, or else too many neutrons produced in the fission process were lost in one way or another without continuing to produce successive fissions. The experiment did serve as a basis for a more effective design soon to be followed at the University of Chicago.

On December 2, 1942, the first self-sustaining atomic pile was put into operation under the west stand of the University of Chicago athletic field. Considerable trepidation was felt over the possibility that the chain process, if it proved to be effective, might run away with itself and release energy with explosive violence. Provisions for the control of the process had been carefully worked out, but no one could be absolutely sure ahead of time that they would be effective. Later all experimentation was transferred to a less thickly populated region at Lemont, Ill., at what is now the Argonne National Laboratory.

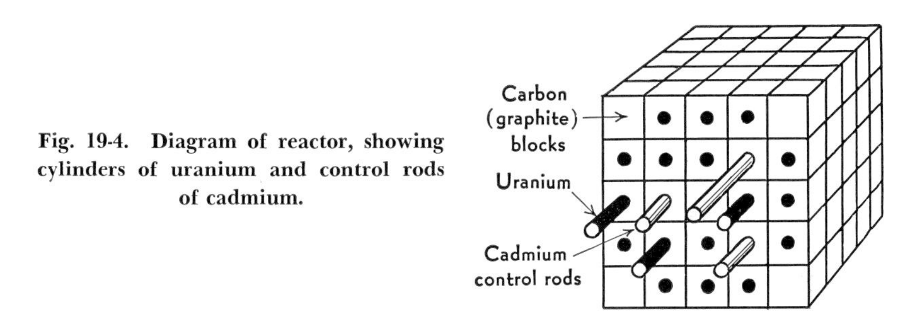

Fig. 19-4. Diagram of reactor, showing cylinders of uranium and control rods of cadmium.

The method of control for this atomic pile (Fig. 19-4) was that of inserting a number of bars of cadmium into the pile. Cadmium strongly absorbs neutrons, particularly those of low energy (Fig. 19-5), and with the bars pushed into the pile there would not be enough neutrons to sustain the chain reaction. It was hoped that, by pulling the bars out, a point would be reached where the chain reaction would become self-sustaining, and also that it would grow at such a rate as to be controllable by further moving the bars in or out. As a matter of fact, if all neutrons in the fission process had been emitted promptly the atomic pile would probably have run away. The saving feature was that, although the delayed neutrons emitted in the fission process are not many in number, they are sufficient to give time to control the process. Of course, if anything should go wrong with the control sys-

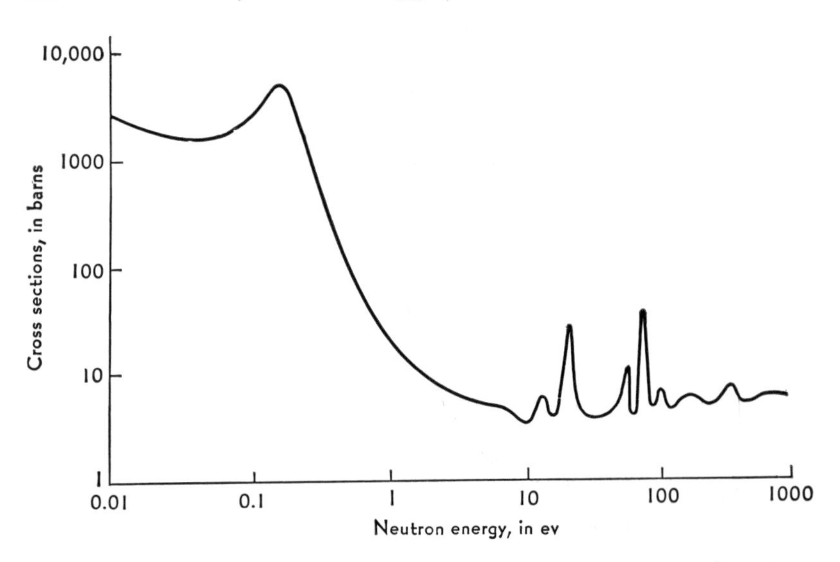

Fig. 19-5. Capture cross sections of cadmium for neutrons. Peaks represent resonance capture, and curve shows the very-high-capture probability of cadmium for slow neutrons.

tem a run-away chain reaction would occur, and if a violent explosion did not take place at the least the pile would probably destroy itself with much danger and damage. Something like this actually happened some years later at the Chalk River Laboratory in Canada.

The success of the Chicago atomic pile or reactor, as such devices are now called, led to the development of reactors on a larger scale at Oak Ridge, Tenn., in the great government project there. When it became evident, with the discovery of plutonium, that such a pile could serve to produce plutonium on a large scale, the Hanford, Wash., plant on the Columbia River was built for that purpose, and the production of fissionable plutonium became a large-scale operation.

19-10. Elementary Theory of Nuclear Reactor

The basic problem in the design of a nuclear reactor can be put very simply. It is to so design the apparatus that the number of neutrons present after those injected have been lost or absorbed will be larger than the number originally injected by at least a small amount. Then the process will become self-sustaining and will continue to grow. The increase or decrease in number is represented by a multiplication factor or reproduction factor k. If k is greater than 1 the number of neutrons in the pile constantly increases, and the process is not only self-sustaining but self-increasing and would run away if it were not limited by suitable controls. If k is less than 1 the number of neutrons in the pile constantly decreases unless more are supplied from the outside. For constant operation at a given level the average value of k for that level must be unity.

To better understand the meaning of the multiplication factor and what it represents, it may best be broken up into four separate factors representing the four chief processes that occur. Assume that only fast neutrons are present in a reactor, as, for instance, in a uranium carbon pile. A few of them may produce fission in U^{238} nuclei before being slowed down. The additional neutrons lead to an increase in the total number by a factor ν, which may have a value in the neighborhood of 1.03. There are now $N_0 \nu$ neutrons. These are slowed down by passing through the graphite moderator, but some of them will be lost from the original beam in resonance capture by U^{238} without producing fission. This will occur before they are slowed down enough to avoid capture. To avoid capture they must be slowed down to energies less than 5 ev, and this means many collisions with atoms of the moderator. Let p represent the fraction thus slowed down that escape resonance capture. The active beam now consists of $N_0 \nu p$ slow neutrons. Assume that of these a fraction f succeed in producing fission in U^{235} nuclei, the remainder being lost, perhaps by escape from the pile or by absorption in impurities or in the moderator itself. The number of neutrons thus producing fission in U^{235} is $N_0 \nu p f$. Now assume that, for each fission in U^{235}, ϵ fast neutrons on the average are produced. The total number then becomes, after one cycle or one generation in the reproductive process,

$$N = N_0 \nu p f \epsilon \qquad [19\text{-}6]$$

The quantity k, the multiplication factor, is defined as

$$k = \nu p f \epsilon \qquad [19\text{-}7]$$

The basic problem in the design of a reactor is to choose just the right amounts of uranium (including the richness in U^{235}) and of the moderator, and to so arrange these geometrically that k will be as large as possible even though it may never be much greater than 1. Estimates for the original Columbia University pile showed that k would most probably be less than unity. Consequently it was hardly expected that this pile would become self-sustaining in action. However, by measurement of the neutron flux at different distances from the point where fast neutrons were injected at the bottom of the pile, estimates could be made of the actual value of k. This information made it possible to design the Chicago reactor and later reactors to achieve k greater than 1.

The first atomic pile at Columbia University was called an exponential pile because it was found that the neutron density decreased exponentially with increasing distance from the neutron source. This type of exponential decrease (or increase) should be distinguished from the exponential way in which neutron density may increase with the time when the action of the pile is growing. Theory shows that the density of thermal neutrons in a reactor may be expressed by the formula

$$N = N_0 \epsilon^{\rho t/\tau} \tag{19-8}$$

where N_0 is the density of thermal neutrons injected into the pile or the density in the pile just at the start of a chain reaction. The quantity τ is the mean lifetime of a neutron in the pile, and ρ (defined as $\rho = k - 1$) represents the fractional increase or decrease in the number of neutrons in one neutron generation. If ρ represents a decrease in neutron density it is a negative quantity, and if it represents an increase it is a positive quantity. Consequently the number of neutrons grows or decays exponentially with time depending upon ρ. When ρ is zero the exponential term in the formula is unity, and a steady state is reached.

Since the average lifetime of a thermal neutron in such a pile is in the neighborhood of a thousandth of a second, even though ρ may be only a few parts in a thousand positive, the neutron density can build up at an enormous rate. A catastrophe would thereby result if control

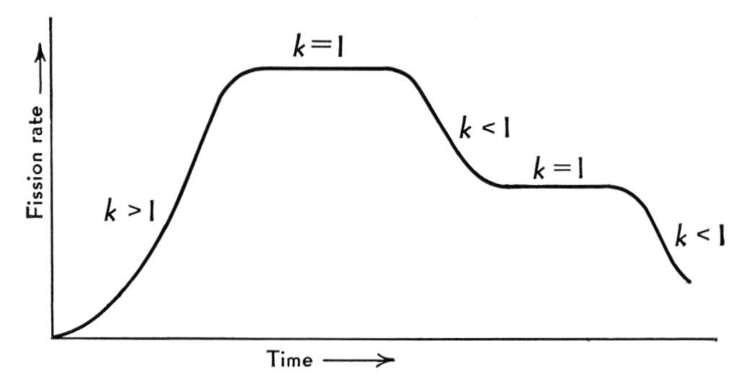

Fig. 19-6. Curve illustrating control of power generated in a nuclear reactor. With control rods in, k is less than 1; with rods out it is greater than 1. For steady operation the rods are set for $k = 1$.

rods could not be moved fast enough to prevent a run-away reaction. However, it is here that the importance of delayed neutrons enters. Although less than 1 per cent of the neutrons are delayed, the delay in seconds is sufficient to enable control of the pile to be accomplished.

It should be pointed out that while an atomic reactor is working at a given power level there is no further increase in the production rate of neutrons, that is, no multiplication, and ρ equals zero. Thus no multiplication occurs at a constant power level, no matter what that particular power level is. Only when the control bars are pulled out does ρ become greater than zero and the action increases; only if they are pushed in does ρ become less than zero and the action decreases (Fig. 19-6). The critical point is where ρ is just zero or $k = 1$. Strange as it may seem, if a pile were to be too efficient it would be difficult to control, and if the design were such that ρ approached a value of 10 parts in 1000 the pile would become supercritical on prompt neutrons and consequently would be unmanageable.

Critical size An atomic reactor has what is called a critical size. In the reactor, if the dimensions are too small, too many neutrons may escape from the surface by diffusion without producing fission. Although a reactor may be surrounded by a poor neutron absorber which may behave to a certain extent as a reflector of neutrons, nevertheless some will always escape through the surface. Critical size then depends upon the ratio of surface to volume. By an increase in the volume a point is reached where the ratio of surface to volume is small enough so that surface losses do not prevent the reactor from operating. This is the critical size.

In determining the critical size of a reactor (or a bomb) an important quantity is an "average path distance," called the diffusion length L. It depends on the average distance l_c that the neutron travels from its source between collisions with a nucleus and the average distance l_a that it travels before it is absorbed. The first distance may be only a few centimeters, whereas the average distance that a neutron travels before it is absorbed may be a thousand or more centimeters. L is defined as

$$L = \sqrt{\frac{l_c l_a}{3}} \qquad [19\text{-}9]$$

Theory indicates that under ideal conditions the critical radius r of a spherical reactor is approximated by the relation

$$r = \frac{\pi L}{\sqrt{k - 1}} \qquad [19\text{-}10]$$

where k is the neutron multiplication factor of the system. This formula indicates that the critical radius varies directly as the diffusion length L but that an increase in the multiplication factor would decrease the critical radius. For carbon L has been computed to be in the neighborhood of 20 to 30 cm.

A complete theory of reactors must include many factors such as the concentration of the U^{235} in the uranium. With a high concentration of U^{235} and only a small total amount of uranium, the total volume is small and the surface area may be too large with respect to the volume. When all factors are suitably balanced, theory indicates that in the ideal circumstance of a spherical reactor the critical radius can be considerably less than 100 cm. In this volume, along with the moderator, there should be at least 10 or 12 pounds of U^{235}.

19-11. Types of Reactors

Heterogeneous and homogeneous reactors Nuclear reactors may be classified in several ways. The type of reactor discussed so far is called a heterogeneous reactor because the fissionable material and the moderator are not uniformly mixed together but are in separate elements such as blocks, lumps, or cylinders. If the fissionable material and the moderator are in finely divided form and are uniformly mixed together the reactor is called a homogeneous one.

Most reactors have been of the heterogeneous type. For one thing, when the first reactors were built only natural uranium was available, and a homogeneous reactor with graphite as a moderator will not work because too many neutrons fail to produce fission. Indeed, it is now known that a homogeneous reactor with natural uranium will work only if heavy water is used as the moderator. However, heavy water in the quantities required is not only scarce but also expensive. Other moderators may be successful only if the natural uranium is enriched with U^{235} or plutonium.

Moderators Graphite is not the nearest to an ideal substance for a moderator, and heavy water has certain advantages. It is better than carbon in slowing down neutrons because of the presence of lighter nuclei. Heavy water contains heavy hydrogen or hydrogen already loaded with neutrons so that the likelihood of further absorption is very small. The oxygen in heavy water, like carbon, consists of closed groups of neutrons and protons and consequently has a very low absorption coefficient for neutrons. The use of heavy water as a

Fig. 19-7. One face of the Brookhaven reactor, showing holes through which cylinders of uranium and control rods may be inserted into the graphite moderator. Through the holes may also be inserted substances to be irradiated by neutrons generated in the reactor. The technician, who is shielded by 5 feet of concrete in front of him, is making observations on the manipulation of radioactive material in the reactor by remote control. (Courtesy, Brookhaven National Laboratory, Upton, N. Y.)

moderator at the Argonne Laboratory in 1944 showed that the effective size of a reactor could be greatly reduced, and a larger heavy-water pile was later built at the Chalk River Laboratory in Canada. An enriched uranium-water (ordinary water) reactor has been built at Los Alamos, N. M.

Reactors may also be classified according to whether they operate by slow-neutron fission in the manner just described or by fast-neutron fission. If the uranium is sufficiently enriched with U^{235} or plutonium, the moderator may be dispensed with and the reactor operates by fast-neutron fission. One such "fast reactor" has been built and operated at Los Alamos, N. M.

The purposes which reactors serve form another basis for classification. Some are purely for research purposes, and their number throughout the country is rapidly increasing. Reactors for producing plutonium from uranium are called production reactors. On the other hand, power reactors are designed to supply energy for heat, light, power, and transportation. The first of this kind was used in the atom-powered submarine.

The Atomic Energy Commission has put into action a broad program of reactor construction and study. An experimental breeder reactor in Idaho has been put into operation with the objective of solving one of the most important problems in connection with the utilization of atomic energy. Since the operation of a nuclear reactor depends upon fissionable material such as U^{235} or plutonium, the problem is being studied of how to use either of these in a reactor and at the same time breed as much as, or more than, the amount consumed. The production of fissionable material, by breeding or otherwise, is of utmost importance because of the limited natural resources. Solving the problem of nuclear fuel production would bring about a revolution in world-wide power distribution and utilization.

The scarcity of U^{235} puts a limiting value on the production of atomic energy. A much greater abundance of U^{238} makes it desirable to find ways of converting as much U^{238} into plutonium as possible. There is also the possibility of using thorium. Thorium is several times as abundant as uranium, and if found in ores sufficiently rich to be commercially useful it would be possible to produce fissionable material from thorium. Th^{232} can serve to produce U^{233}, and U^{233} undergoes fission with the release of a large amount of energy in the same way as does U^{235}. Th^{232} absorbs neutrons, and by two successive beta emissions forms U^{233}, which is a fairly stable isotope and could be of great value.

Another government reactor in Idaho is designed to give high-intensity neutron beams with which to study the properties of various materials. These studies will involve neutron diffraction, neutron scattering, and other properties.

19-12. Nuclear Power

The more immediate peacetime uses of atomic energy include chiefly the production of power from nuclear reactors especially designed for that purpose, the propulsion of ships and perhaps rockets, and the production of intense neutron beams. The neutron beams may be used directly for research, or they may help to produce a variety of radioactive products, some for tracer studies in biophysical and physiological research, and some as substitutes for the rare, naturally radioactive elements.

In the development of power the operation of a nuclear reactor must be so adapted that the heat produced can be utilized and little lost. In the Hanford plant the object was to obtain plutonium for military purposes, and the Columbia River was at hand to carry away the tremendous amount of heat liberated. This energy was, of course, lost. In the efficient utilization of the thermal energy of fission, an extremely important problem is that of developing heat-resistant materials for the construction of atomic "furnaces" and heat exchangers. The satisfactory operation of nuclear reactors to produce electricity has been demonstrated, and such plants are now being built rapidly to furnish heat, light, and power. As the scale of this development increases, large reactors may furnish central power and at the same time breed atoms for smaller reactors around the country. Engineering study and developments in this direction are now embraced in the new field of nuclear engineering.

Plasma fusion of hydrogen In the usual type of nuclear reactor, energy is released by fission of uranium or a similar "fuel." However, our bountiful resources of hydrogen offer far greater potentialities in the release of energy by the *fusion* of hydrogen nuclei into heavier nuclei (§ 17-3) than by *fission* of heavy nuclei. This means, in effect, "slowing down" the action of a hydrogen bomb, or more exactly it means utilizing a source of sufficiently high temperature in such a way that fusion can proceed at a controlled rate. Experiments in which the plasma of an electric discharge (§ 4-9) is made exceedingly intense have achieved important results. When the plasma of an electric discharge carries a very large current, it tends to contract in cross section because of electromagnetic attraction between charges moving in the same direction. This contraction is called the *pinch effect,* and it may produce very high pressures and temperatures of a million or more degrees Centigrade. The possibilities of using these properties to produce continuous fusion of hydrogen resulting in the liberation of almost unlimited amounts of energy is one of the exciting fields of research today.

19-13. Poisoning of Reactors and Radioactive Waste

After reactors have been in operation for some time the fissionable materials gradually become exhausted, and the percentage of byproducts increases to such a point that the efficiency of the reactor is reduced. If the process were carried much further the reactor would stop operation altogether. The cylinders of uranium must then be removed from the reactor and put through a chemical clean-up process, after which they are enriched with more fissionable material. In a large reactor, automatic means are employed to remove the various units at specified times, and by remote control they are cleaned up, reloaded with fissionable material, and returned to the reactor.

The problem of what to do with the radioactive waste from nuclear reactors to prevent ultimate widespread contamination is a very serious one, for which there is as yet no good solution. The problem will become graver as more reactors are built and as reactors for commercial power, heat, and light become more common. The waste could be buried in some remote spot, or it could be sealed in noncorrosive cylinders and sunk in the ocean, but there are drawbacks even to these measures. One solution of the problem would be to put the material into a rocket and fire it into interstellar space, but that would be a difficult and costly operation.

19-14. Nuclear Bombs: the A-Bomb and the H-Bomb

The problem of constructing an atomic or nuclear bomb was successfully solved under the auspices of the Manhattan Project during the latter part of World War II. The bomb that was exploded over Hiroshima on August 6, 1945, was direct evidence before the whole world of the success of the project. This bomb was roughly estimated as having the power of 20,000 tons of TNT and a radius of destruction of approximately 1 mile. Since that time bombs have been made and tested that are far more efficient and more powerful, and they are rated as high as 15 or 20 or more millions of tons (megatons) of high explosive rather than in thousands of tons.

The A-bomb It is beyond the scope of this textbook to do more than mention some basic problems involved in the production of the uranium-plutonium bomb, called the A-bomb. The bomb in a sense is a run-away reactor operating on somewhat different design principles. To be effective as an explosive it must reach maximum liberation of energy in a small fraction of a second. The critical size for this type of action had to be carefully determined, and a mechanism for detonating the bomb had to be devised. Although the "trigger" mechanism was one of the top secrets of World War II, it became evident soon after the war that it was only necessary to bring two or more separate portions of subcritical size together very quickly to form a critical mass which could then immediately be exploded. Indeed, it would probably be triggered by a cosmic ray if more positive methods were not applied. The subcritical masses could be brought together quickly by blowing them together with a small amount of ordinary explosive. That such bombs may now be made of relatively small size is witnessed by the released information that they have been adapted for the war-heads of shells for large-caliber guns.

The chief effects of a nuclear explosion are: (1) the intense heat, forming thermal waves traveling with the speed of light, causing fatal burns and great damage due to fires; (2) the mechanical shock wave, consisting of a blast of air pressure which in itself could produce death and destruction; (3) radioactivity of the fission products, themselves not only poisonous but emitting dangerous radiations of gamma and other rays.

The H-bomb The second phase of nuclear bomb production came with the development of the hydrogen bomb or H-bomb, which operates on the principle of nuclear fusion. Fission bombs and fusion bombs must be carefully distinguished. **Fission** is the process by which heavy nuclei are split to form nuclei of intermediate mass. **Fusion** is the process of combining light nuclei to form those of larger mass. The large, available energy surplus when heavier atoms are formed by fusion out of the lightest atoms has been mentioned (§ 17-3) and can be realized from examination of Fig. 17-2.

The fusion of hydrogen and other light elements to form heavier elements is possible only at extremely high temperatures and pressures such as occur in the stars. These are approached in an A-bomb explosion, and it is presumed that the hydrogen bomb requires an A-bomb for its starter. There are various possibilities of energy release by fusion, depending upon the type of light atoms used; for instance, favorable reactions might be obtained with ordinary hydrogen, or heavy hydrogen, or the still heavier H^3 atom known as tritium. Lithium has also been suggested. The energies to be released and the speeds of the reactions have been carefully computed. Such details need not concern us here since much is yet a military secret, but it is widely understood that important simplifying discoveries have been made.

Whereas in the case of the A-bomb there is a minimum critical size and also a maximum critical size, in the H-bomb or fusion bomb there is no critical upper limit. The intense fusion flame, on being started, can spread through any amount of material. Thus the destructiveness of the A-bomb may be far surpassed by the H-bomb. It is one of the misfortunes of human existence that scientific discoveries are often as available for man's destruction as for his advancement, but it should be pointed out that man alone is responsible for how these forces are used. Now that he has these forces at his disposal, it is up to him to control them.

19-15. Heat of the Stars and the Carbon Cycle

Before the twentieth century all theories of the origin of the sun's heat and the heat of the stars were woefully inadequate. The discovery of radioactivity revealed a source of energy which had previously been unknown, but even this seemed scarcely adequate to account for the enormous amounts of energy involved. With the discovery of the large-scale release of atomic energy the answer seemed to be given. It became easy to say that the heat of the stars and the sun comes from fusion of complex atoms from lighter atoms, that the center of a star is a giant furnace operating at extremely high pressure and temperature, and that thus fusion can occur. Nevertheless, such general statements lacked the definiteness required of a true scientific theory.

Finally a definite series of nuclear reactions was suggested by Bethe, called the carbon cycle. This seemed at least to be one of the most probable ways in which nuclear energy is released from the sun and the stars. The process involves carbon nuclei and hydrogen nuclei, helium being formed in the process and the carbon acting as a kind of catalyzer. The series of reactions is given as follows:

$$_6C^{12} + {}_1H^1 \rightarrow ({}_7N^{13}) \rightarrow {}_6C^{13} + {}_{+1}e^0 \quad [19\text{-}11]$$

$$_6C^{13} + {}_1H^1 \rightarrow {}_7N^{14} \quad [19\text{-}12]$$

$$_7N^{14} + {}_1H^1 \rightarrow ({}_8O^{15}) \rightarrow {}_7N^{15} + {}_{+1}e^0 \quad [19\text{-}13]$$

$$_7N^{15} + {}_1H^1 \rightarrow ({}_8O^{16}) \rightarrow C^{12} + He^4 \quad [19\text{-}14]$$

In effect the carbon nucleus captures four successive protons. After first ejecting two positrons, the four remaining particles group themselves together as an alpha particle, which is then thrown off by the compound nucleus leaving carbon as at the start of the cycle. By this process the sun (or a star) is no longer merely an incandescent mass which is gradually cooling off; indeed, it may retain a fairly constant temperature for a long period of time, or its temperature may even rise.

The only requirement, for the temperature to remain constant, is that the stellar object consume sufficient mass every day to release energy equal to that lost by radiation in the same length of time. The sun, for instance, could apparently retain its temperature constant by a decrease in mass of about 400 million tons per second. However, the total mass of the sun is so large that even at this rate it would take about 1 million million years (10^{12}) for the sun to use up 1/16 of its mass. More recently, the carbon cycle of Bethe has been modified by suggestions from other scientists, but generally some such process is believed to account for stellar and solar heat.

PROBLEMS

1. Compute the energy in ergs equivalent to one atomic mass unit (1 amu). Convert this to electron volts.

Ans. 1.49×10^{-3} erg; 931 Mev.

2. How many fissions per second of U^{235}, each releasing 200-Mev energy, would be required to give 100 kilowatts of power?

Ans. 3.12×10^{15}.

3. Assuming that a nuclear bomb could be made of 100 lb of uranium, what could be the minimum diameter of a sphere to contain the active material if the density of uranium is 1164 lb/ft^3?

Ans. 6.56 in.

4. One pound of coal may be converted into 1.25 kwh of electric energy in a power plant. Find approximately how many tons of coal will give the same energy as that given by the complete fission of 1 gram of U^{235}.

Ans. 9.1 tons.

5. If all the energy equivalent of an ice cube having a mass of 100 gm could be liberated, what distance in kilometers could a 10,000-metric-ton submarine be propelled if all retarding forces were lumped together to give a coefficient of friction of 0.01?

Ans. 9.2×10^6 km.

6. Find three pairs of atoms, any pair of which U^{235} might likely form by fission after absorbing a neutron. Write the symbols for the reactions, assuming that 3 neutrons are emitted at each fission.

7. If the neutron flux from an atomic pile is 10^{12} neutrons/cm^2 sec, how does it compare in intensity with a cyclotron beam of deuterons of 10 microamperes (μa)/cm^2?

Ans. 1.6×10^{-2} times less intense.

8. If a nuclear bomb contains 100 kg of U^{235} and if 0.001 of the atoms undergoes fission in 0.001 sec, what is the approximate horsepower of the bomb if an energy of 200 Mev is released per fission?

Ans. 1.1×10^{13} hp.

9. If the average binding energy of the nucleons in the products of fission of U^{238} is 8.7 Mev and if the average binding energy of the nucleons before fission is 7.8 Mev, find the expected energy release due to fission. (Assume 3 neutrons are emitted in fission.)

Ans. 188 Mev.

10. Can fission occur spontaneously when a U^{235}-atom of mass 235.11392 absorbs a neutron of mass 1.00898 with zero kinetic energy? (Take the mass of the U^{236}-atom (compound nucleus) to be 236.11559 and the energy required for fission of U^{236} to be 6 Mev.)

Ans. Yes; 0.00726 amu or 6.8 Mev is available for fission.

11. Electric power production in the U. S. is approximately 100 million kilowatts. If operated at 100 per cent efficiency, 36 gm of U^{235} will give 100 kw for 1 year. How many tons per year of U^{235} are required to supply all needs if conversion to power is at an over-all efficiency of 30 per cent?

Ans. 132 tons.

12. Approximately how many tons of radioactive fission products would be produced in 1 year under the conditions of problem 11? How would you suggest that these dangerous products should be disposed of?

13. Find the critical radius of a spherical uranium-carbon reactor for which the diffusion length is 20 cm and the neutron multiplication factor is 1.16.

Ans. 157 cm.

14. In order to design a chain-reacting device having a critical diameter of 30 cm with a multiplication factor of 1.25, what will be the maximum average distance that a neutron can travel before being absorbed if the average radial collision distance is 1 cm?

Ans. 17 cm.

SUGGESTED READING

G. Gamow, *Atomic Energy in Cosmic and Human Life* (New York, Macmillan, 1947).

E. Pollard and W. L. Davidson, *Applied Nuclear Physics*, 2nd ed. (New York, Wiley, 1951).

H. D. Smyth, *Atomic Energy for Military Purposes* (Princeton, Princeton Univ. Press, 1945).

S. Glasstone and M. C. Edlund, *The Elements of Nuclear Reactor Theory* (New York, Van Nostrand, 1952).

S. Glasstone, *Source Book on Atomic Energy*, 2nd ed. (Princeton, Van Nostrand, 1958).

CHAPTER 20

COSMIC RAYS AND NEW PARTICLES

20-1. What Are Cosmic Rays?

The earth is being continually bombarded from all directions by high-energy rays, called cosmic rays, coming from outer space. They pass into our atmosphere where they produce many secondary rays, a large number of which reach the surface of the earth. Many are far more penetrating than even the most penetrating man-made rays. Their discovery and study date from the early part of this century when their penetrating nature was first recognized. Although at the time they seemed to be of minor importance, their study has now led to many important discoveries, including that of the positron or positive electron and those of the various new particles, known as mesons and hyperons.

Great scientific interest and much speculation have been aroused as to the origin of these rays, and ingenious suggestions have been made as to the mechanism by which they may be produced with such high energies either from the sun or from more distant sources. Perhaps no portion of physical science has attracted so many investigators all over the world, and the rapid expansion of the field has been phenomenal. Now we recognize the study of cosmic rays as one of special interest, with its results bearing on the nature of matter, in addition to more general implications regarding the nature of physical processes throughout our universe.

20-2. Discovery and Early History of Cosmic Rays

The study of cosmic rays sprang from a very small beginning near the turn of the century, when C. T. R. Wilson and also Elster and Geitel found a small unaccountable leakage of charge in an electroscope which had been carefully insulated. The leakage was more than could be accounted for by any imperfection in the insulation. It appeared to be due to ions formed by some penetrating radiation.

At first it was thought that the radiation came from radioactive material distributed throughout the earth's surface. Yet an amount of shielding that would in effect cut off the rays from all known radioactive substances did not cut off this penetrating radiation, and some of the early experiments by McLennan and Burton in Toronto showed that many of the rays could penetrate a thick brick wall or as much as 18 feet of water. At this time the rays were not dignified by the name *cosmic rays,* but were simply called "an extremely penetrating radiation."

In 1910 experimentation took a different direction. Gockel in Germany ascended to an elevation of 14,000 feet in a balloon and found to his surprise that the intensity of the radiation did not decrease with elevation, as would be expected if the rays came from the earth; if anything they seemed to increase. The next year Hess in Austria and later Kohlhörster in Germany took instruments up in balloons to much higher altitudes and found the intensity of the unknown rays to be as much as 10 times that at the surface of the earth. This increase of intensity with increasing altitude was detected by means of sensitive electroscopes, which showed a greater leakage of charge with increased altitude. Hess then proposed the new theory that the rays originated from somewhere outside the earth's atmosphere. This bold suggestion led to the award to Hess of a share of the Nobel prize in 1936 for the "discovery of cosmic rays."

The name *cosmic rays* was given to this penetrating radiation by Robert A. Millikan whose fertile mind had also led him, as we have seen, to studies of the electron and of the photoelectric effect, and who began the study of these rays shortly after World War I. Millikan soon became one of the most active and productive workers in the new field, and in 1922 Millikan and Bowen undertook a series of experiments with small sounding balloons which could be sent higher than the previous passenger balloons. In that year they reached an altitude of

50,000 feet, which was later greatly exceeded. The sounding balloons carried extremely sensitive electroscopes, together with suitable recording apparatus weighing as little as half a pound, which would record the cosmic-ray intensity at different elevations. The instruments and recorded data were recovered after having been floated back to earth by means of parachutes. They found that the higher their balloons went the more intense became the rays. Later measurements at still higher altitudes (§ 20-5) further confirmed Hess's theory that the origin of the rays must be somewhere outside the earth's atmosphere.

Millikan and his coworkers also investigated the energies of the rays by measuring their penetration into water. In order to avoid possible contamination from radioactive material in the earth's surface, they sank electroscopes deep in the water of snow-fed lakes high in the mountains. Some radiation was found to penetrate as much as 150 feet of water. This indicated that the more penetrating rays must have energies of a billion electron volts or more, far greater than any other then-known type of radiation.

At that time the great penetrating power of cosmic rays made it appear that the incoming rays were probably of the same nature as x-rays or gamma rays, only far more energetic and penetrating. In 1930, however, Arthur H. Compton began to organize an intensive study of cosmic rays, and he and Millikan independently made extensive surveys at many places on the earth's surface, from near the equator to near the poles, and from sea level to the high mountain tops. Evidence now began to accumulate that the incoming rays were not gamma rays, as had been believed by Millikan, but that they were chiefly positively charged particles. This view was supported by Compton and others and was to receive confirmation later.

Soon the cloud chamber began to supplement electroscope measurements. With the help of the cloud chamber the effects of individual rays could be studied, and the observed tracks indicated the presence of high-speed electrons. However, high-speed electrons could hardly account for the extreme penetrating power of cosmic rays. As it later turned out the electrons were not actually primary rays coming in from outside the atmosphere but secondaries formed in the atmosphere itself. About this time it became possible to distinguish between two principal components of cosmic rays. The less penetrating (soft) component was identified as chiefly electrons, whereas the more penetrating (hard) component, thought perhaps to be primaries, was then unexplained.

The mystery of the more penetrating cosmic rays remained until after 1937 when the first evidence was found, in cloud-chamber studies, of the existence of particles intermediate in mass between that of a proton and an electron. The evidence was obtained by Street and Stevenson at Harvard University, and by Anderson and Neddermeyer at the California Institute of Technology. This was the same Anderson who had previously discovered the positive electron. The possibility that these new particles might account for at least a part of the hard component of cosmic rays was in agreement with theoretical studies which indicated that heavy particles (even as heavy as protons) of extremely high energy, traveling with velocities close to that of light, could have extremely great penetrating power.

Out of the complexity of observed data and conflicting theories, it finally became evident that the incoming primary rays are mostly protons with a few nuclei of heavier atoms also present. Gamma rays, however, may be produced by these particles as they enter the earth's atmosphere and must be classed along with other secondary rays. The complexity of the subject and its many aspects make it desirable to discuss a number of the phenomena in more detail.

20-3. Means of Detecting Cosmic Rays

The chief means of detecting cosmic rays are: (1) sensitive types of electroscopes; (2) ionization chambers (§ 14-10); (3) the Wilson cloud chamber (§ 14-13); (4) the bubble chamber (see this section); (5) the Geiger-Müller tube (§ 14-11); (6) scintillation counters (§ 14-12); (7) the Cherenkov counter (§ 20-13); (8) the type of photographic plate coated with what is called a nuclear emulsion (§ 20-11).

Neher and other ingenious experimenters have devised very sensitive types of electroscopes for cosmic-ray measurements at high altitudes. They are extremely light in weight, compact, and self-recording. In one form, to be sent up with small sounding balloons (Fig. 20-1),

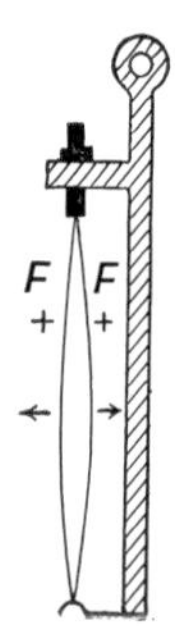

Fig. 20-1. One type of sensitive electroscope for cosmic-ray measurements, to be carried to high altitudes by small balloons. Two gold-plated quartz fibers *F*, *F* repel each other when similarly charged. The separation at different altitudes can be recorded on moving photographic film, and from this the rate of change of separation can be obtained.

two very delicate quartz fibers, plated with gold to make them conducting, were substituted for the usual gold leaves. The fibers when similarly charged repel each other, as indicated. The separation of the fibers gradually decreases as the charge escapes. The rate of decrease measures the intensity of the ionizing radiation that is present. The separation of the fibers at successive intervals of time may be recorded on photographic film wound around a small cylinder and made to rotate by means of clockwork.

Compton put electroscopes on ocean-going vessels to obtain a record of cosmic-ray intensities at different latitudes. The electroscopes were enclosed in airtight containers, the pressure of the air being increased to as much as 30 atmospheres in order to render residual effects of contamination less important. In making measurements near the surface of the earth, such an apparatus is usually shielded with lead of 10-cm thickness or more in order to reduce the effects of rays from radioactive substances to a negligible amount.

The ionization chamber (§ 14-10) frequently serves to measure the total ionization produced by a group of rays such as are present in what is called a shower.

The cloud chamber has been indispensable in the study of cosmic rays, especially when combined with a large magnet to produce bending of the paths in the cloud chamber. This not only enables positive and negative particles to be distinguished, but from the curvature of the path or rather from the Br value (§ 20-7) the momentum of the particle can be obtained. The early horizontal type of cloud chamber was of little value in cosmic-ray study, and a different form with bellows or piston expansion was invented for operation with face vertical, as described earlier (Fig. 2-2). Many of its applications have already been mentioned (§ 14-13).

A new and interesting modification of the conventional type of cloud chamber has been developed recently. It is called a *bubble chamber,* and it is filled with liquid propane. When high-energy charged cosmic-ray particles, or particles from an accelerator, pass through the propane they leave tracks in the form of a series of bubbles which may readily be observed or photographed. Neutrons and neutrinos do not leave visible tracks. Many studies of the newer particles are now being made by means of this device.

The Geiger-Müller tube with a suitable circuit for registering counts of cosmic rays is an extremely versatile instrument and serves many purposes, particularly when a large number of tubes is involved. The special value of both the cloud chamber and the G-M tube, as previously mentioned, and also the bubble chamber, is that each responds to individual rays whereas the electroscope and the ionization chamber give only an average value of the intensity over a period of time.

An important application of the G-M tubes is in the controlled expansion of a cloud chamber. In early experiments with cloud chambers, many expansions were produced at the wrong time because the operator did not know whether or not a cosmic ray had entered the chamber. In 1933 Blackett and Occhialini put the cloud chamber between two G-M tubes and arranged the tubes electrically, so that a switch would be operated only when an ionizing ray passed through both tubes and the cloud chamber between them. Closing the switch then produced an expansion. Thus a cosmic ray would in effect notify the apparatus when it was time to take its own picture, or rather the picture of its own track.

Two or more G-M tubes are said to be connected in **coincidence** when the circuit is so arranged that there is no response unless the cosmic ray goes through all the tubes. Two tubes arranged in coincidence, as in Fig. 20-2, may serve to form what is called a cosmic-ray telescope. A ray passing through one tube only is not counted. Incident rays coming within the angle θ pass through both tubes and are counted. With this kind of device it has been possible to scan the sky to try to find directions of greater or lesser intensity. Although some general variations in intensity have been found, such as the variation with latitude and the east-west effect, there is no evidence of a preferred

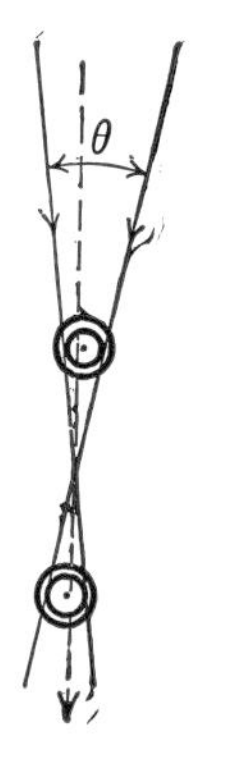

Fig. 20-2. Two G-M tubes connected in coincidence form a directional detector or "telescope." Any ray falling within the angle θ will pass through both G-M tubes and be recorded.

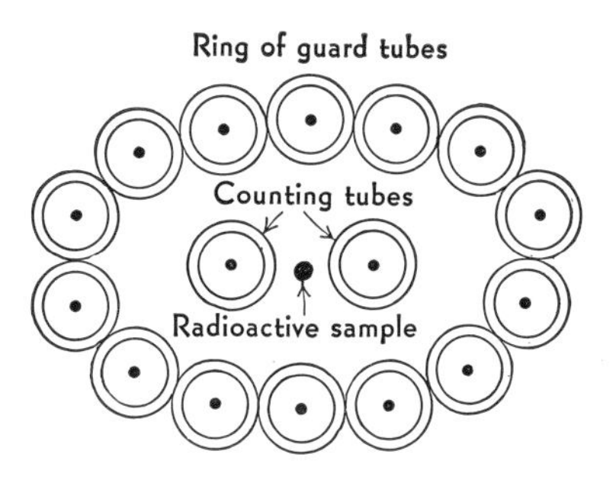

Fig. 20-3. Simplified arrangement of G-M tubes for counting rays from a weak source. Guard tubes are connected in anticoincidence, so that rays from outside passing through a guard tube are not counted.

direction in space which could be considered the direction of the source of cosmic rays (§ 20-6).

During the early days of the G-M tubes in the study of cosmic rays much could be done with only a few tubes. However, today the tubes are often combined, involving as many as 100 tubes or more. Another method of connecting tubes of great importance is called **anticoincidence.** For instance, two tubes may be connected in such a way that counts are registered only when a cosmic ray goes through one tube or the other but not through both. The circuit is so arranged that when a cosmic ray goes through two tubes in anticoincidence the separate pulses cancel and no count is registered. An example is shown in Fig. 20-3, where the method of counting radioactive rays from a feeble source is illustrated.

If an attempt were made to count the radioactive rays from a feeble source with a single G-M tube the counts due to cosmic rays would also be registered. It would then be next to impossible to separate the counts produced by the feeble radioactive source from the even larger background of cosmic rays. In the figure a ring of overlapping G-M tubes surrounds the weak radioactive source, near which are placed one or more other counting tubes. The surrounding ring of guard tubes is connected in anticoincidence with the counting tubes that are near the source. A cosmic ray passing through one of the counting tubes would not be counted because it would first have to pass through one of the anticoincident guard tubes. Thus the only rays to which the counting tubes would respond would be those from the weakly radioactive source that pass only through a counting tube.

Nuclear-emulsion plates for the study of cosmic rays will be discussed later in this chapter (§ 20-11).

20-4. Carbon Dating

The method just described for counting weak radiation is applied in what is called carbon dating. It is well known now that living objects absorb, from their surroundings and from foods, a certain number of carbon 14 atoms which exist in small numbers in the air. Carbon 14 is a rare isotope of ordinary carbon produced in the air by the indirect action of cosmic rays. In the upper air neutrons are liberated in considerable numbers from the nuclei of air molecules. If one of these is captured by the nucleus of a nitrogen 14 atom a proton is ejected, leaving carbon 14, as follows:

$$_{7}N^{14} + {_0}n^1 \rightarrow {_6}C^{14} + {_1}H^1 \qquad [20\text{-}1]$$

Carbon 14 is a beta-ray emitter, decaying to nitrogen 14.

$$_6C^{14} \rightarrow {}_7N^{14} + {}_{-1}e^0 \qquad [20\text{-}2]$$

with a half-life of 5600 years.

If, for instance, a piece of organic material from archaeological remains of 1000 or more years ago is studied, it is found still to possess some radioactivity due to carbon 14. The amount of this radioactivity per gram gives a means of measuring the time that has elapsed since the object was part of a living organism. When the organism died it stopped absorbing carbon 14. Such measurements are the most accurate method of dating archaeological specimens, and the error may be as little as a few decades for specimens that are not too old. Unfortunately the increasingly wide dispersal of radioactive material from atomic explosions threatens to provide a background of radioactivity which will in time cover up the effects of carbon 14.

20-5. Altitude Variation of Cosmic Rays

In the earlier measurements of variation of cosmic-ray intensity with altitude, it was found that the radiation continually increased with increasing altitude, but since the measurements did not go as high as the "top" of the atmosphere there was no positive proof that the rays did not originate in some very high atmospheric layer, although this seemed improbable. It was desirable, therefore, to make measurements as near the top of the atmosphere as possible, if not actually beyond any appreciable atmosphere. Another reason for doing this was that no other method would give direct evidence of the nature of the primary radiation coming from outside the atmosphere if it existed.

A considerable amount of information was secured from high-altitude balloon flights, known as stratosphere flights, in manned and especially designed stratosphere balloons, but even at the maximum they could not get higher than about 90 per cent of the atmosphere. In this connection it should be noted that at the higher elevations the quantity with most meaning is not the altitude in feet but the fraction of the total earth's atmosphere below the observer.

Millikan in this country and Kohlhörster in Europe were pioneers in extremely high-altitude work with small balloons, called sounding balloons. They carried especially designed and very delicate instrumental equipment of very light weight. With these balloons, Millikan and others sent instruments to 100,000 feet or more above sea level. At such altitudes approximately 1 per cent or less of the atmosphere remained above the balloons. Later in a record flight a balloon was sent to 116,000 feet by Curtiss, Aston, Stockman, and Brown near Washington, D. C., in 1938; on this flight only ½ per cent approximately of the atmosphere remained above the balloon. Whereas earlier measurements had not been able to reach a maximum peak on the cosmic-ray intensity-versus-altitude curve, the later measurements not only were able to reach such a peak but went high enough above to show a marked decrease of intensity with further elevation (Fig. 20-4).

In plotting such curves and in making comparisons of results, it is desirable not to indicate cosmic-ray intensities at different altitudes but to plot them with reference to the absorbing power of the air remaining above the instruments. This is most conveniently measured in terms of the water equivalent of the atmosphere. Air itself is an extremely poor absorber because of its low density. The standard pressure of the atmosphere is equivalent to 76 cm of mercury. The height of a water column which would give the same pressure is 1033 cm or 10.33 meters. At sea level, then, the water equivalent of the atmosphere is a

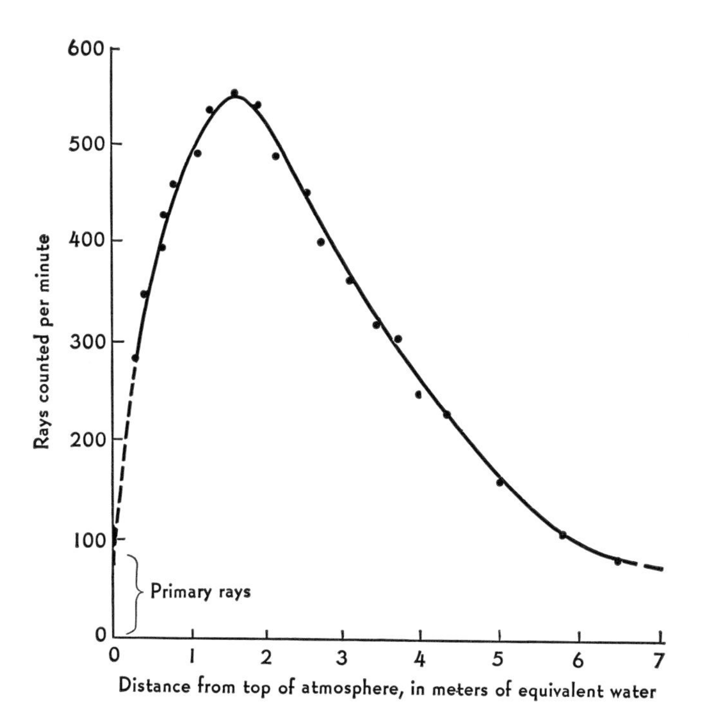

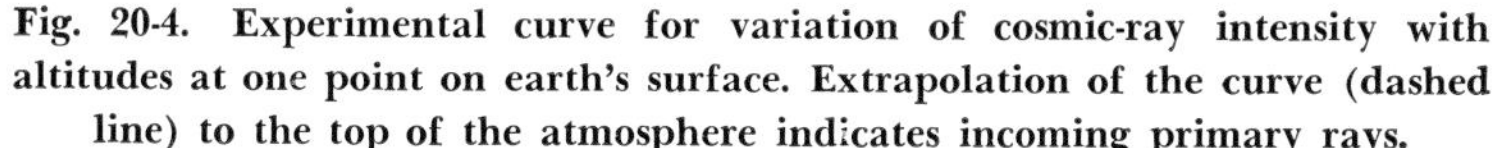

Fig. 20-4. Experimental curve for variation of cosmic-ray intensity with altitudes at one point on earth's surface. Extrapolation of the curve (dashed line) to the top of the atmosphere indicates incoming primary rays.

layer having a thickness of 10.33 meters. At an elevation for which the water equivalent is 5.16 meters, half the atmosphere would yet remain above that point. Thus, it is convenient to indicate the amount of air remaining above the measuring instrument in terms of the water equivalent.

The attempts, just described, to measure variations of cosmic-ray intensity with altitude could hardly have been more successful. The existence of primary radiation is clearly indicated in Fig. 20-4. If the upper end of the curve is extrapolated (dashed line) to zero absorber above the apparatus (top of the atmosphere) it does not fall to zero. The residual intensity at this elevation, of course, represents the primary rays which come into our atmosphere from outer space. Representative curves obtained at different latitudes by Millikan, Bowen, and Neher are given in Fig. 20-5. These show that cosmic-ray intensities vary considerably with latitude and also that the position of the maximum of the curve depends upon the latitude where the measurements were made.

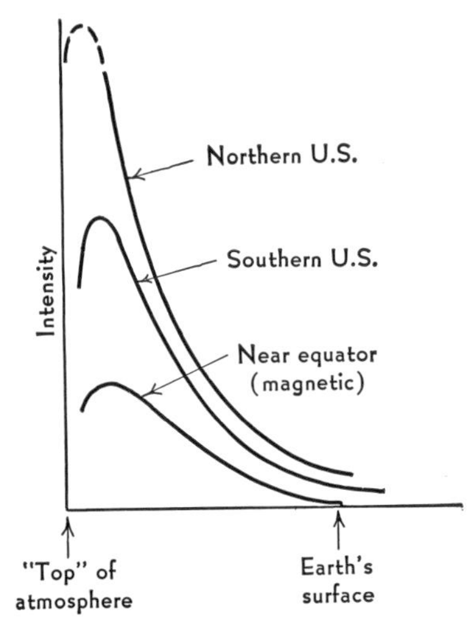

Fig. 20-5. Altitude variation of cosmic rays at different latitudes. (After Millikan, Bowen, and Neher.)

That the curves show a maximum clearly indicates the production of secondary rays in the atmosphere, reaching a maximum in the neighborhood of an atmospheric depth of one-half to a meter of water equivalent. These curves explain the early results of Hess and Kohlhörster, who found increasing intensity as they went to higher and higher altitudes in their balloon flights. They also show that the number of cosmic rays actually filtering down to the surface of the earth at a little more than 10 meters of water equivalent is very small compare with the intensity in the upper regions of the air.

Measurements at the surface of the earth show that about 0.5 ray per cm^2 per minute of all energies reaches sea level in our latitude, and, although the energies of some incoming rays may run above a thousand billion electron volts, the total amount of energy per second received by the earth is estimated to be not more than that of starlight. Despite the fact that something like 10^{18} primary cosmic rays have been estimated to enter the earth's atmosphere every second, and despite the fact that this amounts to a total of something like a million kilowatts of energy, the available energy at sea level per unit area is insignificant.

Rocket measurements Scientists ever seeking more complete data realize that limiting altitudes have been reached with pilot balloons, and that measurements at higher altitudes must be accomplished by some other method. The development since World War II of rockets that are capable of rising to very high altitudes suggested their use in cosmic-ray measurements. A number of experiments have been carried on by several groups, and some of the difficulties of making the measurements have been overcome. Instruments are housed under a plastic cover in the nose of the rocket. They must be designed to be sufficiently shock-proof to withstand the stresses involved in rocket acceleration. One of the difficulties of rocket measurements is that, to measure primary rays directly, little or no absorbing material must intervene between the rays and the detector. For this purpose thin windows have been devised to produce as little disturbance of primary rays as possible. Now that earth satellites have been successfully launched, the possibilities of high-altitude cosmic-ray measurements have been extended considerably.

Useful information has now been obtained concerning the intensity of primaries and other related effects at rocket altitudes, and the measurements indicate that the average energy of primary cosmic rays coming from outside the atmosphere is between 5 and 10 billion electron volts, but maximum energies are far higher.

20-6. Latitude Effect and Earth's Magnetic Field

Clay of Holland, on a trip to Java in 1927, was the first to notice variations of cosmic-ray intensity with changes of latitude. This matter was vigorously pursued by many investigators, including Millikan and Compton in this country, and many measurements were made on both sides of the equator, and to the far north on both land and sea. It was found that in a wide band on each side of the equator there was a considerable drop in intensity compared with the intensity further north or south.

It had been suspected for some time that, if primary cosmic rays consisted of charged particles, the earth's magnetic field could deflect the rays sufficiently so that they might not reach the surface of the earth. This effect should be more noticeable nearer the equator than nearer the poles, and here now was experimental confirmation. At the magnetic poles of the earth circumstances are different. Charged particles could move along paths pretty much parallel to the direction of the field with little or no appreciable deflection. If they were moving at a slight angle to the field they would only spiral around somewhat on the way in.

Near the equator incoming rays of a given electric charge, upon crossing the earth's magnetic field, would be bent away from the earth or toward the earth depending on the direction in which they were moving. Some of those bent away from the earth would, of course, miss it altogether. Those bent toward the earth, if possessing enough energy, would hit it as in Fig. 20-6 at *B*. Those possessing less energy would

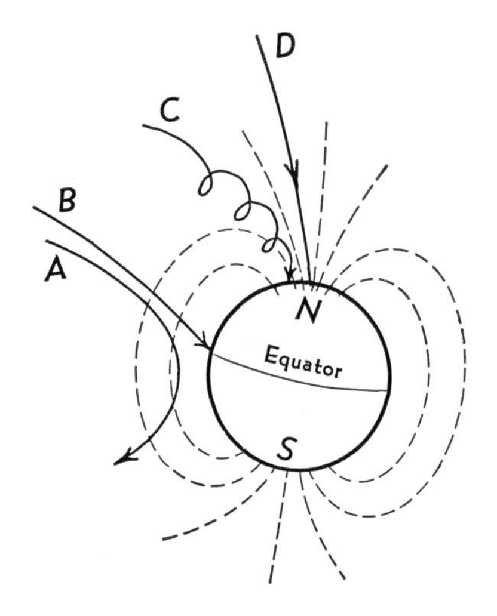

Fig. 20-6. The earth's magnetic field may bend incoming particles so that at *A* they miss the earth completely. If the energy of a particle is large enough, as at *B*, it will reach the earth. Nearer the earth's magnetic pole, lower-energy particles may spiral in, as at *C*, or move along the lines of force, *D*, of the magnetic field.

be bent completely around and either just miss the earth, or completely miss it, as at *A*. Since the atmosphere surrounding the earth is mostly in a relatively thin layer, any bending of the rays in the atmosphere itself is of negligible importance, and most of it occurs at very much greater distances from the earth.

The magnitude of the latitude effect indicates that incoming rays are chiefly charged particles, not gamma-ray photons. Measurements by various investigators show that there is as much as a 10 per cent drop in the intensity of the cosmic rays at the equator and that the intensity rises to a fairly constant value for latitudes above 40°, as represented in Fig. 20-7.

Consideration of the energies required by particles to enable them to reach the earth indicates that protons of approximately 60 billion electron-volts energy are bent in the equatorial plane of the earth, so that the radius of curvature of path is smaller than the earth's radius; therefore these protons can reach the earth regardless of direction in the equatorial plane. Such particles, with energies of less than 10 billion electron volts, will not be able to reach the earth at all at the equator; those of 10 billion volts or a little more will arrive from a

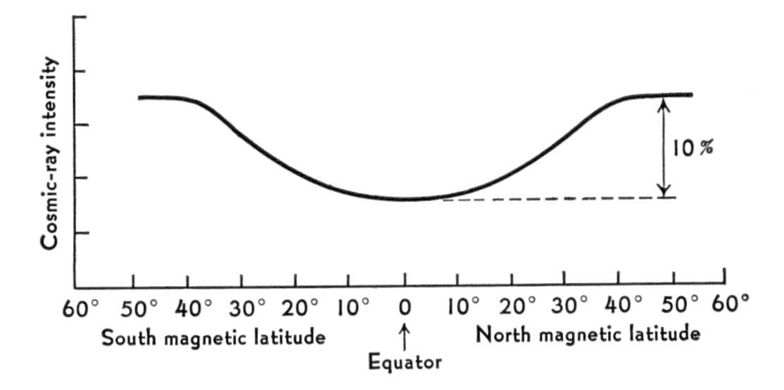

Fig. 20-7. Approximate curve of variation of cosmic-ray intensity with latitude, the result of a number of sets of measurements made with electroscopes.

westerly direction if they are positively charged and from an easterly direction if they are negatively charged. If they have energies of 15 or more Bev, they can arrive at any angle between the western horizon and the zenith. At the poles particles of any energy can reach the surface of the earth except for losses such as those due to collision, radiation, and ionization. These losses usually amount to about 1.5 Bev per particle on the average, another reason why low-energy primary cosmic rays cannot reach the surface of the earth. Great credit is due Lemaître and Vallarta for developing the theory and computing the orbits of cosmic-ray particles bent by the earth's magnetic field under a variety of conditions.

Through the efforts of Johnson and Swann, measurements were made of the relative numbers of cosmic rays arriving from the east and from the west. These measurements indicated that slightly more rays come from the west than from the east. This is known as the east-west effect. Its importance is its indication that the primary rays are mainly positively charged particles; these have now been identified chiefly as protons.

20-7. Energies and Penetrating Power

Measurements of the penetrating power of cosmic rays have led to traces of cosmic rays being found as far below the surface of the earth as 2000 feet down in a coal mine. Although only about 1 in 20,000 of the rays falling on the earth is able to penetrate to this depth, it shows the extraordinary energies of some of the rays, running perhaps to as much as 10 thousand billion electron volts. This penetration is roughly equivalent to nearly a mile of water or 400 feet of lead. Evidently a ray capable of passing through that much lead could pass through the human body without being noticeably impeded; in fact, it might not hit anything.

In computing the absorption coefficients for penetrating rays, there seemed to be not a single but several absorption coefficients. From this it was suspected that not only protons enter the atmosphere from the outside but also nuclei of heavier atoms. This has been confirmed by high-altitude studies showing traces of primaries as high in the atomic number series as iron 26, with measurable peaks for carbon, nitrogen, oxygen, magnesium, and silicon. This poses the interesting question, whether identification of the source of the particles as coming from the stars or the sun is thus possible.

The formula for bending in a magnetic field of a particle of charge Ze may be written

$$Br = \frac{mv}{Ze} = \frac{p}{Ze} \qquad [20\text{-}3]$$

where m is the relativistic mass at velocity v, and p is then the actual measured momentum, all quantities being measured in one system of units. Since mass may vary with velocity, no longer is the bending a function of the velocity alone in a particle of a given charge but of mass times velocity which is momentum p. When a relativistic correction is involved the momentum then is the all-important quantity. As the velocity of a particle approaches that of light it cannot increase much in magnitude, whereas the mass does increase relativistically. From the formula, then, it is seen that the momentum is measured in terms of the product of the magnetic flux density and the radius of curvature.

For very-high-energy particles the magnetic field may not be intense enough to produce appreciable bending, but where bending can be observed the product Br is proportional to the momentum and is a measure of it for particles of a given charge Ze. This quantity, Br, is called the **magnetic rigidity** of the particle and is commonly used in comparing results. Because of relativistic effects it may be difficult to distinguish between extremely-high-energy electrons, mesons, and protons, and even the density of ionization along the tracks may differ but little for these particles. Consequently identification of particles becomes difficult and must involve all available evidence, including collision properties or capacity to produce nuclear disruption.

20-8. Secondary Cosmic Rays

Any cosmic ray produced by action of a primary is called a secondary ray. Secondary rays may be produced by a variety of processes, and they may include a number of different types of rays. Measurements of secondaries indicate that there are present in the atmosphere high-speed electrons, positrons, mesons, high-energy gamma rays, and even neutrons, together with other particles not so well known. The processes by which the secondaries are produced have been given much consideration by theoretical physicists as well as by experimentalists.

Cosmic rays entering the atmosphere produce three chief effects besides that of disruption of nuclei. A primary ray, as it comes down, gives up energy by ionization, by radiation of gamma rays, and by direct collision with an atomic nucleus, which if not disrupted may be hurled onward. When a primary is suddenly slowed down by collision it may lose energy in the form of a gamma-ray photon very much as, in an x-ray tube, sudden slowing down of the electrons by the target produces x-rays. However, with cosmic rays the energies of primary particles are so large to begin with that, after production of a gamma ray, a primary may have most of its energy left for further processes. The gamma ray can now be transformed in the presence of a suitable nucleus into an electron pair. When this occurs we have the original primary ray and two secondary electrons. The secondary electrons may likewise produce gamma rays by collision, and the name given to this process by the Germans is bremsstrahlung or "slowing-down radiation." The gamma rays may then in turn produce further electron pairs. Thus, as this process proceeds and repeats itself, gamma rays and electrons multiply by one process or another, as indicated in Fig. 20-8. At the same time many nuclei undergo either transmutation or total disruption in the nature of an atomic explosion. It is by the latter proc-

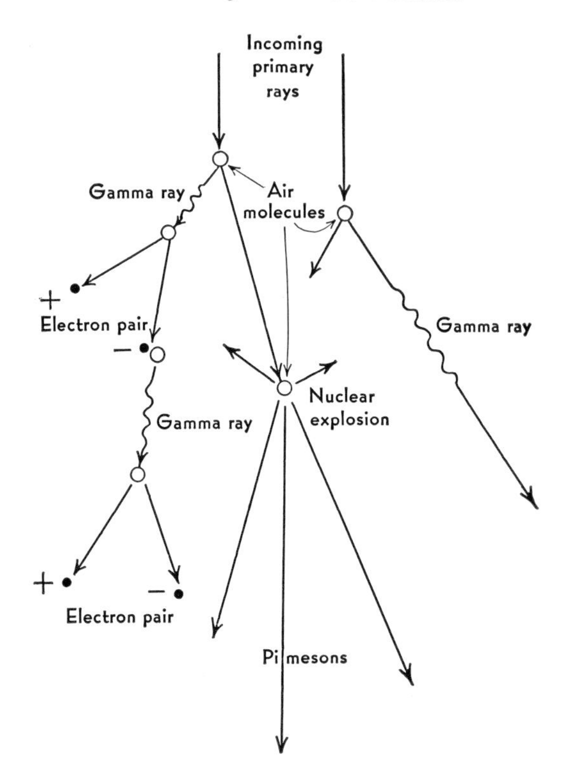

Fig. 20-8. Production of secondary cosmic rays in atmosphere by incoming primary rays. For simplicity no attempt has been made to show such phenomena as pi-meson decay or capture and the production of neutrons and neutrinos.

esses that mesons are ejected from nuclei, as well as protons and neutrons.

20-9. Showers and Bursts

In making cosmic-ray measurements it is sometimes found that occasional, very intense amounts of ionization are produced as if owing to large numbers of cosmic rays close together. Such a group of cosmic rays is called a shower; in air it is called an air shower. It is also noticed that when a counter is shielded with a relatively thin layer of lead the counting rate often goes up. The reason was discovered when layers of lead were put into a cloud chamber and it was observed that many rays issuing from the same spot in the lead were produced by a single particle entering the lead at that spot. Thus the particle produces a shower from the lead plate. If the shower particles strike another lead plate they may in turn produce showers, and the entire process is called a cascade shower, as shown on the right of Fig. 20-9. The maximum intensity of such a shower is usually obtained by a thickness of about 1.7 cm of lead, but it depends on the energy of the shower-producing particle.

Frequently there is an extraordinary multiplication of particles in successive showers, as shown in Fig. 20-10, where the bars in the photo are layers of lead of equal thickness inside the cloud chamber and they are separated by gaps where the tracks are visible. Often the shower particles are almost too numerous to count and may number as many as 10,000. Evidently such showers (sometimes called bursts) can only be produced by high-energy particles, since the energies of all the shower particles added together cannot be greater than the energy of

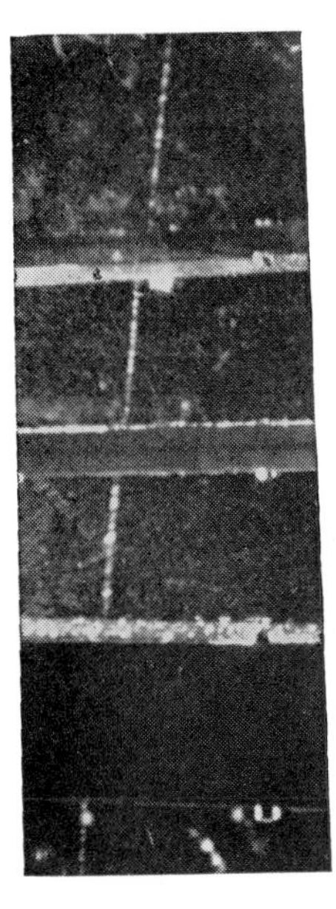

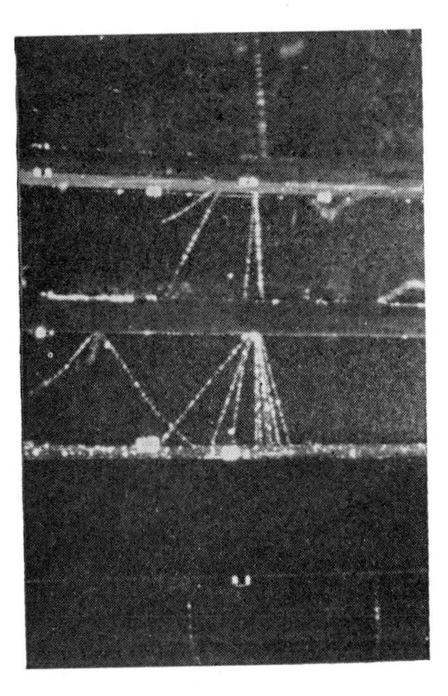

Fig. 20-9. Cloud-chamber photographs. Left, a penetrating particle (high-energy meson) passes downward and completely through three lead plates 4 mm, 10 mm, and 39 mm thick. Most cosmic rays at the surface of the earth are of this type and seldom produce showers. Right, a shower-producing particle (presumably an electron) forms a two-stage cascade shower. Nearly all the particles are absorbed in the bottom plate. The two V-tracks may be electron pairs, formed by gamma rays produced when the high-speed particle is slowed down by a lead plate. (Courtesy, Harvard University, Physics Laboratory.)

Fig. 20-10. Intense multiplication of cosmic-ray secondaries by shower process in lead plates in a cloud chamber. (Courtesy, University of California, Berkeley.)

the incoming particle or particles except for possible, relatively small increments due to nuclear processes. Extensive air showers are formed by primary rays having energies of 10^{10} to 10^{19} ev.

20-10. The Penetrating Component of Cosmic Rays

For a considerable time before the discovery of mesons in 1937, it was recognized that there were at least two chief components in cosmic rays, called the hard and soft components. The hard component was of high energy and extremely penetrating, as shown on the left of Fig. 20-9. The soft component was much less penetrating and was more frequently the cause of showers. Theory indicated that a particle more massive than the electron might be responsible for the high penetration of the hard component although in earlier days it had been supposed that more massive particles would have more difficulty in passing through matter than less massive ones. For instance, electrons could be made to penetrate a thin window in a discharge tube that was impenetrable to the more massive positive ions.

However, at very high speeds the situation is different. As massive a particle as a proton produces little more ionization than an electron when both travel with speeds approximately that of light, but the momentum of the more massive particle is much greater and consequently it is not so easily stopped. At high speeds the loss of energy by ionization may be relatively low, and radiation losses become more important. Yet the radiation loss of a more massive particle is less than that of a less massive one since by classical electrodynamics the radiation loss is proportional to the second power of the acceleration, which in turn is inversely proportional to the mass. Consequently more massive particles lose considerably less energy by radiation than less massive particles.

Many studies of the more penetrating component of cosmic rays led to the conclusion that they are particles heavier than electrons. Although protons come into our atmosphere from the outside, few penetrate as far as the surface of the earth. On the other hand, mesons intermediate in mass between electrons and protons are plentiful near the earth's surface, and approximately two-thirds of the rays at the surface are mesons. The penetrating component of the cosmic rays is thus identified as consisting of high-speed mesons.

20-11. Mu and Pi Mesons

When the new particles of intermediate mass were discovered in 1937 by Anderson and Neddermeyer, and by Street and Stevenson, they were first called heavy electrons, and then mesons (§ 17-4). When similar particles of somewhat larger mass were found later, the particles of the first type were called mu (μ) mesons. This is frequently shortened to *muons.* The closely related but somewhat more massive particles discovered later are called pi (π) mesons, or in shorter form simply *pions.*

The mu meson was discovered from a study of cloud-chamber tracks which showed an occasional track intermediate in character between the known tracks of electrons and protons. Since the differences in observed tracks were small the original identification was made with difficulty. When it was found that this particle did not show

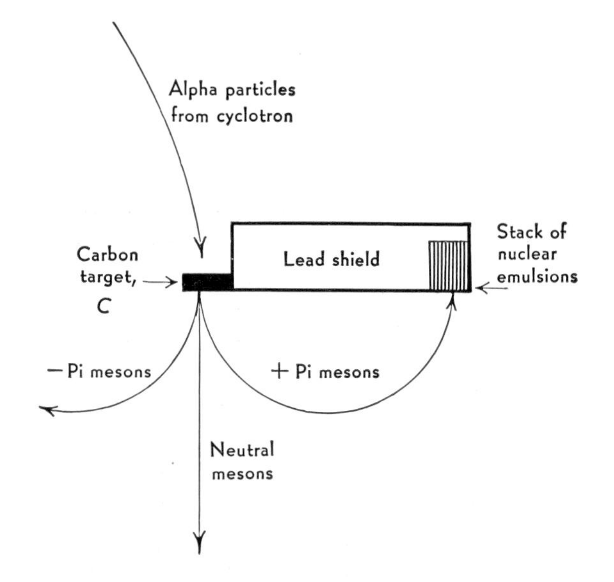

Fig. 20-11. Experimental method developed at the University of California for producing and detecting pi mesons.

properties as total energy, range, and ionization. Cloud-chamber photographs of the newly discovered pi mesons were also obtained, and the tracks of some of these particles are shown in Fig. 20-12. In the quite remarkable cloud-chamber photograph numerous and different types of tracks are visible. The long thin tracks are mostly electrons. The short thick tracks are more massive particles, presumably protons. The intermediate tracks of mesons are readily discernible.

Both pi- and mu-meson masses have now been obtained with considerable accuracy (Table 20-1).

TABLE 20-1. MASS OF MU AND PI MESONS
(m_e = mass of electron)

Particle	Mass in m_e
$\pi^{\pm}$ meson	273.0 ± 0.5
π^0 meson	263.8 ± 1
$\mu^{\pm}$ meson	206.6 ± 0.5

By an application of quantum-mechanical analysis it has been possible to correlate pi and mu mesons with the newer types of quantum statistics. Pi mesons are found to be describable in terms of Bose statistics, and mu mesons are describable by Fermi statistics.

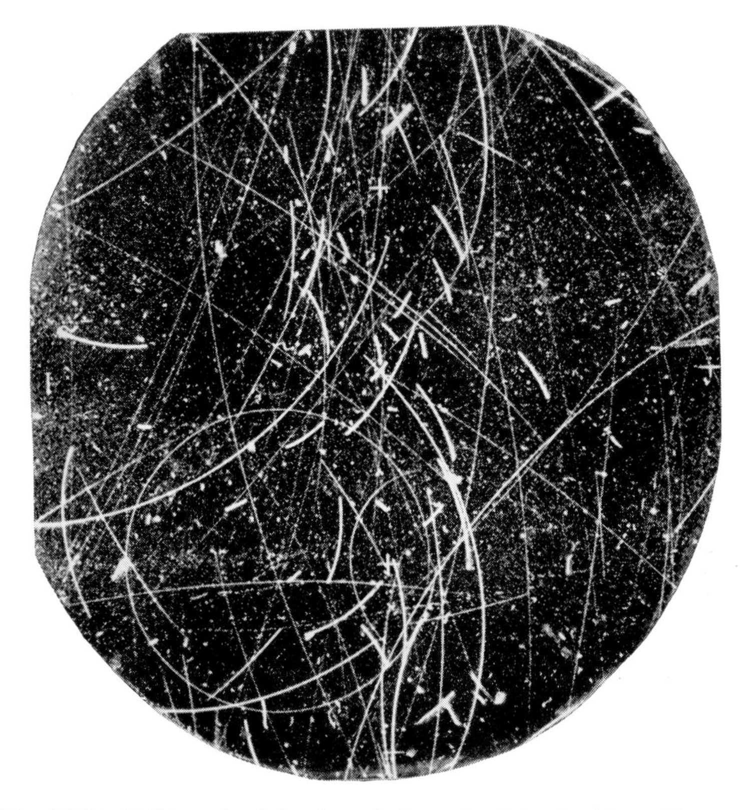

Fig. 20-12. Striking cloud-chamber photograph of tracks of particles expelled from atoms bombarded by high-energy particles from the 184-inch cyclotron at the University of California. The spiral (almost circular) track in lower left-hand part of photo is a positively charged pi meson artificially produced by the bombardment. (Courtesy, Radiation Laboratory, University of California.)

20-12. Decay of Pi and Mu Mesons

Pi-meson decay When it is possible to follow the track of a pi meson to the point where it apparently ends and a new track begins in a different direction, the event occurring at the branch point very evidently represents the decay of the pi meson (Fig. 20-13). In addition to the visible track of the decay particle, however, it is necessary, in order to conserve momentum, to assume the emission of at least one other particle which does not leave a visible track. Since the mu meson has the same charge as its parent, the pi meson,

rays, whereas mu mesons are plentiful, suggests that they are mostly found in the upper atmosphere where high-energy collisions are more frequent. It also suggests that their mean life is much less than that of mu mesons. Measurements indicate that it is probably of the order of a hundredth that of mu mesons, the latter being of the order of a few microseconds. Recent measurements gave 2.6×10^{-8} sec for the mean life of a pi meson and 2.2×10^{-6} sec for that of a mu meson.

Pi mesons are now produced by bombardment of a variety of targets with high-energy protons, neutrons, alpha particles, and even gamma rays. For instance, when protons are used as bombarding particles they are presumed to interact with individual protons or neutrons in a nucleus, and possible reactions are:

$$p + p \rightarrow p + n + \pi^+ \qquad [20\text{-}6]$$

$$p + n \rightarrow p + p + \pi^- \qquad [20\text{-}7]$$

These two reactions have been confirmed by bombarding with high-energy protons. Since protons and neutrons have half-integral spin this indicates that pi mesons have zero or integral spin.

If pi mesons are responsible for internucleonic forces it would seem that neutral pi mesons would be required to explain forces between two protons or between two neutrons. Whether or not this assumption is justified, the existence of neutral pi mesons has now been demonstrated, though as free particles they are found to have an extremely short mean life ($\sim 10^{-15}$ sec), and their mass (263.8 electron masses) is unaccountably different from that of charged pi mesons. To conserve charge, spin, and statistics they could decay by either of the following processes:

$$\pi^0 \rightarrow \gamma + \gamma \qquad [20\text{-}8]$$

$$\pi^0 \rightarrow e^+ + e^- + \gamma \qquad [20\text{-}9]$$

The first process of decay into two gamma-ray photons has been confirmed experimentally, and the coincident pairs of gamma rays have been detected. In the second process the decay would be into an electron pair, plus a gamma-ray photon.

Mu-meson decay In mu-meson decay two "mysterious strangers," presumably neutrinos, are required to conserve spin and statistics, and the following decay processes are believed to occur:

$$\mu^+ \rightarrow e^+ + \nu + \nu \qquad [20\text{-}10]$$

$$\mu^- \rightarrow e^- + \nu + \nu \qquad [20\text{-}11]$$

In the early nuclear-emulsion plates, electrons were difficult to detect because they did not leave satisfactorily observable tracks, but in the more recently developed emulsions they are now easily detected, and in the decay of a mu meson at the end of its track the path of the particle emitted is very evidently that of an electron. Although it is assumed that, in the decay of a mu meson, two neutrinos are emitted there are again no visible tracks. Since the spin quantum number of the mu meson is believed to be ½, and since the spin of the electron emitted is ½ there might either be no other particle emitted, or a particle of zero spin, or else two particles the sum of whose spins is zero. To account for the great variation of energy of the decay electrons similar to ordinary beta decay, as well as to account for the angles at which they may be emitted, other particles must be assumed to conserve energy and momentum. The assumption that two neutrinos are emitted is then in harmony with the idea of conservation of energy and conservation of spin since the two neutrinos may spin in opposite directions and the sum of their spins may be zero.

20.13. Cherenkov Radiation

In 1934, P. A. Cherenkov found that a charged particle moving through a transparent medium excites visible radiation when traveling fast enough to produce a kind of "shock wave." The formation of a shock wave is a familiar phenomenon in other forms of motion through a medium but had not been known to occur in the motion of charged particles. Such a wave front is formed similarly to the way that a bow wave is formed by a boat moving through water except that the wave picture becomes electromagnetic and also three-dimensional. The necessary condition for the production of the wave front, representing Cherenkov radiation, is that the particle move with a speed greater than the speed of light in that medium. The speed of light in a medium of index of refraction μ is c/μ where c is the speed of light in free space. The ratio of c/μ to the speed of the particle v determines the direction of propagation of the wave front, and

$$\cos\theta = \frac{c}{\mu v} \qquad [20\text{-}12]$$

where θ is the angle of propagation with respect to the direction of motion of the particle (Fig. 20-15).

Cherenkov radiation is often used as a means of detecting high-speed particles in cosmic rays or in nuclear experiments, and it played an

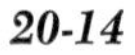

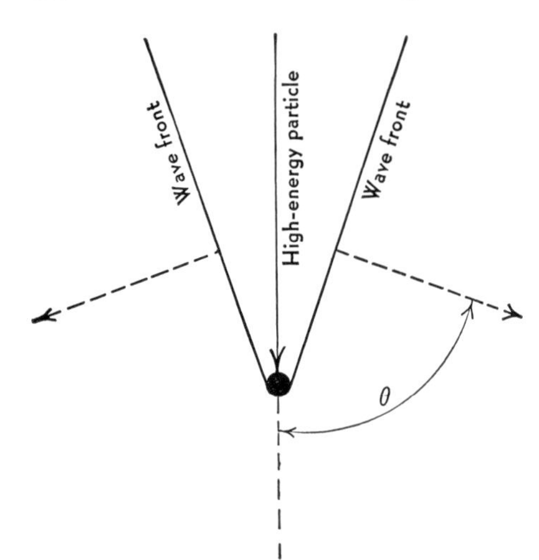

Fig. 20-15. Cherenkov radiation. A high-speed charged particle forms a wave of visible radiation like the bow wave of a boat when moving through a medium with a speed greater than that of light in the medium.

important part in the detection of the antiproton (§ 15-18). If the angle of propagation of the wave front is measured, a simple means is furnished of computing the speed of the particles.

20-14. Other Mesons and Hyperons

In addition to pi and mu mesons known as light or *L* mesons, other particles have been discovered having masses intermediate between that of the pi meson and that of the proton. These have been given a variety of names but are now classed as heavy or *K* mesons, and they may have positive, negative, or zero electric charge (Table 20-2). Still other new particles have been found to have masses larger than that of a proton or of a neutron. They do not fit into the category of intermediate particles and are now often called *hyperons*. When strange inverted V-shaped tracks were found in cloud chambers it was realized, since there was no visible track of a particle coming toward the point of the *V*, that they must be produced by a new type of neutral particle. These were first called *V* particles. Later it was found that there must be two kinds of such events: one formed by a neutral *K* particle and the other formed by a much heavier particle, a hyperon, now appropriately called a lambda (Λ) particle. Lambda particles carry zero charge and may decay into a proton and a negative pi meson.

A more massive hyperon is the sigma (Σ) particle, which may carry either a positive or a negative charge and decays into a pi meson of either sign, plus a proton or a neutron so as to conserve charge. A still higher-mass particle, called the xi (Ξ) particle, apparently produces V-shaped tracks when it decays. This is explained by the fact that in the decay process a lambda particle is formed first, and it in turn decays to form the V-shaped tracks.

TABLE 20-2. MESONS AND HYPERONS

Class	Particle	Mass (m_e)	Decay Products	Mean Life (sec)	Statistics
L mesons	$\pi^{\pm}$	273.0	$\mu^{\pm} + \nu$	2.6×10^{-8}	Bose
	π^0	263.8	2γ	10^{-15}	Bose
	$\mu^{\pm}$	206.6	$e^{\pm} + 2\nu$	2.2×10^{-6}	Fermi
K mesons	$K^{\pm}$	$\sim$966	$\pi^{\pm} + \pi^+ + \pi^-$	$\sim 10^{-8}$	Bose
	K_1^0, K_2^0	$\sim$965	$\begin{cases} \pi^+ + \pi^- \\ \pi^+ + \pi^- + \pi^0 \end{cases}$	$\sim 10^{-8}$	Bose
Hyperons	Λ^0	$\sim$2181	$p + \pi^-$	$\sim 10^{-10}$	Fermi
	$\Sigma^{\pm}$	$\sim$2326	Various	$\sim 10^{-10}$	Fermi
	Ξ^-	$\sim$2580	$V^0 + \pi^-$	$\sim 10^{-10}$	Fermi

20-15. Parity and Strangeness

With the present rapid development of nuclear physics, old concepts may often be discarded as new ones arise. The conservation of parity (§ 16-18) was called into question when two types of mesons (then called tau and theta but now called K mesons) were found to be indistinguishable except that one decayed into three pi mesons whereas the other decayed into two. It was concluded that the two mesons could actually be one and the same particle, but if so only one mode of decay would be permitted if parity was always conserved. If such a particle could undergo either one or other of these two modes of decay, parity could not be conserved. Two young theoretical physicists, T. D. Lee of Columbia University and C. N. Yang of the Institute for Advanced Studies (Princeton), unremittingly pursued the idea that parity might not always be conserved, particularly in what are called "weak interactions" such as are involved in the radioactive emission of beta particles. Their work set the stage for a full-scale experimental test, and the two were awarded the Nobel Prize for 1957. The problem was how to make such a delicate test.

The critical experiment which showed that parity is not always conserved was performed in December, 1956, at the National Bureau of Standards, Washington, D. C., by C. S. Wu of Columbia University and her collaborators at the Bureau under E. Ambler. They cooled radioactive cobalt 60 to a temperature of less than 1° above absolute zero. At this temperature it was possible to obtain alignment of the nuclei of the cobalt atoms in a magnetic field so that the magnetic moments of the nuclei nearly all pointed in one direction. When the beta-ray emission from the nuclei was measured it was found to occur predominately in one direction. This was direct evidence that the emission is not mirror-symmetrical and that parity is not conserved. Other experiments were soon performed confirming the work of Wu and Ambler.

Four of the particles mentioned in Table 20-1, the xi, sigma, lambda, and *K* particles have been classed under a new name, *strange particles,* because of certain apparent contradictions in their predictable properties. It has been found possible to associate the "strangeness" with factors in the mathematical description of the nucleus, and the suggestion has been made that a quantity, which may be called the degree of strangeness, can be represented by small integers in such a way that the strangeness may be conserved in nuclear transformations. Thus does man ever seek permanences in the midst of change, guideposts in the midst of uncertainties.

20-16. Fundamental Particles

Before the discovery of mesons and hyperons, the structure of matter seemed to be much more simple. The nucleus was thought to consist of protons and neutrons, and to form an atom only electrons needed to be added in external shells. It seemed appropriate at that time to speak of protons, neutrons, and electrons as the fundamental particles of which all matter is composed. Even then, however, the problem was complicated by the emission of positrons and electrons from the nucleus in certain types of radioactive decay.

With the discovery of still more particles, it became increasingly difficult to set up a simple plan of organization by which all known particles can be fitted into an architectural scheme describing the structure of matter. Consequently the term *fundamental particle* has lost a considerable amount of significance. Those particles which have an extremely short life and decay into other particles can hardly be considered fundamental, but their behavior in the nucleus may be different from their behavior outside the nucleus. Just which particles are fundamental and which are not is a question that cannot be completely answered at present.

20-17. Sources of Cosmic Rays

Investigations of different parts of the sky with a cosmic-ray telescope (§ 20-3) give no indication of a favored source for cosmic rays. They seem to come equally from all directions in space. To answer the question of the source of the rays, one must not only find where they come from but also find a mechanism by which particles of such tremendous energies can be produced. It seems most probable that large numbers of the lower-energy particles, which we speak of as cosmic rays, have their source in the sun and are scattered throughout the solar system by means of the magnetic fields of the sun, the earth, and the other planets in such a way that they seem to come uniformly from all directions of space. However, no satisfactory theory has yet been able to account for the higher-energy particles in terms of any mechanism connected with the sun.

One source that seems possible is the type of star known as a nova or supernova. In the apparent atomic explosion of such a star, it seems that particles of sufficiently high energy could be produced if the nova were surrounded by a time-changing magnetic field enabling it to act as a huge particle accelerator. However, it is difficult to see how enough particles could be produced since the occurrence of these novae is comparatively rare. Certain pulsating stars may have pulsating magnetic fields and might act as giant accelerators to speed up such particles. If the type of nuclei coming to the earth as primary rays could be identified with sufficient accuracy it might be possible to correlate them with the abundances in the stars, as obtained from spectroscopic analysis. However, the final answer to the question of where cosmic rays come from is fraught with great difficulties and does not appear to be near satisfactory attainment.

SUGGESTED READING

F. K. RICHTMYER, E. H. KENNARD, and T. LAURITSEN, *Introduction to Modern Physics,* 5th ed. (New York, McGraw-Hill, 1955).

B. ROSSI, "Cosmic-Ray Phenomena," *Reviews of Modern Physics, 20,* 537 (1948).

L. LEPRINCE-RINGUET, *Cosmic Rays* (New York, Prentice-Hall, 1950).

B. ROSSI, *High Energy Particles* (New York, Prentice-Hall, 1952).

A. M. THORNDIKE, *Mesons, a Summary of Experimental Facts* (New York, McGraw-Hill, 1952).

M. M. SHAPIRO, "Mesons and Hyperons," *American Journal of Physics, 24,* 196 (1956).

G. D. ROCHESTER and J. G. WILSON, *Cloud-Chamber Photographs of the Cosmic Radiation* (New York, Academic Press, 1952).

P. MORRISON, "The Overthrow of Parity," *Scientific American,* April, 1957, p. 45.

M. GELL-MANN and E. P. ROSENBAUM, "Elementary Particles," *Scientific American,* July, 1957, p. 72.

APPENDIXES

APPENDIX 1. IMPORTANT PHYSICAL CONSTANTS

Velocity of light in a vacuum	c	2.9973×10^{8} m/sec 2.9973×10^{10} cm/sec
Planck's constant	h	6.625×10^{-34} joule sec 6.625×10^{-27} erg sec
Avogadro's number	N_0	6.0247×10^{23} atoms/gm-atomic wt
Boltzmann's constant	k	1.3804×10^{-23} joule/°C 1.3804×10^{-16} erg/°C
Gas constant	R	8.3166 joule/gm-mol wt/°C 8.3166×10^{7} erg/gm-mol wt/°C 1.9870 cal/gm-mol wt °C
Volume of 1 gm-mol wt of perfect gas, normal temperature and pressure		22.421 liters
Electron charge	e	1.6021×10^{-19} coulomb 4.8029×10^{-10} esu
Electron rest mass	m	9.1085×10^{-31} kg 9.1085×10^{-28} gm
Proton rest mass	M_p	1.6724×10^{-27} kg 1.6724×10^{-24} gm 1.00759 amu
Neutron rest mass	M_n	1.00898 amu
Ratio of proton mass to electron mass	M_p/m	1836.1
Charge-to-mass ratio of the electron	e/m	1.7589×10^{11} coulomb/kg 5.2730×10^{17} esu/gm
Rydberg constant	R_∞	109,737.31 cm^{-1}
Radius of first hydrogen orbit	r	0.52916 angstrom
Atomic mass unit, grams	1 amu	1.6598×10^{-24} gm
1 X unit	XU	1.002020×10^{-11} cm

APPENDIX 2. USEFUL CONVERSION CONSTANTS AND UNITS

Electron mass, ev	m	0.51098 Mev
Atomic mass unit, ev	amu	931.16 Mev
Constants, mks units	ϵ_0 μ_0	8.8542×10^{-12} farad/m $4\pi \times 10^{-7}$ henry/m
Electron volt (ev)	1 ev	1.6021×10^{-12} erg 1.6021×10^{-19} joule
	1 Mev 1 Bev	10^6 ev 10^9 ev
1 coulomb	0.1 abcoulomb (emu)	3×10^9 statcoulomb (esu)
1 weber per square meter		10^4 gauss
Base of natural system of logarithms	ϵ	2.718

APPENDIX 3. PERIODIC TABLE OF THE ELEMENTS

Period	Group I a	Group I b	Group II a	Group II b	Group III a	Group III b	Group IV a	Group IV b	Group V a	Group V b	Group VI a	Group VI b	Group VII a	Group VII b	Group VIII a	Group VIII b
I	1 H 1.0080															2 He 4.003
II	3 Li 6.940		4 Be 9.013			5 B 10.82		6 C 12.010		7 N 14.008		8 O 16.0000		9 F 19.00		10 Ne 20.183
III	11 Na 22.997		12 Mg 24.32			13 Al 26.98		14 Si 28.09		15 P 30.975		16 S 32.066		17 Cl 35.457		18 A 39.944
IV	19 K 39.100	29 Cu 63.54	20 Ca 40.08	30 Zn 65.38	21 Sc 44.96	31 Ga 69.72	22 Ti 47.90	32 Ge 72.60	23 V 50.95	33 As 74.91	24 Cr 52.01	34 Se 78.96	25 Mn 54.93	35 Br 79.916	26 Fe 55.85 27 Co 58.94 28 Ni 58.69	36 Kr 83.80
V	37 Rb 85.48	47 Ag 107.880	38 Sr 87.63	48 Cd 112.41	39 Y 88.92	49 In 114.76	40 Zr 91.22	50 Sn 118.70	41 Nb 92.91	51 Sb 121.76	42 Mo 95.95	52 Te 127.61		43 Tc [99] 53 I 126.91	44 Ru 101.7 45 Rh 102.91 46 Pd 106.7	54 Xe 131.3
VI	55 Cs 132.91	79 Au 197.2	56 Ba 137.36	80 Hg 200.61	57 to 71 Rare earths*	81 Tl 204.39	72 Hf 178.6	82 Pb 207.21	73 Ta 180.88	83 Bi 209.00	74 W 183.92	84 Po 210	75 Re 186.31	85 At [210]	76 Os 190.2 77 Ir 193.1 78 Pt 195.23	86 Rn 222
VII	87 Fr [223]		88 Ra 226.05		89 to 102 Actinides†											

* Rare earths: 57 La 138.92, 58 Ce 140.13, 59 Pr 140.92, 60 Nd 144.27, 61 Pm [145], 62 Sm 150.43, 63 Eu 152.0, 64 Gd 156.9, 65 Tb 159.2, 66 Dy 162.46, 67 Ho 164.94, 68 Er 167.2, 69 Tm 169.4, 70 Yb 173.04, 71 Lu 174.99

† Actinides: 89 Ac 227, 90 Th 232.12, 91 Pa 231, 92 U 238.07, 93 Np [237], 94 Pu [242], 95 Am [243], 96 Cm [243], 97 Bk [245], 98 Cf [246], 99 E [253], 100 Fm [255], 101 Mv [256], 102 No [253?]

Atomic weight in square brackets is of the isotope of longest half-life or in some instances the first one identified.

APPENDIX 4. ALPHABETICAL LIST OF THE ELEMENTS*

Element	Symbol	Atomic Number, Z	Element	Symbol	Atomic Number, Z
Actinium	Ac	89	Hydrogen	H	1
Aluminum	Al	13	Indium	In	49
Americium	Am	95	Iodine	I	53
Antimony	Sb	51	Iridium	Ir	77
Argon	A	18	Iron	Fe	26
Arsenic	As	33	Krypton	Kr	36
Astatine	At	85	Lanthanum	La	57
Barium	Ba	56	Lead	Pb	82
Berkelium	Bk	97	Lithium	Li	3
Beryllium	Be	4	Lutecium	Lu	71
Bismuth	Bi	83	Magnesium	Mg	12
Boron	B	5	Manganese	Mn	25
Bromine	Br	35	Mendelevium	Mv	101
Cadmium	Cd	48	Mercury	Hg	80
Calcium	Ca	20	Molybdenum	Mo	42
Californium	Cf	98	Neodymium	Nd	60
Carbon	C	6	Neon	Ne	10
Cerium	Ce	58	Neptunium	Np	93
Cesium	Cs	55	Nickel	Ni	28
Chlorine	Cl	17	Niobium	Nb	41
Chromium	Cr	24	Nitrogen	N	7
Cobalt	Co	27	Nobelium	No	102
Copper	Cu	29	Osmium	Os	76
Curium	Cm	96	Oxygen	O	8
Dysprosium	Dy	66	Palladium	Pd	46
Einsteinium	E	99	Phosphorus	P	15
Erbium	Er	68	Platinum	Pt	78
Europium	Eu	63	Plutonium	Pu	94
Fermium	Fm	100	Polonium	Po	84
Fluorine	F	9	Potassium	K	19
Francium	Fr	87	Praseodymium	Pr	59
Gadolinium	Gd	64	Promethium	Pm	61
Gallium	Ga	31	Protactinium	Pa	91
Germanium	Ge	32	Radium	Ra	88
Gold	Au	79	Radon	Rn	86
Hafnium	Hf	72	Rhenium	Re	75
Helium	He	2	Rhodium	Rh	45
Holmium	Ho	67			

* The Commission on Inorganic Nomenclature of the I.U.P.A.C. (International Union of Pure and Applied Chemistry) has recommended the following changes in symbols: Ar for argon, not A, Es for einsteinium, not E, and Md for mendelevium, not Mv.

Alphabetical List of the Elements—*Continued*

Element	Symbol	Atomic Number, Z	Element	Symbol	Atomic Number, Z
Rubidium	Rb	37	Thallium	Tl	81
Ruthenium	Ru	44	Thorium	Th	90
Samarium	Sm	62	Thulium	Tm	69
Scandium	Sc	21	Tin	Sn	50
Selenium	Se	34	Titanium	Ti	22
Silicon	Si	14	Tungsten		
Silver	Ag	47	(Wolfram)	W	74
Sodium	Na	11	Uranium	U	92
Strontium	Sr	38	Vanadium	V	23
Sulfur	S	16	Xenon	Xe	54
Tantalum	Ta	73	Ytterbium	Yb	70
Technetium	Tc	43	Yttrium	Y	39
Tellurium	Te	52	Zinc	Zn	30
Terbium	Tb	65	Zirconium	Zr	40

INDEX